Environmental Laboratory Data Evaluation

by

Walter Berger
Harry McCarty
Roy-Keith Smith

Apichemical Consultants
9401 Grace Lake Drive
Douglasville, GA 30135

1996

ABOUT THE AUTHORS

Walter Berger is an independent consultant specializing in Department of Defense environmental analysis and contracts. Harry B. McCarty, PhD, is employed as a Senior Scientist with Science Applications International Corporation (SAIC). Roy-Keith Smith, PhD, is the Quality Assurance Manager and Analytical Methods Manager with Analytical Services, Inc., and owner/operator of Apichemical Consultants.

ACKNOWLEDGMENTS

The authors thank the many scientists, regulators, and other persons who have contributed either directly through their suggestions or indirectly through their work to this effort. Special thanks are due to Frederick W. Whitehurst, J.D., PhD, FBI Central Laboratory, and Robert G. Owens, Jr, Analytical Services, Inc. for their painstaking review of the complete manuscript. Thanks are also due to Michael Stevens, JD. of Arnall, Golden & Gregory for his digging out references and review of Chapter 3. If it was not for the suggestion of G. Wyn Jones at Analytical Services to prepare and present a course to clients on Data Evaluation, this book would never have been written.

TABLE OF CONTENTS

LIST OF FIGURES

LIST OF TABLES

CHAPTER 1

Introduction

While environmental samples are collected and analyzed in the United States for a variety of reasons, the most common one is in order to demonstrate compliance with one of many Federal or state environmental regulations. Beginning with the Federal Water Pollution Control Act (FWPCA) in 1948, the U.S. Congress has enacted a series of Federal environmental regulations designed to improve the quality of the water in which we fish and swim, the water that we drink, the air that we breathe, and the land on which we live. The majority of the Federal environmental regulations are administered by the U. S. Environmental Protection Agency (EPA), formed in 1970. Major Federal legislation that requires compliance monitoring includes:

- Clean Air Act, first enacted in 1970
- Clean Water Act, first enacted in 1972
- Safe Drinking Water Act, first enacted in 1974
- Resource Conservation and Recovery Act, first enacted in 1976
- Comprehensive Environmental Response, Cleanup, and Liability Act (Superfund), first enacted in 1980.

Additional legislation includes the Federal Insecticide, Fungicide, and Rodenticide Act of 1972 and the Toxic Substances Control Act of 1976. While there are some testing requirements associated with these latter laws, those requirements primarily apply to product testing, not environmental media, and will not be a focus of this discussion.

In response to the five major laws listed above, EPA originally organized a program office around each statute, opting in recent years to consolidate some similar programs in a single office within the Agency. These acts have been reauthorized periodically, sometimes adding new acronyms and new requirements. They have also spawned a number of state regulations in those states that have been granted authority to administer more stringent programs. In addition, the Departments of Defense (DOD) and Energy (DOE) have authority to require the collection and analysis of environmental samples in support of both their respective programs and in order to ensure compliance of these Federal agencies with existing Federal and state environmental statutes.

The overall result has been a sometimes confusing collection of programs designed to monitor compliance with the various statutes. There have been efforts in recent years to consolidate the sampling and analysis approaches used by the Program Offices within EPA and to forge common approaches among EPA, DOD, and DOE. It is too early to claim victory in this consolidation effort, and the proliferation of methods and approaches will likely continue for a number of years to come.

Despite these differences, the common thread among the various programs is that they employ the results of some environmental measurement to determine compliance with some statutory limit, regulatory objective, or "acceptable" level of risk to human health and/or the environment. Given the costs associated with avoiding, controlling, or mitigating environmental contamination, the quality of the measurement data is likely to be subject to scrutiny. Each of these environmental measurements is based on a series of assumptions and judgments, which are, in turn, subject to evaluation by parties other than those making the measurements.

The purpose of this book is to provide:

- An overview of many of the Federal environmental regulations that require compliance monitoring

- An introduction to the sampling and analysis methods associated with those programs

- A generalized discussion of the quality control procedures that are associated with environmental analyses

- A philosophical introduction to data validation (e.g., why validate?)

- Guidance on how to conduct a data validation program tailored to specific program needs.

A. Federal Regulations

The Clean Air Act (CAA) of 1970 grew out of a 1948 law that had been administered by the Department of Health, Education, and Welfare. At present, the CAA regulates air emissions from mobile, stationary, and area sources. It establishes national standards for ambient air quality, mobile sources, hazardous air pollutants, and new emission sources. Monitoring requirements associated with the CAA range from state-administered programs for testing tailpipe emissions from automobiles to relatively sophisticated methods for the collection and analysis of toxic organics in ambient air. In addition, some CAA monitoring may require testing of wastewaters that have the potential to emit volatile organics to the air during treatment. Responsibility for the CAA methods lies with the EPA Atmospheric Research and Exposure Assessment Laboratory (AREAL) in Research Triangle Park, NC.

The Clean Water Act (CWA) of 1972 was an updated version of the Federal Water Pollution Control Acts of 1948 and 1965. The goal was to return the surface waters of the U.S. to a "fishable and swimmable" condition through the regulation of wastewater discharges. The heart of the CWA approach is the National Pollutant Discharge Elimination System (NPDES) permit system, which places numerical limits of the concentrations of a variety of pollutants ranging from suspended solids to toxic organics. Section 304(h) of the CWA stipulates that the EPA administrator "promulgate guidelines establishing test procedures for the analysis of pollutants." The 304(h) methods include the familiar "200 series," "300 Series," and "600 Series" methods, as well as the "1600 Series" methods. Originally the purview of the EPA research laboratory in Cincinnati, OH, the responsibility for the 304(h) methods recently has been shifted to the Office of Water's Office of Science and Technology, Engineering and Analysis Division, in Washington, DC. While most of the 304(h) methods contain explicit allowances for flexibility, the CWA requires the use of these methods and precludes use of methods from other programs or organizations unless specifically stipulated in an individual NPDES permit.

The Safe Drinking Water Act (SDWA) of 1974 is designed to protect the quality of drinking water sources. It establishes national priority drinking water standards for a variety of contaminants. The SDWA requires compliance monitoring be carried out on a somewhat complicated schedule that depends on the contaminant and the size of the water system. The responsibility for analytical methods rests in the Technical Support Division of the Office of Ground Water and Drinking Water, and is based in Cincinnati, OH. Relevant methods include the "200 Series" and "300 Series" methods along with the "500 Series" methods for organics. The Drinking Water Program is also evaluating innovative screening techniques such as immunoassays and a performance-based methods system as means to reduce the costs of compliance monitoring.

The Resource Conservation and Recovery Act (RCRA) of 1976 was designed to provide "cradle to grave" regulation of solid and hazardous wastes. As a result, the regulations issued under the authority of RCRA may involve monitoring not only the solid wastes themselves, but also monitoring of wastewaters, groundwaters, air emissions, etc., to ensure that the handling and disposal practices do not simply cause the pollutants to be moved from one medium to another to escape regulation. RCRA employs a permitting system somewhat similar to that used under the CWA. RCRA programs are managed under the EPA Office of Solid Waste (OSW). Given the wide variety of wastes that may be encountered, OSW does not generally mandate the use of specific methods. Rather, they have developed a lengthy guidance document, *"Test Methods for Evaluating Solid Waste,"* commonly known as SW-846. It cannot be overemphasized that with the exception of five specific applications mandated under RCRA rules, the use of methods in SW-846 is *not required* for testing under subtitle C of the RCRA statute. The principal exceptions include monitoring requirements associated with:

- Delisting petitions (attempts to have a waste removed from the list of those subject to specific regulations)

- Incinerator trial burns

- Free liquid determination (a test required under the Land Disposal rules)

- Characteristics (determining if a waste meets the definitions of a toxic or characteristic waste)

- Preparation (but not analysis) of the Toxicity Characteristic Leaching Procedure (TCLP) leachate.

Beyond that, RCRA regulations allow the permitted entity to employ any analytical methods that provide data of adequate quality to support the decision-making process. Unlike the stand-alone methods from the CAA, CWA, and SDWA programs, by and large, SW-846 methods are divided into sample preparation, cleanup, and determinative categories. The analyst should choose the most appropriate of the preparation, cleanup, and determinative methods to achieve the necessary data quality. Despite OSW's educational efforts regarding the guidance nature of SW-846, some states and other Federal agencies have developed specific requirements that mandate the use of SW-846 methods without regard to their obvious limitations.

The Comprehensive Environmental Response, Cleanup, and Liability Act (CERCLA, or Superfund), was enacted in 1980 in response to well-publicized incidents of the risks posed by abandoned hazardous waste dumps. The intention was to clean up such abandoned sites as well as accidental chemical spills by providing a Federal "Superfund" through a tax on chemical feedstocks. At the time that Superfund was authorized, EPA's internal laboratory capacity for the analysis of soil and water samples was clearly not capable of meeting Congressional expectations for the rapid evaluation of a large number of old waste sites. Since the political climate of the time favored privatization efforts, EPA's Office of Emergency and Remedial Response (OERR) established an extramural contracting program for routine laboratory services associated with Superfund. This program came to be known as the National Contract Laboratory Program (CLP).

As part of the formal contracts with as many as 100 commercial laboratories, EPA developed formal detailed Statements of Work (SOWs) that described how the laboratories were to perform the analyses and report the results. The analytical methods were based on the earlier CWA methods with modifications necessary to address solid matrices. The hallmark of the CLP methods was that the level of detail in the SOW would allow a laboratory to provide data of "known and defensible quality." The intent was to minimize the government's reliance on the expert witness capabilities of the laboratory personnel during legal proceedings. An analyst need only testify that he/she had performed the tests, performed them as described in the SOW, and that the lengthy data package submitted by the government as evidence was the product of those analyses. With time, the methods were further "refined" to eliminate areas of misunderstanding, to improve the technical capabilities of the methods, to add or delete analytes to the target lists, and to increase the data-reporting requirements. The result is a rigid protocol for a narrow subset of relevant environmental analyses.

Perhaps the greatest success of the CLP approach has been the relative standardization of data reporting requirements and formats. The CLP SOWs are developed by the Analytical Operations Branch of OERR, in Washington, DC. As with the use of SW-846 as guidance, it cannot be overemphasized that the specifications in the CLP SOWs represent a contract document between EPA and the laboratory. While any competent laboratory should be able to perform the analyses described in the SOW and may be able to produce a CLP-like data package given the proper software, the fact remains that CLP analyses are those that are performed under contract to EPA. Any other use of the SOW is dependent on the ability of the person paying the bills to incorporate the specifications of the SOW in an enforceable contract with a commercial laboratory.

B. Transition from Academia

Environmental analytical chemistry is not a discipline that mysteriously dropped out of the sky on the day in 1970 that EPA was formed. Its roots are founded in the basic research aimed at understanding the biosphere and performed in universities around the world and in applied research aimed at exploiting such diverse resources as agricultural production, petroleum deposits, and the vast uncharted ocean depths.

In the early 1970s, when EPA first proposed to use gas chromatography in combination with mass spectrometry (GC/MS) to analyze environmental contaminants, the proposal was met with skepticism and a fair dose of incredulity. While GC/MS clearly had a role as a research tool in academic laboratories and sophisticated industrial settings, few believed it could be employed for quantitative measurements of organics at part per billion levels in environmental matrices by commercial laboratories. The results depended entirely too much, it was said, on the interpretive skill of the analyst. If applied to a wide range of contaminants in a single sample, the resulting data would overwhelm the analyst: it would take years to get useful results. We now know that these predictions (or prejudices) were wrong. As primitive as they may seem today, computer systems became available that could deal with much of the data interpretation. No longer did the analyst have to rely on years of training and the dog-eared copy of McLafferty's mass spectral interpretation book that may have hung on a string from the side of the instrument. It also meant that these analyses could move from the academic laboratories to commercial laboratories geared towards production of results in days, instead of months.

This shift was accompanied by a host of new concerns. Whereas the careful, deliberative approach employed in academia relied on the skill and reputation of the analyst and the conservative approach of peer review of results before publication, commercial production laboratories entailed no such approach. When environmental analyses were used to monitor compliance with the various regulations enacted in the 1970s, and lack of compliance might result in substantial financial penalties, it became obvious that one could no longer depend on the reputation of a few skilled professors and their legions of graduate students. The paradigm of "Trust us, we know what we're doing" just did not apply.

EPA's response to this problem under the Clean Water Act was to develop a series of standardized test methods for wastewater analyses. The "Methods for Chemical Analysis of Water and Wastes" (MCAWW) was an early result. As the methods were expanded to cover organic compounds, EPA received critical feedback from its own Science Advisory Board who determined that a common, systematic approach to assuring the quality of the analytical results was needed. This approach was adopted in the early 600 Series methods, and included considerations of precision, accuracy, sensitivity, and specificity, as evidenced by the results of such laboratory quality control operations as method blanks, spiked samples, duplicate analyses, calibration checks, the use of surrogate compounds, etc. Subsequently adopted by every EPA program office in one form or another, it is these quality control operations that permit the data to be "validated."

C. Why Validate?

Given the sometimes lengthy quality control requirements of analytical methods from EPA or other sources, why is it necessary to validate the results? Perhaps the simplest answer is that people are involved. Despite the degree of automation that may be involved in many analyses, there are still major aspects of the process that are controlled by people, whether they be the analyst operating the instrument, the technician extracting the sample, or the person receiving the cooler at the loading dock. Errors happen. And whether they are errors of commission or omission (things done and left undone), they can have drastic effects on the results. Examples include every-day problems from transcription errors that mix up the sample number to misread instructions. Problems that are sometimes more difficult to uncover are the use of an inappropriate method, say one with less sensitivity than is required to meet a regulatory threshold, as a result of a lack of communication within the laboratory or between the client and laboratory.

Two other reasons that data are validated are monetary. If the results of a $150 analysis can cause a facility to incur a $25,000 fine for noncompliance with their NPDES permit, it makes sense to validate those results, even if that validation costs as much as the original analysis (it usually doesn't). Similarly, if the results of an analysis are to be used to design and construct a treatment facility that may cost millions of dollars, it only makes sense to check the validity of the data that are the basis for the design.

Unfortunately, the second monetary reason for validation is also a result of human nature, namely greed. Economic pressures and the chance to make a fast buck have led some laboratories to cut corners. While such cost-savings measures are not necessarily a problem, a few laboratories have resorted to out and out fraud, falsifying sample results, quality control data, etc. Data validation is not a panacea in these cases. It will not uncover every instance of fraud. It does, however, provide a reasonable level of assurance that the results are what they purport to be.

D. Data Quality Objectives

The last reason to validate results is that the end user of the data is much more likely to understand how the data are to be applied than the laboratory. Despite the use of standardized analytical methods and sometimes exacting quality control specifications, there remain some aspects of the analyses of environmental samples that are legitimately open to professional judgments and interpretations. We believe that the end user may be in the best position to determine how to apply the results to the problem at hand and how to interpret those issues that fall outside of simple black-and-white decisions.

EPA developed the concept of data quality objectives (DQOs) as an aid to its environmental decision-making processes. While much of the DQO process is beyond the scope of this book, it is the driving force in data validation. DQOs are the expression of the degree of uncertainty that the decision-maker can tolerate in the environmental data being employed to make the decision. DQOs are often expressed in terms of precision, accuracy, reliability, representativeness, and comparability (PARRC). Some of these can be readily transposed into quality control limits for the analytical process. If a decision will change if the input data differ by as little as 25%, then the QC limit for the precision of duplicate analyses should be set at 25% or less. Similarly, accuracy specifications can be transposed into recovery limits for spiked samples. Other organizations have adopted the DQO concept or developed similar means of establishing data quality requirements.

Since the laboratory performing the analyses often has limited knowledge of the intended end use of the results, the DQOs allow the end user to establish the requirements for those results up front, at the beginning of the sample collection and analysis process, and, hopefully, to determine the appropriate analytical methods to be employed, the quality control limits that apply, and the nature of any corrective actions to be taken by the laboratory or the data user in response to problems. Data validation becomes part of the evaluation process inherent in the DQO concept.

E. Data Validation History

Just as the specifics of the analytical methods differ between EPA programs, so do the specifics of the data validation procedures. The only formal data validation guidance available from the EPA for many years was that developed for the Contract Laboratory Program. Given the nature of the CLP and the fact that many laboratories could be producing results related to a single hazardous waste site, the EPA recognized the need to review the specific analytical results. This review was performed at the level of the EPA Region, as the Regional offices were responsible for the decisions on cleanup and remediation. As one might expect, the reviews performed in ten different EPA Regions did not always have a common focus. Thus, the "National Functional Guidelines for Data Validation" were developed by the OERR Program. The purpose was to establish a common approach and framework for validation of CLP results while still allowing for the necessary degree of professional judgment and understanding of the specific activities to be carried out at a given site. The guidelines were based on the existing CLP statements of work, and provided a series of data qualifier flags[1] to be applied according to common rules.

The guidelines can be seen as breaking the analytical results down into three categories: data that are completely acceptable without reservation, data that are qualified and might be used with appropriate caution, and data that should be rejected for use. The first category posed no great problems. The latter two categories eventually spawned a whole new level of data validation: contractual compliance. Because the CLP results were produced under a contract between EPA and the laboratory, some at EPA believed that the data review process should be coupled to a feedback process that sought to control laboratory performance through monetary consequences. If the analysis did not meet the letter of the contract, there ought to be some financial penalty associated with poor performance.

Recognizing that the data review process was already sufficiently time-consuming and that its technical personnel were not necessarily the most appropriate ones to be making contractual determinations, EPA developed the data acceptability screening (DAS) process that sought to evaluate the laboratories contractual performance irrespective of the technical utility of the results. DAS eventually became codified as the Contract Compliance Screening (CCS) procedures and was incorporated into the government's contractual right of inspection clause in all CLP contracts in 1987. Thus, EPA had in place procedures to evaluate both the technical quality of the results and the contractual performance of the laboratory and could separate the effects of the two. Data might be both technically correct and the laboratory contractually compliant, the data might be technically usable and the laboratory contractually non-compliant, the data might be unusable and the laboratory compliant, or the data might be unusable and the laboratory non-compliant. Data usability was determined by the end users in the Regions while the contractual issues of performance were addressed by the CLP National Program Office.

---

[1] "Quality" as an adjective applied to data is a good term and connotes confidence in the results. On the other hand "qualified" used as an adjective is a pejorative term and indicates that there are problems with the data.

At present, the only other formal data validation guidance available from EPA is from the Office of Water. Although the overall focus is on laboratory resolution of analytical problems, *Guidance on Evaluation, Resolution, and Documentation of Analytical Problems Associated with Compliance Monitoring*, June 1993, EPA 821-B-93-001, provides a basic outline of procedures that may be used for data review associated with CWA compliance monitoring. Often referred to as the "pumpkin book" due to the color of the cover and the length of the title, this guidance document also contains a chapter that discusses, in relatively simple terms, various aspects of contracting for analytical services. The Office of Water performs data validation on results that it collects in developing effluent guidelines. Those procedures are determined on an industry-by-industry basis, depending on the specific analyses to be performed. There is no national guidance on validation of NPDES results.

Compliance monitoring data are collected under the Safe Drinking Water Act, however, there is not yet any data validation guidance nor a formal program used by the EPA for these results. Instead, the Office of Ground Water and Drinking Water relies on its laboratory certification program to ensure the quality of the results.

The Office of Solid Waste also has no formal guidance on data validation, nor is it discussed to any degree in the SW-846 manual. While the RCRA Program validates the results it collects in the course of hazardous waste listing determinations and other regulatory efforts, the details are usually spelled out in a Quality Assurance Project Plan for the specific project. By and large, the procedures resemble those from the CLP, with allowances made for the fact that many of the SW-846 analytical methods bear little resemblance to the limited number in the CLP.

There is no known guidance for validation of data from the air methods.

The Army Corps of Engineers and other DOD agencies have extensive data validation procedures in place, and guidance is available on these procedures.

F. Data Validation Versus Contractual Compliance

The distinction between the usability of the data and the contractual performance of the laboratory is a critical one. Based on EPA's experience with the CLP, the evaluation of a laboratory's contractual compliance is best separated from the validation of the data themselves. This book is designed to address the validation of environmental data to determine their usability. We make no attempt to address the contractual responsibilities incumbent upon both a commercial laboratory and its clients beyond the simple statement that a well-written contract between these two parties is often essential to the successful analysis of environmental samples.

Data validation is best divorced from any thoughts of penalties to the laboratory. The job of the data validator is *not* to "get" the laboratory or to find problems. While the results of a data validation effort may lead to corrective actions by the laboratory or to changes in their procedures, those actions must be secondary to determining the suitability of the data for the end use. Leave the contractual issues to the lawyers and the accountants. Establish a good rapport with the laboratory staff, as effective communications are often the key to efficiently resolving those problems that do occur during validation.

G. Goals of This Book

One goal of this book is to provide an overview of the data validation process so that the reader can then examine the particulars of any formal data validation program in current use. In addition, we hope to walk the reader through a discussion of why particular techniques of quality control are used with certain analytical methodologies under one monitoring program and not in others. It is also a goal that readers will develop an understanding of how quality control results are used to interpret the data that has been reported on their samples.

Analysis is expensive. If this book helps purchasers of analytical data get their money's worth from the information they have bought, then we, the authors, have met our objectives.

CHAPTER 2

Scientifically Valid Data

Scientifically valid data result from the proper application of the techniques of qualitative and quantitative analysis. Qualitative analysis is the identification of what is in the sample. To a great extent the answer that is obtained from a qualitative analysis depends on what techniques were used to generate the information. If the desire is to know if the sample is acidic or basic, then a simple qualitative test with a piece of litmus paper will provide a suitable answer. However, if the desire is to determine what acids or bases are present in the sample, the results from the litmus paper test are only the starting point for the rest of the identification procedure. It is important to understand that correct identification of target analytes results from a series of qualitative tests performed on the sample, each test serving to eliminate a subset of other possible chemicals. If the litmus test turns red, that eliminates the possibility of bases being in the sample. It is known that acids are present, but not which ones. Further testing is needed.

Once the sample components are identified then the question can be asked "how much is present?" Quantitative analysis provides the answer to the "how much" question. Quantitative analysis is performed by testing a series of prepared solutions of known concentration (standards) of the target analyte to establish a calibration, then testing the unknown solution and comparing the response obtained from the unknown with those of the standards.

Of the two types of analysis, qualitative analysis is the more important. That a particular sample is reported by a laboratory to contain 5.00 mg/L of "methyl ethyl bad-stuff," is irrelevant if the identification of the "methyl ethyl bad-stuff" is in question. For example, benzene is a cancer-causing pollutant commonly associated with gasoline spills from underground storage tanks. Most samples being tested for benzene are analyzed on a gas chromatograph (GC) coupled to either a photoionization detector (PID) or a mass spectrometer (MS). The GC-PID combination is a good quantitative tool if benzene is known to be present; however, it is severely limited as a qualitative instrument. The compounds in Table 2-1 are a partial listing of the known compounds that can be misidentified as benzene when a GC-PID is used for analysis. Most regulations are compound-specific, and even though some of the compounds in Table 2-1 can pose considerable health threats, the misidentification of benzene for one of them can create severe economic problems for the site owner if benzene is the regulated compound.

Table 2-1. **Partial Listing of Compounds that Can Co-elute with Benzene During Analysis with a GC-PID.**

Methyl acrylate	Hexafluorobenzene	Ethyl acetate
Cyclohexene	Cyclohexadiene	Trimethylstilbene
Dichlorocyclohexene	Bromocyclohexene	Methylhexylether
Dimethyl-isobutylamine	2,3-Dichloro-1,4-dioxane	1,3-Dioxolane
Diphosphine	Diisopropylamine	1,2-dichloroethane

Table 2-1. **Partial Listing of Compounds that Can Co-elute with Benzene During Analysis with a GC-PID.** *Continued*

Isocyanoethane	Ethylisobutylether	Ethylchloromethylether
Nitroethane	Ethylpropargylether	Bromochloroethene
1,2-Dimethoxyethane	Diisopropylfluorophosphate	Ethylal
Allyl formate	Propyl formate	beta-Furlyl chloride
2-Methyltetrahydrofuran	Hexadiene	Hexatriene
Dichlorohexadiene	Divinylacetylene	3-Methyl-1-hexene
Hexyne	Dichloropropionaldehyde	Pyran
Dimethoxydimethyl silane		

The absence of any response for "benzene" on the GC-PID means that most of the above compounds, including benzene, can be eliminated as present in the sample; however, a positive response means that benzene and/or any of the chemicals in Table 2-1 could be present. For a completely uncharacterized sample any identifications claimed by the GC-PID procedure are at best tentative, akin to claiming that nitric acid is present based on a litmus test for acids and bases. The GC-MS procedure on the other hand is primarily an identification tool that is capable of providing quantitative information. Using a GC-MS, benzene can be qualitatively and quantitatively differentiated as present from all the compounds in Table 2-1, whether benzene is in the saimes and Pixture of any of the above compounds.

A. Individual Sample Concerns

There are five general questions[1] the analyst must answer to be able to claim that the result of the test is correct and accurately reflects the content of the sample. They are:

1. Is the test capable of measuring the analyte?

This is a research question and deals with method development. Most regulatory agencies with environmental responsibilities publish lists of methods approved for use. The basic assumption is that one individual or group within the regulatory agency has performed an assessment of the procedure and established that, in fact, it does work on the particular types of samples at question. If an approved method is not used for the analysis it is up to the method user to generate a method validation package that establishes in considerable detail that the method does work. The validation package should include exhaustive comparison of the results obtained from the proposed method with those obtained from approved methods in both an inter-laboratory and intra-laboratory framework, in addition to interference studies, method and instrument detection limit studies, multiple-level matrix spikes studies of representative sample types, and precision and accuracy determinations.

---

[1] Smith, R.-K., Chapter 10, *Water and Wastewater Laboratory Techniques*, 1995, Water Environment Federation, Alexandria, VA

2. How close is the test result to the real level of the analyte in the sample?

This is the concept of accuracy, which is how close the result is to the true level of target analyte in the sample. Accuracy can be determined through the analysis of matrix spikes: addition of a known amount of target analyte to a portion of the sample, then analyzing the sample and comparing the result with the true added amount.

3. Can the same result be generated repeatedly on the sample?

This is the concept of precision, which is the ability to repeatedly obtain the same result on analysis of the sample. Precision is determined by analysis of sample replicates and comparison of the obtained results.

4. What is the lowest level of analyte that can be determined in the sample?

Detection limits are an expression of this concern. Factors that contribute to this concept are:

- Innate ability of the instrument to differentiate a signal generated by the analyte from the background instrument electronic or chemical noise (Instrument Detection Limit - IDL)

- Imprecision that is added to the detection capabilities of the analyte due to the sample processing manipulations (Method Detection Limit - MDL)

- Imprecision that is added to the detection capabilities resulting from processing of the sample phase or matrix (Practical Quantitation Level - PQL, Minimum Level - ML, Reporting Limit - RL, *etc.*)

- Adjustments made to the detection limits based on difficulties encountered in analyzing the real sample (dry weight adjustments, dilution factors, *etc.*).

5. Is the target analyte really present at the site?

There are a number of considerations that fall under this question. First, has the target analyte been convincingly shown to be present in the sample, or is an interference actually being measured? Interferences can be positive or negative, *i.e.* they can either hide the real presence of the target analyte in the sample (a false negative) or they can generate a positive signal in the test without the target analyte actually being present (a false positive). Second, given that the target analyte was detected correctly at the end of the analytical process, was the target analyte in the sample at the time of sample collection or was it added to the sample during the analytical process? Laboratory contamination is an insidious problem all analysts have to face, and an active program must be in place to combat it. Third, was the analyte originally in the sample but was lost from the sample during the transport or analytical processing?

B. Analytical quality control procedures

Scientists have been aware of the above concerns about the analysis, and over a period of many years, have developed specific procedures for generating data to satisfying them. Collectively these procedures are called **Quality Controls**. Quality controls are designed to produce a quantitative measure of the success of a specific part of the analytical procedure. The results of the quality controls performed on a sample serve as the scientific proof that the analyte is really in—or not in—the sample and that the concentration reported is correct. Without quality control data there is no confidence in the reported results of the sample analysis.

The terms quality control (QC) and quality assurance (QA) have been used by many within the industry as if they are synonomous. They are not.

> *Quality Assurance - An integrated system of management activities involving planning, implementation, assessment, reporting and quality improvement to ensure that a process or service meets the requirements of the customer.*

> *Quality Control - The routine technical activities that quantitatively measure the success of a process or service against standards of performance established to meet the needs of the customer.*

As a client of a laboratory you can review the QC results for a particular sample and make a decision as to whether the results on that sample are acceptable or not. Or you can review the QA systems in place at the laboratory that cover the ordering of supplies, training of the analysts, preparing the final reports and detail the QC that will be performed on each sample. QC indicates nothing about the systems, while QA tells you nothing specific about the validity of the results on your particular sample.

1. Calibration

Calibration is the establishment of a quantitative relationship between the response of the analytical procedure and the concentration of the target analyte. Calibration is the technique that performs the quantitative analysis on the sample. A necessary prerequisite is that a confident identification of the target analyte has already been established.

The main assumption that underlies most calibrations is that there is a regular change in response from the analytical procedure as the concentration of the target analyte in the sample changes. All calibrations have a limited range of concentrations over which this basic assumption is valid. pH electrodes have the longest calibration range of any common laboratory instrument; however, even they are limited to the pH range 1 to 13. Outside these limits erratic response and even irreversible damage to the electrode can occur.

The physical boundaries of the calibration are generally established by the electronic or chemical noise that contributes to a background signal in the instrument on one end and a phenomenon called saturation on the other. Saturation is where a change in concentration of the target analyte produces no corresponding change in the instrument response. This is illustrated in Figure 2-1, where saturation is demonstrated to occur at phosphate levels of 2.0 mg/L and higher. Determination of the electronic noise level is the object of the Instrument Detection Level (IDL), which is discussed in detail below. Between these limiting boundaries calibration is possible.

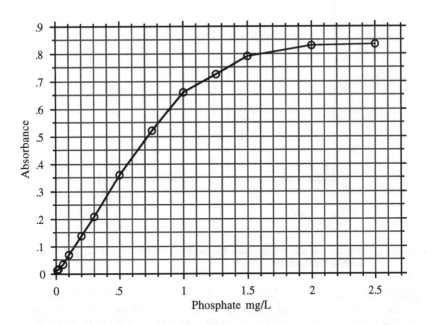

Figure 2-1. **Calibration plot of phosphate analysis by EPA method 365.3, demonstrating saturation at the higher levels of the calibration.**

There are a number of different techniques used by laboratory instruments to quantitate a response. Most instruments in the organic section of the laboratory generate a chromatogram (a plot of signal intensity *vs.* time). In the environmental industry, computers are used to handle the data, and the data are most easily dealt with in digital form, *i.e.* the strength of the signal is represented by some number of units of signal collected over a period of time such as picoamps per 10 milliseconds. The chromatogram is thus a collection of time slices with a signal count representing the intensity of the time slice, as illustrated in Figure 2-2. This method of data handling offers choices in the manner in which a target analyte response is quantitated. The beginning of the analyte response is established as the rise in the signal counts above that of the background and the end of the analyte response is when the signal counts return to the background level. An example is illustrated in Figure 2-2, where the analyte response begins at time 5.5 and ends at time 12.5.

The target analyte response can either be determined as the maximum signal occurring during the peak over the background, a peak height mode, or as the sum of all signals over the duration of the peak, a peak area mode. When a mass spectrometer or other 3-D[2] detector is used, the time slice height can represent either the total signal reaching the detector during the time interval, or it could be only the signal from one particular mass ion or wavelength that is characteristic of the target analyte. Either approach has advantages and disadvantages.

---

[2] 3-D detector is one that generates a third axis of information in addition to time of response and gross intensity of response. Examples of 3-D systems include infrared spectrometer (FTIR), mass spectrometer and photodiode array UV-Vis spectrometer.

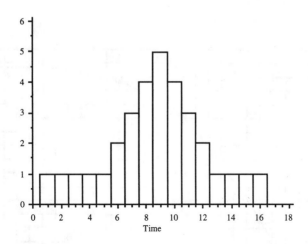

Figure 2-2. **Digital data from a detector used to visualize a target analyte signal in a chromatogram.**

Spectrophotometers and colorimeters used in most wet chemistry laboratories measure the decrease in light of a set wavelength that is capable of passing through a sample. Normally the absorbance is recorded. Absorbance is the mathematical inverse of the light received by the photodector. This results in a single number representing the signal maximum for the sample. Another type of photometric response is found in the metals laboratory where the intensity of a characteristic wavelength of light emitted from excited atoms in a sample is measured as the sample flows through an excitation source. A photodetector is used to transform the light that hits it to an electrical signal. The total light received by the photodetector during a set time period (exposure period) becomes the analyte response. The background light is measured by shifting the path of the light and again collecting the light received by the photodetector. Often the background signal is divided into the analyte signal to generate a background corrected quantitative response.

For some instruments the signal generated from just the target analyte present in the sample is sufficient to establish a quantitative analysis. However, for other instruments there is variation in how much sample actually enters the instrument and gives rise to the signal, or there may be reproducibility problems with the detector itself. It these cases it is necessary to add another analyte, called an internal standard, in known amount to the sample and then relate the signal resulting from the target analyte to that obtained from the internal standard. This technique is called an internal standard calibration. Even in the simplest form, the calibration calculation is made somewhat more complicated by having to deal with the amount and response of the internal standard in addition to that of the target analyte. The equation is as follows:

$$\text{amount} = \frac{(\text{Response}_{TA})(\text{Amount}_{IS})}{(\text{Response}_{IS})\ R_f}$$

where TA and IS stand for target analyte and internal standard respectively, and R_f is the response factor, which is often treated as a constant. The advantages resulting from minimization of sample introduction variability offsets the increased use of computer time.

Most laboratory instruments in use exhibit a very regular change in response within the bounds of the calibration. This change may be in a straight line (linear) or it may be in the form of a gentle curve. This has prompted the widespread use of computer-based mathematical curve fitting algorithms (regression analysis) to generate an equation of the calibration. The "goodness" of fit is measured by either the correlation coefficient (r) or the coefficient of determination or variance (r^2), which are direct products of the regression procedure. Regression procedures are available for fitting the best linear equation through the calibration points.

amount = A + B(response)

Alternately, higher level polynomial equations may be more appropriate of the form:

amount = A + B(response) + C(response)^2 + D(response)^3

where A, B, C and D are constants. Most instruments are capable of being calibrated to obtain a correlation coefficient of >0.995 with the appropriate choice of degree of regression equation.

During the course of performing a calibration, occasionally one of the calibration standards will generate a response that is completely out of line with the responses of all the other standards. An example would be if in Figure 2-1, the 0.3 mg/L standard had generated a 0.05 response rather than the 0.2 response from the instrument. The 0.05 value would clearly be out of line with all the other standards, and a decision must be made as to what to do about it. The choices to be considered are to re-analyze the errant point, to scrap the calibration and start all over again, or to fix the calibration. The root causes for the errant point may be an operator blunder, an instrument malfunction in either sample introduction, analysis, or data collection, or a totally unknown reason. A clearly identified and obvious reason for the errant result can lead to a desire to fix the calibration. The idea is that if this obvious incident reoccurs during analysis of samples, it will be immediately recognized as such and the sample re-analyzed. If the fix is performed by dropping the point from the calibration, this is called calibration data censoring. This becomes an important issue if six calibration points are required for method compliance and only six standards were run. Dropping one of the results generates a good curve, but then there are only five standards in the calibration. The calibration can generate good data but it is non-compliant.

On the other hand, there may be no definitive reason for the errant point. Censoring the calibration point in this situation to obtain a pretty curve is highly questionable as the operator has no way of knowing when the same thing has reoccurred with a sample. The bottom line is that there may be a scientifically valid reason for calibration data censoring; however, in general, the practice is viewed with a great deal of well-deserved mistrust. The best remedy is to scrap the calibration and start all over again.

2. Multiple Standard Addition (MSA)

Multiple standard addition is a calibration technique performed in each individual sample. It is used to overcome analytical interferences in the sample. The procedure is to first perform the normal analytical test on the sample against a calibration curve to obtain an approximate idea of how much target analyte is in the sample. Next additional portions of the sample are spiked with the target analyte at 50%, 100% and 150% of the approximate level already determined. Each of these samples is then run through the test procedure and the response recorded. A plot of the response *vs.* added amount in each sample is prepared, and a linear regression is performed on the three points. If a regression coefficient of greater than 0.995 is obtained the regression line is extended until it intersects the amount axis. The intersection point is the negative of the amount of target analyte in the unspiked sample. An example of the plot is presented in Figure 2-3. The amount of target analyte determined in this sample is 1.52.

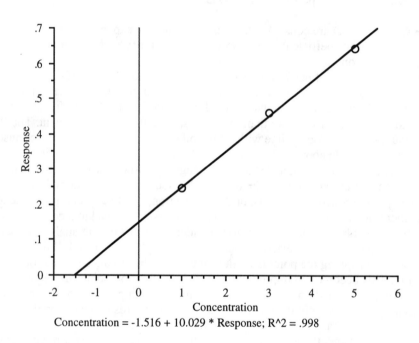

Concentration = -1.516 + 10.029 * Response; R^2 = .998

Figure 2-3. Multiple Standard Addition plot.

3. Calibration Verification

There are two aspects to calibration verification. First, there is a need to independently check the accuracy of the calibration curve immediately after it is prepared. This is generally termed an Initial Calibration Verification (ICV). Second, there is a need to periodically check the calibration curve to determine if it is still reliable. This is generally termed a Continuing Calibration Verification (CCV).

The initial calibration verification is performed to determine if, in fact, the calibration curve that has just been generated is valid. In essence it is a check upon the accuracy of the individual calibration standards used to perform the calibration. The ICV solution is, at a minimum, prepared from a different manufacturer's lot number than that used for preparation of the standard or better yet, obtained from a different manufacturer than that of the calibration standards. Further, the ICV solution should be at a different concentration than that of any of the standards but still within the bounds of the calibration curve. Most methods have acceptance criteria for ICV; however, in the absence of specific criteria, normally the ICV concentration obtained from the calibration curve should agree within ±5% of the true value of the ICV solution.

Failure to obtain ICV results within the acceptance criteria is interpreted that the calibration curve is not valid. Possible causes for the failure are that:

1. The concentrations of either the calibration standards or the ICV solution are not accurate.
2. There is a problem with the calculation of the calibration curve.
3. The instrument developed a problem between the completion of the calibration and the analysis of the ICV.
4. An instrument problem which existed during the calibration was corrected prior to the ICV analysis.
5. The analysis of the ICV was botched.

The analyst should take investigative measures to find which of the possible causes was the reason for the failure. Re-analysis of the ICV is often taken as the first step. Other steps are taken until a root cause for the problem is found. Remedial measures then are taken to correct the problem. If standard or ICV purity or concentration accuracy are the possible cause, then a third or fourth standard solution from different manufacturers may be used to trace the problem. The instrument must be completely re-calibrated if no identifiable cause for the ICV failure can be found. Under no circumstances is the calibration used for unknown sample analysis until acceptance criteria for the ICV are met.

The continuing calibration verification (CCV) is used to ascertain that the initial calibration is still holding and correct as the instrument is used to process samples. For instruments that incorporate analyte identification into the procedure such as retention time matching from a gas chromatograph or spectral matching from a mass spectrometer, CCV also serves to determine that the identification criteria are still being met. The source of the CCV solution could be one of the calibration standards, the initial calibration standard at a different concentration than those used for the initial calibration, or it could be from an independent source than that of the initial calibration standards. The CCV should be at a different concentration than the ICV. The minimum frequency for performance of the CCV is once each day that the instrument is used for sample analysis. Some methods specify more frequent CCV such as at the beginning and end of each analytical day, every ten samples or even every four samples as in the case of sulfate analysis by turbidimetric determination of barium sulfate.

Some instruments, particularly GC and GC-MS, may overwrite the quantitation files with the results obtained from the daily CCV to update identification and quantitation criteria as software default settings. This is an improper use of continuing calibration verification. What this practice does in essence is replace the multi-level initial calibration with a daily one-point calibration, with the string attached that the daily one-point results have to be within the method acceptance criteria for CCV as compared to the initial full calibration, for instance ±20% of the initial calibration. There is no scientifically rigorous justification for this practice. The size of the acceptance window of the CCV criteria is recognition of the random error inherent in the analytical process. A big acceptance window, such as ±20%, is linked to a procedure that has large amounts of random error, while a small acceptance window such as ±5% is linked to a measurement with lesser amounts of random error. The use of the daily CCV results for quantitation converts the original random error allowance into an allowable systemic error that still has the random error superimposed upon it. Thus an original ±20% quantitation variation is translated into a ±40% variation.

Failure to pass CCV acceptance criteria is interpreted that the calibration curve is no longer valid. The actual cause for the CCV failure may have little to do with the calibration curve and includes all the possible scenarios listed above for the ICV. However, if no identifiable cause for the CCV failure is found, and re-analysis of the CCV to obtain acceptable results is not performed, then the accuracy of the calibration curve becomes questionable. Further, all sample results obtained from the instrument since the last acceptable CCV are also in question. Sample results that are regarded as valid will always be bracketed in time by acceptable CCV analyses.

4. IDL and MDL

IDL stands for Instrument Detection Limit, while MDL is the abbreviation for Method Detection Limit. These are two different but complementary concepts used to evaluate the lowest level of detection of which the method is capable. The IDL and MDL together are very similar in concept to the signal-to-noise ratio that many manufacturers will report as a performance characteristic of their product. The procedures for determining MDL are published at 40 CFR 136, Appendix B and all programs across the EPA cite this reference. There is no formal procedure for IDL outside of the CLP-SOW for inorganic analyses.

The instrument detection limit (IDL) acknowledges the presence of baseline electronic or background noise in the instrument and then attempts to provide guidance as to what signal should be regarded as noise and what signal arises from a target analyte. The IDL is determined by repetitively using the instrument to test a target analyte-free sample or extract over several days, then calculating the standard deviation of the repetitive determinations. The standard deviation is multiplied by three. The resulting value is the IDL. Any signal higher than the IDL is regarded as statistically significant as compared to the noise level of the instrument.

The method detection limit study attempts to answer the question, "What is the lowest level of analyte in a sample that will result in a signal different than zero?" The study is based upon repetitive analysis of an interference-free sample spiked with a known amount of the target analyte. In general, seven aliquots of the spiked sample are taken through the entire sample preparation and instrument analysis protocol. Seven is frequently used as the best balance between effort put into the study and the desire to use as small a one-tailed *t*-statistic multiplier as possible. (As the number of replicates decreases the *t*-statistic increases dramatically.) Four replicates are allowed in MDL determinations under methods included in SW-846; however, the one-tailed *t*-statistic is 4.541. The standard deviation of the results is determined, then multiplied by the one-tailed *t*-statistic at the 99% confidence level for the number of degrees of freedom in the study (one less than the number of repetitions used to calculate the standard deviation). For seven repetitions this is a multiplier of 3.143. The resulting value is finally compared to the spike level in the sample. If the sample spike level is within five times the calculated MDL then the procedure is considered successful. If not, the spike level in the sample is adjusted, and the study is repeated.

Table 2-2. **Method Detection Limit Study for Total Organic Carbon (TOC) by EPA Method 415.2.** Analyte-free water spiked at 0.90 mg/L.

Trial	Result
1	0.76
2	0.72
3	0.74
4	0.77
5	0.70
6	0.64
7	0.53
8	0.54
9	0.77
10	0.59
Mean	0.68
SD	0.094
MDL	0.27

Presented in Table 2-2 are the results of an MDL study performed using EPA method 415.2, Total Organic Carbon (TOC). This particular study is what would be regarded as a perfect example of an MDL determination. The analyte spike level was 0.90 mg/L. The spike level is 3.33 times the calculated MDL of 0.27, which is almost exactly in the middle of the desired 2-5 times range. No single result was less than the calculated MDL. However, these results indicate that for samples containing TOC at the 0.90 mg/L level, there is a distinct bias for low answers. Sample repetitions give values from 0.53 mg/L to 0.77 mg/L and an average result of 0.68 mg/L; but the answers will not be zero, or lost in the instrument noise. The MDL is specifically not a measure of the accuracy of the test to give the right result. The MDL measures exactly what it is supposed to measure, based on the wording of the definition.

The IDL is not a measure of the capability of the test procedure to measure target analyte in a sample. It is only a measure of the maximum performance capability of the instrument in the absence of any other effects. The MDL is not a measure of the lowest level of analyte in the sample that can be reported with accuracy. The MDL is only a measure of the ability of the test procedure to generate a positive response for the target analyte in the absence of any other interferences from the sample. It is actually a determination of the precision of obtaining a response from very low levels of target analyte and has no bearing on quantitative accuracy. The minimum level of target analyte in a sample that can be detected and accurately quantitated is generally defined as some multiple of the MDL that is not required to be determined as a method performance characteristic. There is no uniform procedure by which this level is determined, and depending on the procedure, it may be from 5 to 20 times higher than the MDL. The value is frequently called the Practical Quantitation Level (PQL), although many other terms are used to present the same idea.

Real samples contribute noise to the analytical procedure and the instrument response, which is independent of the procedure and instrument. MDL and IDL are performance characteristics that do not take into account any contribution to analytical inaccuracy by sample noise. This is of particular concern if the method does not provide a high degree of certainty in the identification of target analytes, for example the GC and HPLC methods using two-dimensional detectors. For these technologies, the MDL serves as a good indication of the false negative threshold, *i.e.* a non-detect at the MDL really indicates a lack of analyte in the sample. However, there is a substantial probability that a reported detect at or near the MDL is actually due to random noise in the sample, which, by random coincidence, happens to fall in the retention time windows on both the analytical and confirmation column, resulting in a false positive. A variety of techniques are used to express the effect of the sample noise on the ability to detect and quantify the target analyte in the sample. Normally these boil down to some multiplier used on the MDL to give a number that is variously called Minimum Level (ML), Reporting Level (RL), Practical Quantitation Level (PQL), and a number of other terms. Minimum Level has a set multiplier of 3.18 times the MDL; however, the other values have arbitrary multipliers of from 2 to 20 ,which, in reality, should be dependent upon individual samples. Samples that are interference- and noise-free could have very small multipliers, while "dirtier" samples would have larger multipliers.

These considerations should give persons who are using analytical results as input data to risk assessment and site modeling programs some pause for reflection. There are a number of ways in which data reported as "Below Detection Limit" have been handled in these evaluations. One technique is to give the BDL result the value of the quantitation limit, another is use one half the quantitation limit as the input and still another is to use the value zero. As a suggestion it may be a more accurate reflection of the data generation process to use the IDL as the default value and require the laboratory to report estimated values for analytes detected in the IDL-QL range. Values at or above the quantitation level are—and should be—expected to possess a measure of reliability; values below the quantitation limit are admittedly guesses and subject to frequent false positives and false negatives but useful as an indication of trace contamination. It is frequently necessary to differentiate between "trace" contamination and "not detected" in site assessment. Although the use of "zero" is unscientific from the laboratory point of view, it may be very appropriate for site evaluation as a value for a "non-detect," particularly when non-scientists are involved in a decision-making process.

5. Holding Times and Preservatives

Holding times are defined as the amount of time that elapses between the collection of the sample from the source in the field and the beginning of the analysis procedure. Preservatives are defined as techniques used to maintain the target analytes at concentrations representative of those in the source sampled until the sample is analyzed in the laboratory. Published holding times are viewed as valid as long as the associated preservation and container requirements have been met.

There are a number of choices for containers. For the most part the construction materials are either high density polyethylene (HDPE) or borosilicate glass, frequently with a Teflon® liner to the cap or lid of the container. As a general rule of thumb metal containers should not be used for metal analytes, and plastic containers not be used for organic analytes. Glass containers are not suitable for either boron or silica analysis. The containers are of a variety of shapes and sizes, the appropriate choice being dependent upon the type of sample and the target analyte. Of major concern is the cleanliness of the container. It must be demonstrated to be target analyte-free, generally accomplished by filling a representative container from a lot with reagent water, then analyzing the water. Records of these container blanks should be kept on file by the laboratory.

Preservatives are used to counter the naturally occurring biological, chemical and physical processes that change the phase and concentration of target analytes in samples. For the most part sources of environmental samples are in a non-equilibrium state. The removal of a portion from the source as an analytical sample allows the sample to come to an equilibrium prior to analysis, which is not representative of the source. Thus metals may precipitate from water samples; air can mix with soil samples and change the oxidation state from anaerobic to aerobic; and micro-organisms may degrade organic analytes. In the case of chlorinated sources, collection and storage of the sample may allow for more complete oxidation and disinfection, which is not representative of the source.

Common preservation techniques are cooling, dechlorination and pH adjustment of the sample. Preservations almost always have some measurable specification that determines whether appropriate preservation has been accomplished. Thus the directions "Cool to 4°C," indicate the action that is required and a quantitative measure of the success of the action. pH adjustment is always specified to a final pH level such as greater than 12 or less than 2.

For most target analytes in the environmental industry, there have never been any experimental determinations of appropriate holding times or preservatives. The holding time and preservative guidelines that do exist through out the environmental methods and regulations are usually estimates based on how long someone thought a reasonably efficient laboratory would take to generate a result. Within the last several years there have been some holding time studies particularly for mercury[3], volatile organic analytes[4], and explosives residues[5]. What has been found in these few studies is that, as expected, some of the estimates are good and some of them very bad. The estimates in some cases were far too long, while, in others, they are unreasonably short. And not to anyone's surprise, it has been demonstrated that for an analyte group, there are different holding time and preservative needs for individual components within the group. The needed holding times and preservatives for the aromatic hydrocarbons benzene, toluene and ethylbenzene within the volatile organic group were found to be quite different than those suitable for the saturated halogenated analytes.

All of which is not to say that the existing holding time, preservative, and container charts found in the environmental regulations can be safely ignored because they have no founding in scientific experiment. No, much to the contrary for many applications, strict adherence to the tabulated information is an absolute necessity in the context of legal admissibility of analytical data. For the most part courtroom defenses do not deal with the issues of the foundations of individual regulations and laws in the scientific literature

---

[3] Hamlin, S.N. "Preservation of Samples for Dissolved Mercury," 1989. *Water Resources Bulletin*, 25(2):255-262.

[4] Turriff, D., C. Reitmeyer, L. Jacobs and N. Melberg. "Comparison of alternatives for sampling & storage of VOCs in soil;" Hewitt, A. "Determining volatile organic compound concentration stability in soil." Eleventh Annual Waste Testing and Quality Assurance Symposium, July 22-26, 1995, Washington, D.C.

[5] Jenkins, T., and P.G. Thorne, "Evaluation of the new clean solid phases for extraction of nitroaromatics and nitramines from water." Eleventh Annual Waste Testing and Quality Assurance Symposium, July 22-26, 1995, Washington, D.C.

but rather with whether the existing laws and regulations have been followed or not followed.

6. Blanks

Blanks are for the purpose of determining the level of laboratory and field contamination introduced into the samples, independent of the level of target analytes found in the sample source. Similar to the old adage that the best place to catch a disease is in a hospital, the best place to find environmental pollutants is in the laboratory. A survey[6] of groundwater results from over 500 sites found that laboratories reported methylene chloride and bis(2-ethylhexyl)phthalate as the most common pollutants detected in the samples. Although these materials may, in fact, be detected in the environment, they are many times more abundant in the laboratory and are not that prominent in-so-far as industrial production, use and disposal are concerned.

Sources of sample contamination can include the containers and equipment used to collect the sample, preservatives added to the sample, other samples in transport coolers and laboratory sample storage refrigerators, standards and solutions used to calibrate instruments, glassware and reagents used to process samples and the analytical instrument sample introduction equipment. Each area of analysis has its own particular suite of common laboratory contaminants. Active measures must be performed to continually measure the ambient contamination level and steps taken to discover the source of the contamination to eliminate or minimize the levels. Random spot contamination can also occur from analytes that are not common laboratory problems but that can arise as a problem for a specific project or over a short period of time.

Blanks regularly collected and analyzed in the laboratory include:

- Container blanks
- Trip blanks
- Field blanks
- Equipment blanks
- Sample storage blanks
- Sample preparation (batch) blanks
- Instrument blanks.

All of these blanks require the use of analyte-free water. Analyte-free water is defined as water that has been prepared for a specific use in the laboratory and been determined through testing to be free of contamination for that specific use. Water is notoriously hard to purify and keep pure. The traditional Type I, II, and III standards of water purity developed and published by ASTM are generally insufficient for environmental laboratory and sampling purposes. Modern laboratory water purification technology focuses upon the application of the water rather than generic standards. Thus water used for trace metals analysis must be demonstrated to be free of trace metals contamination. Organic and microbiological contamination in water used for trace metals purposes is immaterial as long as it does not interfere with the application. Water used in

---

[6] Plumb, R.H. Jr. "The Importance of Volatile Organic Compounds as a Disposal Site Monitoring Parameter" in *Groundwater Contamination and Analysis at Hazardous Waste Sites*, S. Lesage and R.E. Jackson (Eds), Marcel Dekker, Inc. 270 Madison Ave, NY, NY 10016, 1992, pp. 173-197.

the volatile organics laboratory must be free of volatile organics: the level of micro-organisms, metals and non-volatile organics is irrelevant as long as they do not interfere with the volatile organic analysis. Water suitable for each of these applications is probably not suitable for any other application, and in neither case meets any ASTM standards. The insistence in work and project plans upon Type I or Type II water for laboratory and field use for sample collection and analysis ignores the scientific reality of the level of current technology in water purification.

Laboratory contamination can either occur as a random event, or it can appear in every sample as a systematic problem. Although some examples of laboratory contamination will show up in all samples and blanks at exactly the same level, it is a poor laboratory practice to make the assumption that all laboratory problems are systematic and thus can be dealt with by subtracting the amount of contamination discovered in the blank from all the sample results. Likewise it is a poor practice to have a reporting limit of say 10 ppb, discover laboratory contamination in the blank at just less than 10 ppb, for instance 9 ppb, and then report the analyte found in the samples at any amount at or above the reporting level without flagging the results as being due to suspected laboratory contamination. A good rule of thumb is to regard laboratory contaminants as actually present in the sample only when the blank level is less than 5% of the reporting level for that analyte. A reporting level of 10 ppb would then allow a blank level of no more than 0.5 ppb.

There is also the issue of the statistical validity of assessing laboratory contamination in a batch of 20 samples based on the results of one preparation blank analysis for the batch. Systematic contamination can be discovered in this fashion; however, random contamination is the more frequent occurrence. The statistical occurrence of random contamination needs to be monitored using a statistically valid control. The number of blanks that need to be performed will depend upon the desired confidence level of the results and the number of samples under consideration. The needed number of blanks for a project can be calculated (see the DQO-PRO at the end of this Chapter) and performed. Another approach is to examine the results of all the blanks for a particular test performed in the laboratory over the last 3 to 6 months. This will increase the population of results and build confidence in the results obtained from any particular blank within the group. It will also help distinguish systematic sources from random sources.

Container blanks are performed to monitor contamination in sampling containers. For laboratories that clean and reuse sample containers, one or two containers from each cleaning batch should be filled with analyte-free water, and then the filled container treated and analyzed as a sample. Each container used in sampling and cleaned in a batch should be traceable to that batch and results of the container blank kept on file indicating freedom from contamination. For laboratories that purchase precleaned sample containers and do not perform cleaning operations of their own, there is still a necessity for performing blanks. Normally precleaned containers come labeled with lot numbers traceable to manufacturer's cleaning batches. Random selection of containers from a lot number and performance of container blank analysis is generally sufficient to document freedom from contamination. This procedure should be followed even in the cases where the manufacturer provides container blank analysis documentation. This is because the containers have probably been boxed and definitely been transported from the manufacturer's facility to the laboratory, exposing the containers to possible contamination.

Trip blanks are for the purpose of monitoring possible contamination introduced into the sample containers as the containers are moved from the laboratory to the field and back to the laboratory. The sample containers are filled with analyte-free water at the laboratory, then taken to the field, left unopened, and returned to the laboratory in the same coolers used for sample transport. They are analyzed as regular samples in the laboratory. These are particularly valuable for monitoring any possible airborne contamination due to volatile organic analytes capable of diffusing across the Teflon® lined silicone septa used to seal the volatile organic sample vials. Common contaminants found in trip blanks are aromatic hydrocarbons such as benzene, toluene, ethylbenzene and xylenes arising from exposure of the closed sample containers to fumes from internal combustion engines. Less frequent contamination is detected from analyte vapors diffusing into the blank from very high level samples stored in the same sample cooler. Samples collected for mercury analysis are also subject to vapor phase contamination. Trip blanks should be prepared for mercury analysis.

Field blanks are prepared at the sampling site by filling empty sample containers with analyte-free water, adding preservatives and then taking the samples back to the laboratory where they are analyzed as a regular sample. These type of blanks are used to monitor ambient airborne contamination at the site, contamination introduced by the sample handling procedures, and also to monitor possible contamination traceable to the preservatives added to the samples.

Equipment blanks are used to monitor the effectiveness of the cleaning procedure used for decontamination of sampling equipment in the field and the possibility of contamination at one site being carried over to another sampling site. When disposable field sampling equipment is used, equipment blanks serve to monitor the cleanliness of these items. An example of this type of contamination was discovered at a project site where groundwater monitoring wells had been installed and field filtration was performed to obtain samples for total and dissolved metals content. None of the samples for total metals had any antimony present in them; however, a large number of the dissolved metals samples exhibited antimony present between 10 and 50 µg/L. The equipment blanks revealed that the disposable filtration unit membranes had antimony present on them. The amount of antimony found in the dissolved samples depended on how well the filtration units were rinsed prior to filtration of the sample and how much sample was filtered.

The proper way to prepare an effective equipment blank is to take a quantity of analyte-free water to the sampling site, rinse the piece of equipment with the analyte-free water directly into the sample container, add preservatives and then treat as a regular sample. The same analyte-free water should be used to prepare the field blanks. At least one equipment blank is prepared for each type of analyte group collected with each item of equipment.

Sample storage blanks are used to monitor the transfer of target analytes from one sample to another within the sample coolers and sample storage refrigerators. These are particularly valuable when volatile organic samples and mercury samples are concerned. When used to monitor refrigerators, the blank should remain in the refrigerator for the same length of time that the normal sample will reside in storage, or no longer than one week.

Sample preparation blanks are also referred to as batch blanks or method blanks. They consist of a portion of analyte-free water or solid of the same size as that used for the routine sample preparation. Surrogates and other monitoring compounds are added to the blank, then the blank is taken through the entire sample processing procedure just as if it were a regular sample. If selected samples within the batch are given extra processing, for example alumina column clean-up or gel-permeation chromatography, then additional blanks are prepared to monitor these extra steps. The sample preparation blanks serve as a monitoring control for a variety of possible sources of contamination in the laboratory. These include the laboratory ware used for sample preparation and their cleaning procedures, the quality of the reagents added to the samples, the equipment used in the sample processing, and stray sources of contamination such as that arising from the gloves the technicians use to protect their hands.

Contamination discovered in the sample preparation blank should result in a cessation of production analysis until the contamination is confirmed, the source located and finally the contamination controlled or eliminated. After these steps have been completed, then the batch of samples associated with the contaminated blank should be reprocessed and analyzed. The batch blank associated with the reprocessing should be closely examined to verify that the contamination has been controlled.

Instrument blanks consist of analyte-free solutions or solvent samples processed through the instrument periodically just as if they were samples. These should be performed at a minimum of once each day that the instrument is used for sample analysis. Many methods have a set frequency of performing instrument blanks, such as every ten analytical samples. Instrument blanks serve to verify that the instrument is free from contamination. Another use for these blanks is to process them immediately after samples that contain high levels of target analytes or background contamination. In this mode the instrument blanks are being used to detect carry-over of the contents of the previous sample. The instrument blank also serves in this case to flush the instrument. Instrument blanks that are positive for contamination lead to a cessation of analysis until the instrument is decontaminated and determined through re-analysis of the blank to be clean. Depending on the circumstances, this could also lead to re-analysis of all the samples performed immediately prior to the contaminated instrument blank back to the point of the last clean instrument blank.

7. Sample Replicates

Sample replication is the preparation and/or analysis of two or more aliquots of the same sample. They are used as a measure of the ability of the test to obtain the same result on the same sample on repeated analysis. Sample replicates are the primary source of information for determination of the precision of an analysis. There are several possible interpretations of the results obtained from analysis of replicates. The first case involves a result above the reporting level derived from the replicates. The closeness of the individual results gives a direct indication of the ability of the test to generate a reproducible result on the real sample. It is an approximation of the width of the distribution of the random error associated with the test at that level of analyte, *i.e.* how careful the analyst is in the performance of the test. For a test method where the target analyte is almost always found in every sample, sample replicates are a very useful quality control.

The second case concerns an analyte that is not detected in the sample and the replicate. The inability of the test to detect an analyte in the sample is possible information that can be used in a verification of the lack of contamination in the system. However, it may also be a result of a failure of the test procedure to function properly. Lack of target analyte in the sample is the situation for most organic target analytes and many metals. Precision must be generated by other means, most commonly a matrix spike and matrix spike duplicate (see following for a discussion on matrix spikes).

Although analysis of the results from these procedures will generate estimates of precision, the evaluation is at a single target analyte level, and the information is not quite as useful as that derived from sample duplicates where random variation in target analyte level is normally encountered.

The third case is where the analyte is present in the sample at the detection limit or the reporting level. Sometimes the sample and replicate results will fortuitously lie on the reportable side of the detection limit; however, the more common occurrence is that the values bracket the detection limit. This gives one result as a number and the other as a "BDL."

Some test protocols require the preparation and analysis of each sample in duplicate, triplicate or, in one case, as high as quadruplicate. The reported results are obtained from the average of the replicates. This helps to minimize the random error inherent in either the test protocol or the sample itself, particularly when the samples are solids. Sample duplicates, where each duplicate is performed as a replicate, are not very informative and generally a waste of effort, time, and materials.

Many test procedures require the instrumental analysis of the sample be performed in duplicate with the average result reported. The analysis of duplicate portions of the same prepared sample helps to minimize random error in the instrument results. Preparation of the sample in duplicate and then analysis of each duplicate in duplicate is a good quality control on the repeatability of the sample preparation. This information can be used to separate effects due to sample inhomogenity from sample preparation variation.

Sample replicates can be performed as part of the field sampling, in which case they are termed field duplicates. Field duplicates are consecutive samples taken from the same site, so called co-located samples. They are not a sample split obtained by vigorously mixing a large portion of sample and then portioning the sample into separate containers. Field duplicates are normally inserted as part of the regular sample submission to the laboratory and are processed as a regular sample. Field duplicates are an assessment of the variability in the entire sample collection, shipment, and analysis procedure. The field duplicates should be examined very closely to verify that the same set of target analyte hits are reported for both samples and that they are in approximately the same quantity for both samples. Wide variations in particularly the set of target analytes reported from the samples, is a cause for grave concern.

Although some samples are heterogeneous and will give poor comparability of duplicates, regular occurrences of wide variation in the results of replicate analysis is a cause for alarm. Such wide variation of results may suggest that the analyst is not performing the procedure in exactly the same manner for each sample. This may be an indication of needed training, or it may be an indication that one of the techniques used in the sample preparation or sample collection is not functioning properly. Either scenario requires a close evaluation of the process and a corrective action.

8. Matrix Spikes

Matrix spikes are the addition of a known amount of a target analyte to a sample. Analysis of the sample that has been spiked and comparison with the results from the unspiked sample (background) gives information about the ability of the test procedure to generate a correct result from the sample.

Although the matrix spike procedure seems very straightforward, differences in the manner in which it is performed in the laboratory can give difficulty in the interpretation of the results and their applicability to the actual sample. Most target analytes in samples have had a period of time to interact with the matrix of the sample. This can result in the target analyte becoming very tightly bound to the matrix, part of the process termed "aging." The matrix spike procedure is normally performed by adding the target analytes as a solution in a solvent in which they are soluble to the sample, then immediately beginning the sample preparation steps. The solvent used to dissolve the target analyte frequently prevents or changes the interaction of the matrix spike compounds with the sample matrix. Further, little time is allowed for interaction to occur. Good analytical practice would allow time for the spike to interact with the sample after the evaporation of the solvent. In some laboratories, the matrix spike solution is added to a solution or suspension of the sample in the reagents of the sample preparation. An example of this practice is in the sonication extraction of PCBs from a soil sample, where the acetone-methylene chloride extraction solvent is added to the soil, then the matrix spike solution added to the suspension followed by immediate sonication. This practice leads to great recoveries of the matrix spike components; however, it gives essentially no information about the ability of the test to obtain a relevant answer concerning the PCB content of the soil. Quite different results can be obtained if the matrix spike is added to the sample, the solvent allowed to evaporate and the spiked sample permitted to sit for 24 hours prior to the beginning of the sample preparation.

Another concern in the matrix spike procedure is the quantitative level of the spike itself. In general, the greater the level of the spike, the better the recoveries of the spike. However, with regard to relevance to the use of the data, the matrix spike levels should match the levels of concern. In other words, if a regulatory level of 1 mg/L is established for the sample, results from matrix spikes at the 1 mg/L level are more pertinent for interpretation, than matrix spikes at the 100 mg/L level. At the same time the inherent background level of the analyte in the sample itself must also be taken into consideration. If the sample contains 100 mg/L of methyl ethyl badstuff, and the matrix spike adds 1 mg/L of the analyte, the additional amount of the matrix spike is not going to be discernible from the random variation in the test results around the 100 mg/L background. As a rule of thumb the spike level should be at least one to five times the background level of the analyte in the sample.

Another facet of the matrix spike process concerns the target analytes which constitute the matrix spike. If PCBs are the target analyte, it is doubtful that a matrix spike consisting of Lindane, Aldrin and Heptachlor contributes meaningful information about the ability to analyze PCBs. Another consideration is whether a short list of specified matrix spike compounds adequately represents the behavior of all the target analytes actually in the sample.

The above considerations should lead to the conclusion that for matrix spikes to generate useful data for interpretation they really need to be performed after an initial analysis of the sample, and they should be tailored to the specific sample.

Assuming that the matrix spike has been performed conscientiously, the recovery of the matrix spike can be utilized by end users of the data to perform bias correction. In other words the reported value for the target analyte is adjusted upward based on the recovery of the matrix spike. The normal guidelines for bias correction indicate that for matrix spike recoveries less than 80%, reported analyte amounts are divided by the decimal percentage of the recovery. For example if sulfate is reported at 25 mg/kg from a sample and a matrix spike gives a 65% recovery, then the bias corrected amount for the sample is 38 mg/kg. Laboratories are generally prohibited from reporting data that has already been bias corrected.

There are pitfalls associated with the use of bias correction. The first is that the matrix spike must be performed on that exact sample. Most laboratories process samples in batches through the test protocol and there is commonly only one sample in the batch that is matrix spiked. The matrix spike results would strictly apply for the purposes of bias correction to that single sample and should not be generalized to all the samples in the batch. The second pitfall is that there is a distribution of matrix spike recoveries around an average recovery that is characteristic of the procedure and the laboratory. If an average recovery of 100% for a matrix spike compound is associated with a repeated performance standard deviation of 15%, then all matrix spike recoveries within the 95% confidence range (70-130% or ± 2 standard deviations) would correctly be considered to be 100% recovery, and no bias correction would be justified.

It is only when the matrix spike recoveries fall significantly below the normal performance expectations that there are concerns about the recovery of target analyte from the sample. How these concerns can be translated into a correction factor on the results is not straightforward. The most common occurrence is a low matrix spike recovery associated with no target analyte recovery from the sample. Does this mean that there is target analyte in the sample and none has been recovered, or does it suggest that there never was target analyte in the sample? It is because of these complications that most end users of data avoid general application of bias correction using matrix spike recoveries.

9. Post-digestion Spikes

Post-digestion spikes (PDS) are performed after the sample has been prepared and is ready for analysis. These are also termed "analytical spikes." The technique is used in conjunction with a matrix spike to provide data that can separate interferences produced as part of the sample preparation from interferences that are innate qualities of the sample. When used in the metals laboratory on samples being analyzed by ICP, the comparison of the PDS results and the MS results gives an indication of how well the samples were matched in terms of viscosity and ionic strength with the standards used to calibrate the instrument. Low recoveries of post-digestion spikes may lead to the decision that all the analytical results associated with the PDS are suspect and should be treated as estimates rather than reliable values.

10. Laboratory Control Samples

Laboratory control samples (LCS) are also known as quality control samples, Initial Precision and Recovery samples (IPR), Ongoing Precision and Recovery samples (OPR), Initial Demonstration of Ability samples (IDA), Initial Demonstration of Competence samples (IDC), and Continuing Demonstration of Ability samples (CDA). Laboratory control samples consist of a portion of analyte-free water or solid phase sample that is spiked with target analytes at a known concentration. Frequently the LCS spiking solution will be the same as that used for the matrix spikes into real samples. These samples can be prepared by the laboratory on a routine basis. They are also available commercially, coming with a Certificate of Analysis and acceptance limits for the analytes. The LCS is then processed through the entire method procedure and the results examined for target analyte recovery. Precision evaluations can be generated on a "perfect" sample by performing the Laboratory Control Sample in duplicate (LCSD). The idea is to evaluate on a continuing basis the performance of the method on an interference-free or "perfect" sample.

The LCS and LCSD results are frequently used as a fall-back position by the laboratory in cases where the matrix spike and matrix spike duplicate have failed to achieve acceptable recovery and/or precision. The interpretation generally given is that the sample gave poor results due to matrix interference; however, the perfect samples gave good results, which indicates that the analytical system in the laboratory was in good operational condition. Thus, the results for the particular sample used for the MS and MSD may be in question, however, those MS and MSD results should not be generalized to the rest of the samples processed in that batch. The opposite situation, the case in which the LCS and LCSD fail to generate acceptable results, is cause for grave concern about the validity of the results for all samples in the batch. Inability to obtain acceptable results for the perfect sample is directly related to an inability to generate acceptable results for any sample.

Another important use of laboratory control samples is the evaluation of target analyte recoveries from specific sample clean-up procedures. Examples of possible applications are use of Florisil columns and gel permeation chromatography to reduce interferences in sample extracts. For these applications the laboratory control sample consists of known concentrations of target analytes and surrogates in a suitable solvent for the clean-up step. There may also be compounds added to the mix that are supposed to be removed though the clean-up. Not only is successful recovery of desired analytes evaluated, but also removal of undesired materials can be quantitated.

11. Surrogates

Surrogate recovery is a quality control measure limited to use in organics analysis. Surrogates are compounds added to every sample at the beginning of the sample preparation to monitor the success of the sample preparation on a individual sample basis. Individual compounds used as surrogates are selected based on their ability to mimic the behavior of specific target analytes held to be particularly sensitive to the sample preparation manipulations. Another consideration is that the surrogate compounds should be infrequently found as background in the samples. For these reasons compounds selected as surrogates are frequently isotopically labeled analogs of target analytes. Substitution of deuterium for hydrogen is the most common labeling feature. For example phenol-d_5 and nitrobenzene-d_5 among other compounds are used as surrogates in GC-MS analysis of semivolatile organic compounds.

Although some methods have established surrogate recovery acceptance criteria that are part of the method or contract compliance, for the most part acceptable surrogate recoveries need to be determined by the laboratory. The procedure is based upon collection of a large amount of surrogate recovery data, then evaluation of the data to determine what part of the variation seen in the data is due to normal random events from the analysis. This boils down to finding and eliminating results from botched analyses, commonly termed outlier elimination in statistical circles. Once the outliers have been eliminated, the mean ± 3 standard deviations is computed for the data, and this becomes the acceptance criteria.

A frequency distribution is illustrated for 791 surrogate recovery data points for nitrobenzene-d_5 by Method 625 in Figure 2-4. The recovery criteria for this surrogate based on the complete data set is 0 - 156, which is unacceptably large.

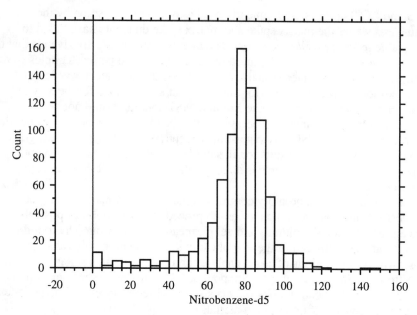

Figure 2-4. **Frequency distribution for nitrobenzene-d5 recovery of Method 625.**
Mean 76.4 and standard deviation of 26.45, n = 791; 5 data points with
recoveries greater than 160% are not shown, but are included in the
average.

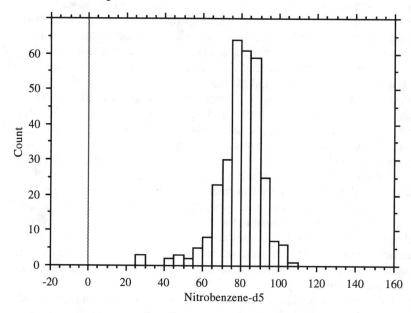

Figure 2-5. **Frequency distribution for nitrobenzene-d5 recovery from blank and
quality control samples of Method 625.** Mean 79.07 and standard
deviation of 11.53, n = 299.

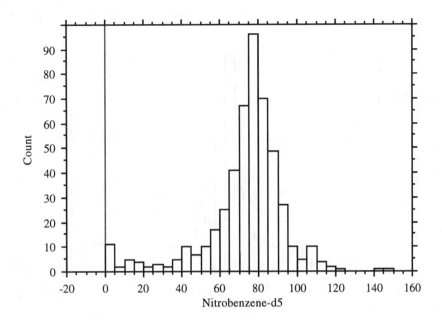

Figure 2-6. **Frequency distribution for nitrobenzene-d5 recovery from actual samples by Method 625.** Mean 74.78 and standard deviation of 32.34, n = 492; 6 data points with greater than 160% recovery are not shown but are included in the average.

Segregation of the data points into those derived from the blanks and quality control samples (laboratory control samples) gives a subset illustrated in Figure 2-5. These data points are considered to be free of the matrix effects encountered in real samples. The mean of this subset is 79.1, and the standard deviation is 11.53, giving three standard deviation acceptance limits of 45-114. The data set derived from samples subject to matrix effects is illustrated in Figure 2-6. Elimination of all the data points above 121% recovery gives a smooth distribution on the high side of the pattern without any breaks in values. The distance between 121 and the median value of 76 leads to elimination of the 26 data points less than 31% recovery on the low side of the distribution, a range that also eliminates the three lowest values obtained for the blanks and LCS. This reduced data set gives an acceptance range of 33-119 and the frequency distribution shown in Figure 2-7. The symmetry of the distribution suggests that the data points represent the range of random variation of the results without the skewing effect of very difficult matrices.

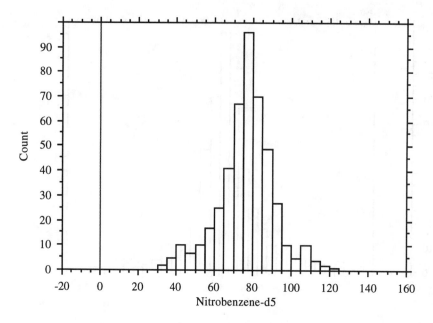

Figure 2-7. **Frequency distribution for nitrobenzene-d5 recovery from actual samples by Method 625.** This distribution results from elimination of all data points less than 31 and greater than 121% recovery and has a mean of 76.2 and standard deviation of 14.3, giving an acceptance range of 33-119 for real samples.

The pattern of surrogate recoveries, as used in the semivolatile organic (SVO) base/neutral-acid extraction procedures, can give specific information about the success of the extraction procedure. An example of these methods is EPA Method 3510, from the solid waste methods manual (SW-846). The six surrogates which are used in Method 3510 are listed in Table 2-3.

Table 2-3. **SVO GC-MS Surrogates used in EPA Method 3510**

Phenol-d$_5$
2-Fluorophenol
Nitrobenzene-d$_5$
2-Fluorobiphenyl
2,4,6-Tribromophenol
Terphenyl-d$_{14}$

The main steps involved in Method 3510 are adjustment of the pH to greater than 12, extraction with three portions of methylene chloride, adjustment of the pH to less than 2, extraction with three portions of methylene chloride, combining the extracts, drying over sodium sulfate, and finally concentration of the combined extracts to no less than 1.0 mL. The key areas of concern are first the efficiency of the extractions from the basified and acidified sample and second the control exercised over the concentration to insure that the volume of the extract never went below 1.0 mL.

With regard to the first concern, the six surrogates can be divided into two groups as to their acidic or base/neutral properties as shown in Table 2-4. Very low or no recoveries for one of the groups, normally the acidic group, accompanied by good recoveries of the surrogates in the other group is frequently diagnostic for the sample not have been acidified to less than pH 2 and extracted, after an initial extraction of the pH 12 adjusted sample. Another frequent occurrence is that the extracts were not combined, a specification in similar methods encountered under other regulatory programs. As none of these surrogates are true bases, the opposite situation, where there is good recovery of the acid surrogates and zero recoveries of the base/neutral surrogates, is not a strong indication that the sample was not pH adjusted to greater than 12. Initial extraction of a pH adjusted sample to less than 2 will recover all six of these surrogates. This pattern of good acidic surrogate recoveries and zero base/neutral surrogate recoveries suggests that the extracts were not combined.

Table 2-4.   **Division of the SVO GC-MS Surrogates used in Method 3510 by Acidic or Base/Neutral Properties**

Acidic Surrogates	Base/neutral surrogates
Phenol-d_5	Nitrobenzene-d_5
2-Fluorophenol	2-Fluorobiphenyl
2,4,6-Tribromophenol	Terphenyl-d_{14}

The concentration step is of great importance in Method 3510 and, in general, in all sample preparation procedures. Reduction of the volume of the extracts below 1.0 mL will lead to significant losses of the more volatile target analytes. As shown in Table 2-5, the surrogates can be evaluated based on their relative sensitivity to the concentration process. Poor to no recoveries of the very labile surrogates suggests the sample extract was concentrated below 1.0 mL. If the somewhat labile surrogates exhibit very low recoveries, and there is zero recovery of the very labile surrogates, this suggests the sample was concentrated to less than 0.5 mL. If the only surrogates present in the sample are the two inert compounds, this is an indication that the sample was reduced in volume to dryness, then solvent added to bring the volume back up to 1.0 mL. The behavior of the surrogates is directly related to the behavior of the target analytes in the sample with regard to concentration technique. Loss of the very labile surrogates translates to loss of very labile target analytes. Loss of the very labile and somewhat labile surrogates is an indication that a significant number of the target analytes have very low probability of being in the extract.

Table 2-5.   **Division of the SVO GC-MS Surrogates Based on Their Sensitivity to the Concentration Step**

Very labile	Somewhat labile	Inert
2-Fluorophenol	Nitrobenzene-d_5	2,4,6-Tribromophenol
Phenol-d_6	2-Fluorobiphenyl	Terphenyl-d_{14}

A similar pattern of surrogate recoveries can result when a sample contains a large amount of organic material (greater than 1 mL), which is extracted in the organic solvent. Attempted reduction of the volume of the organic layer to 1.00 mL using prolonged heating and other techniques can lead to significant losses in surrogates and target analytes. This often occurs when samples contain petroleum oils.

Surrogate recovery patterns can also give information about the condition of the analytical instrument. Residues from previous samples and degradation of the liquid phase inside the gas chromatography column can create "active" sites in the instrument that will irreversibly bind sensitive surrogates and target analytes. Table 2-6 divides the surrogates as to whether they are sensitive to the instrument conditions or inert. Low or zero recoveries of the sensitive surrogates accompanied by good recoveries of the inert surrogates is an indication that the instrument needs maintenance.

Table 2-6. **Division of the SVO GC-MS Surrogates Based on Sensitivity to Instrument Conditions**

Sensitive	Inert
Phenol-d_5	
2-Fluorophenol	2-Fluorobiphenyl
2,4,6-Tribromophenol	Terphenyl-d_{14}
Nitrobenzene-d_5	

Surrogates are used in volatile organic analysis to monitor sample preparation and matrix interferences. EPA Method 5030/8260A lists the surrogates presented in Table 2-7 as appropriate for volatile organic compound (VOC) GC-MS analysis.

Table 2-7. **VOC GC-MS Surrogates from Method 5030/8260A, SW-846**

4-Bromofluorobenzene
1,2-Dichloroethane-d_4
Toluene-d_8
Dibromochloromethane

The VOC GC-MS surrogates are somewhat useful in continued monitoring of the purge and trap system to insure adequate flow of purge gas; however, the system monitoring compounds (see below in 13) are more specifically directed toward diagnosis of problems in the sample preparation/introduction. In VOC analysis the surrogates are more generally useful for evaluation of matrix interferences in the sample itself. Some samples will exhibit low recoveries of the surrogates, which are suggestive of non-specific absorption of the analyte molecules to a non-volatile organic material such as a polymer. However, the more frequent occurrence is due to non-target analyte volatile materials purging from the sample and then co-eluting from the GC-MS with either the internal standards or the surrogate compounds. Co-elution with the surrogate compounds generally is seen as low surrogate recoveries. Co-elution of matrix interferences with internal standards is reflected in high surrogate recoveries, as high as 130-150%.

Surrogate recoveries in VOC are frequently above 100% while this is seldom the case with the SVO GC-MS analysis. Part of the explanation for this observation comes from consideration of the ranges of the masses of the quantitation ions used in the two techniques. As illustrated in Figure 2-8, the quantitation masses for the VOC lie from 40 to 225 with an average value of 93. The median value is 88. On the other hand the mean for the SVO quantitation masses is 172 with the median value 164. The distribution of the SVO quantitation masses is illustrated in Figure 2-9.

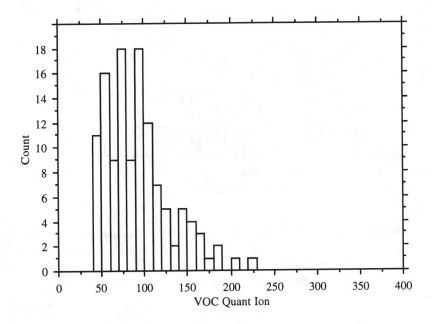

Figure 2-8.   Distribution of quantitation ions for VOC GC-MS analysis.

These differences become significant when the mass spectra of common sample interferences are considered. By far, the most common matrix interference encountered in environmental organic analysis is hydrocarbon contamination of the sample due to petroleum products and wastes. Regardless of the molecular weight, when petroleum-based hydrocarbons are ionized, they fragment to generate a huge number of ions under mass 130. Figure 2-10 illustrates this with the mass spectrum of the common hydrocarbon hexadecane. This phenomenon, with few exceptions, is common for most organic materials, where the bulk of the ions produced from the co-eluting contaminants have mass less than 130. In VOC analysis by GC-MS the quantitation ions of the internal standards, Table 2-8, are subject to this interference as either discrete co-eluting peaks or as non-specific background noise, while for the most part the SVO internal standards are less sensitive. This leads to higher area counts for the VOA internal standards and thus, lower quantities of target analytes reported for samples.

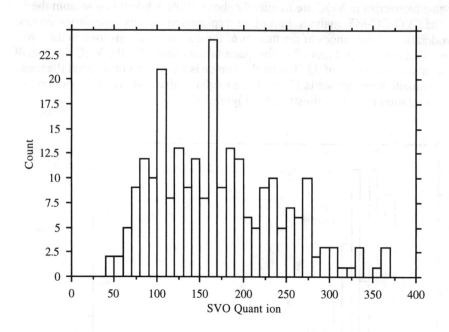

Figure 2-9. **Distribution of quantitation ions for SVO GC-MS analysis.**

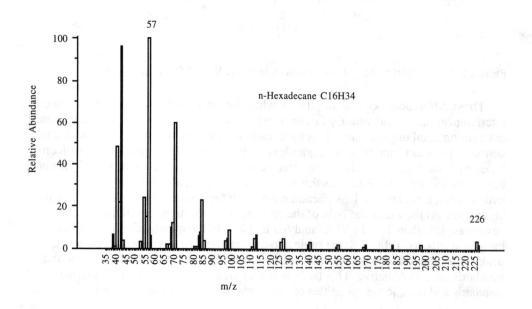

Figure 2-10. **Mass spectrum of the common petroleum constituent, hexadecane.**

Table 2-8. **Comparison of the Quantitation Ions of the Common Internal Standards Used in VOC and SVO GC-MS Analysis**

VOC Internal Standard	Quant Ion	SVO Internal Standard	Quant ion
Fluorobenzene	96	1,4-Dichlorobenzene-d4	152
Chlorobenzene-d5	117	Naphthalene-d8	136
1,4-Dichlorobenzene-d4	152	Acenaphthene-d10	164
		Phenanthrene-d10	188
		Chrysene-d12	240
		Perylene-d12	264

Surrogates are also used in organic analysis procedures that do not employ mass spectrometers as the determinative instrument. The chlorinated pesticide and PCB methodologies variously suggest the use of the three surrogates in Table 2-9.

Table 2-9. **Surrogates Used in Chlorinated Pesticide and PCB Analysis**

Dibutylchlorindate	DBC
2,4,5,6-Tetrachloro-*meta*-xylene	TCMX
Decachlorobiphenyl	DCB

Dibutylchlorindate (DBC) is a very fragile compound that strong acid or base conditions will degrade rapidly. Thus the recoveries of DBC reflect the required pH adjustment of the sample to the range 5-9. 2,4,5,6-Tetrachloro-*meta*-xylene (TCMX) is the more volatile surrogate, being more volatile than any of the target analytes of this method. The recoveries of TCMX are linked to the lowest volume to which the sample extract was concentrated. Low recoveries of TCMX are related to low recoveries of the lighter target analytes such as heptachlor and aldrin. The other two surrogates are less volatile than any of the common analytes of this method. TCMX and Decachloro-biphenyl (DCB) are inert to the strong acid washing of the sample extract which is part of the sample clean-up used in the PCB analysis and therefore function well as surrogates for PCB determination. The higher weight PCBs, such as Aroclor 1254, 1260 and 1262, contain substantial portions of decachlorobiphenyl which will effect the calculated recovery of this surrogate when these analytes are present in the sample.

12. Mass Spectrometer Tuning

Tuning is a quality control that is particular to analytical instruments that use a mass spectrometer as the detector. The mass spectrometer functions by bombarding the target analytes as they enter the analyzer with electrons. The electrons that hit the analyte molecules cause them to ionize. The analyzer then performs a count on the abundance of each ion created from the compound molecules. The software used in conjunction with the mass analyzer prepares a plot of abundance *vs.* mass of the ions, called a mass spectrum. The relative abundance of the ions created and detected from the compound molecules is dependent upon the electrical and magnetic properties of the mass analyzer. These properties are adjusted by the operator of the instrument to:

1. Obtain optimum numbers of ions throughput from the ionization source to the ion detector

2. Obtain adequate resolution of adjacent mass ions to allow differentiation for accurate counting and correct determination of isotopic abundances

3. Calibrate the mass axis to allow correct identification of mass to charge (m/z) positions

4. Obtain an optimum balance between low mass ions and high mass ions.

The spectrum generated by the instrument for any compound is used for identification purposes. Spectra for many compounds including the target analytes are stored in the memory of the computer. The software is used to compare the spectra of the compounds found in the sample with those stored in the memory to find potential matches. The accuracy of the identification comparison depends to a large extent upon the mass analyzers used to generate the library and the analyzer used to examine the sample being able to generate similar results from the electronic and magnetic set-point profiles. The adjustment parameters change from manufacturer to manufacturer since there is no industry standard for the design and construction of the mass analyzers. To establish a standard for the results obtained from the set-points for the mass analyzers, tuning compounds were selected and acceptance criteria developed that assures that similar results would be obtained from different instruments.

The tune of the mass analyzer also has a great effect upon the quantitative results obtained from the instrument. Most of the internal standards used in GC-MS analysis are polyaromatic hydrocarbons, which are deuterium labeled. When ionized in the mass analyzer, these compounds only produce one major ion, which commonly represents over 35% of the ions produced from the compound (Figure 2-11). The relative abundance of the internal standard single ion produced and the number of ions detected is somewhat insensitive to the conditions within the mass analyzer. On the other hand, most target analytes produce a number of different ions (Figure 2-12). The ion used for quantitation for these compounds in general is only one of a number of ions produced from the parent molecule. The relative abundance of the ions produced and detected can be adjusted over wide ranges by varying the set-points of the mass analyzer, thus the relative abundance of the quantitation ion will change based on the set-points chosen. For example if a quantitation ion from a target compound has only 5% relative abundance on one day and 10% relative abundance on another day, the quantitative results based on the amount of that particular ion will be different by a factor of 2 for those days even though the actual amount of target compound has not changed.

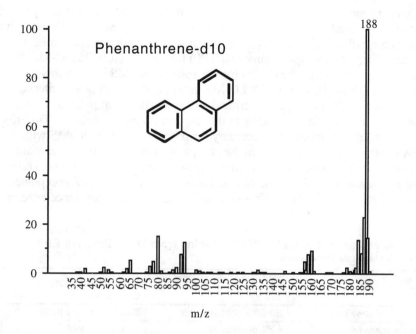

Figure 2-11. Structure and mass spectrum of the internal standard phenanthrene-d10.

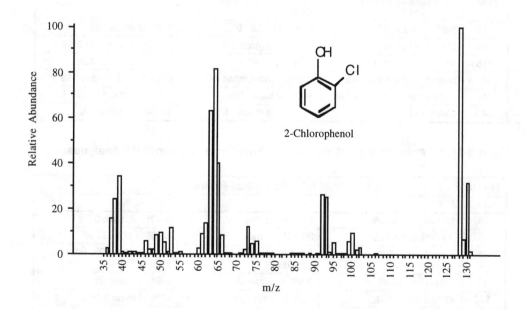

Figure 2-12. Structure and mass spectrum of the target analyte 2-chlorophenol that has quantitation ions of 64 or 128.

To minimize the variations in the mass spectra being produced from the analyzers, a standard compound is used for evaluation of the results from the instrument's set-points. These standards are called tuning compounds. The tuning compounds used in EPA methods are decafluorotriphenylphosphine (DFTPP) for the semivolatile GC-MS instruments, 4-bromofluorobenzene (BFB) for the volatile GC-MS instruments and polyethylene glycol (PEG 400) for the HPLC-MS instruments. Acceptance criteria based on allowable abundance ranges for critical ions of the tune compounds were established and included as quality controls in the relevant analytical methods. Different ideas concerning the degree of control necessary for proper use of the GC-MS within the different EPA programs led to variances in the acceptance criteria for the same tuning compound. Only the CLP SOW mass spectrometer tune requirements were generated out of an in-depth scientific study. Illustrated in Table 2-10 are the DFTPP acceptance criteria for several methods. Table 2-11 presents differences for the acceptance criteria for BFB.

Table 2-10. Acceptance Criteria for DFTPP Tuning from Three Different EPA Analytical Protocols

Mass	EPA Analytical Protocol		
	525.2	625	CLP-SOW
51	10-80% of base peak	30-60% of base peak	30-80% of base peak
68	<2% of mass 69	<2% of mass 69	<2% of mass 69
70	<2% of mass 69	<2% of mass 69	<2% of mass 69
127	10-80% of mass 198	40-60% of mass 198	25-75% of mass 198
197	<2% of mass 198	<1% of mass 198	<1% of mass 198
198	Base peak or >50% of 442	base peak, 100% rel. abund.	Base peak
199	5-9% of mass 198	5-9% of mass 198	5-9% of mass 198
275	10-60% of base peak	10-30% of mass 198	10-30% of mass 198
365	>1% of base peak	>1% of mass 198	>0.75% of mass 198
441	present and < mass 443	present and < mass 443	present and < mass 443
442	Base peak or >50% of 198	>40% of mass 198	40-110% of mass 198
443	15-24% of mass 442	17-23% of mass 442	15-24% of mass 442

Table 2-11. Acceptance Criteria for BFB from Three Different EPA Analytical Protocols

Mass	EPA Analytical Protocol		
	524.2	624	CLP-SOW
50	15-40% of mass 95	15-40% of mass 95	8-40% of mass 95
75	30-80% of mass 95	30-60% of mass 95	30-66% of mass 95
95	Base peak, 100% rel. abund.	Base peak, 100% rel. abund.	Base peak, 100% rel. abund.
96	5-9% of mass 95	5-9% of mass 95	5-9% of mass 95
173	<2% of mass 174	<2% of mass 174	<2% of mass 174
174	>50% of mass 95	>50 % of mass 95	50-120% of mass 95
175	5-9% of mass 174	5-9% of mass 174	4-9% of mass 174
176	95-101% of mass 174	95-101% of mass 174	93-101% of mass 174
177	5-9% of mass 176	5-9% of mass 176	5-9% of mass 176

With regard to which tune criteria is the best, there are several considerations. If the major intention for use of the mass spectrometer is identification of target analytes, then it does not matter which tune is used as most of the methods require daily updating of the library of target analyte spectra. If the intention is identification of unknown compounds, then the mass spectrometer should be tuned to standards used by most of the practitioners who generated the spectra in the NIST or Wiley collections. For almost all instruments commercially available the tuning standard is perfluorotributylamine (PFTBA, TBPFA or FC43). This compound is volatile and contained in a solenoid-closed vial attached to the source of the mass spectrometer. Many instruments have software programs that will open the solenoid to allow small amounts of the TBPFA to bleed into the mass spectrometer source and then automatically adjust the set-points of the mass analyzer to produce an optimum response to the tuning compound. The EPA protocols are the only set of GC-MS procedures that require tuning to some other compound than TBPFA. Most operators of GC-MS who are following EPA procedures begin the workday with an auto-tune of the instrument to tributylperfluoroamine standards, then "de-tune" the instrument to meet the method tuning compound acceptance criteria. Further, in a study for the Contract Laboratory Program[7], the mass spectra of 125 semivolatile and pesticide compounds were obtained under a variety of tune conditions, then searched against the NIST mass spectral library. All compounds were correctly identified under all tune conditions within either EPA or manufacturers' tune specifications with the exception of confusion between benzo(b) and benzo(k) fluoranthene. As long as the mass axis was calibrated correctly and the isotopic abundances met, the tune worked fine for library searching.

If the major intention for use of the mass spectrometer is quantitation of target analytes, then the idea should be to minimize the day-to-day variation of the conditions within the mass analyzer. By maintaining the response of the mass analyzer within tight tolerances, one of the major variables that leads to quantitation fluctuation is reduced, and the calibration curve will remain valid for longer periods of time. Thus while it is important to maintain tight control over the allowable variation of the mass analyzer response, it is not scientifically necessary to attach these tight controls to preconceived ideas of desired relative abundances of any tuning compound other than that of the industrial standard TBPFA. As the instrument operational software already provides automatic tuning to set tolerances on this compound, additional tuning checks become redundant.

The argument has been advanced that it is necessary to evaluate the mass spectral response after the tuning compound has transited the entire instrument, thus TBPFA is not suitable as a standard. This is simply adding complexity to a procedure that already provides adequate controls and checks over the entire system through the daily continuing calibration and system performance evaluations. As previously discussed it should be obvious that if the mass analyzer does not meet the appropriate tune conditions of the initial calibration then the continuing calibration check will fail. The conditions of the gas chromatograph are more specifically and effectively addressed by the system performance compounds rather than rolling the evaluation into the mass spectrometer tune check.

---

7 Bottrell, D.W., D.R. Youngman, A. Sauter, J. Downs, J. Fisk, C. Dempsey, H. McCarty, and P. Isaacson, 1989. Performance based quality assurance criteria for GC/MS data supporting the U.S.E.P.A. Contract Laboratory Program. 1989 Pittsburgh Conference on Analytical Chemistry and Applied Spectroscopy, Atlanta GA.

13. System Performance

Environmental samples and extracts are very complex mixtures and contain large quantities of materials other than the target analytes, surrogates and internal standards. A significant portion of these otherwise unidentified co-extractants are not amenable to the conditions within the heated injector port or the column oven of the gas chromatograph, either through not being sufficiently volatile to enter the gas phase or through compound degradation. Either mechanism results in deposition of organic materials within the injector and column of the GC. The build-up of this deposited material can create unintentional reactive sites for target analytes and other compounds to become mired. This deposited material can also react with the liquid coating of the inside of the column resulting in its depolymerization, and exposing the underlying solid support for interaction with target molecules.

One of the functions of system performance evaluation is to generate data on a continuing basis about the contamination conditions on the inside of the instrument. Another function is to continuously provide a performance check on the set-points of switching times, temperatures and flow rates within the sample introduction mechanisms of the instrument.

There are two approaches to system monitoring encountered within analytical methods. The first approach is injection of representative compounds known to be very sensitive to instrument conditions and examination of the chromatographic response of the compounds. In a very inert system the peaks eluting from the column should be symmetrical, with a nice gaussian shape, Figure 2-13. In active systems the molecules of the compound will be retarded through interaction with the active site and the peaks will be distorted, Figure 2-14.

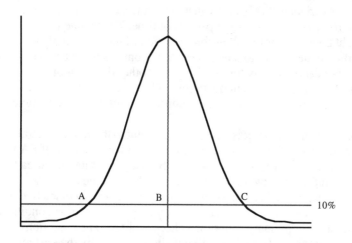

Figure 2-13. Symmetrical (gaussian) peak shape.

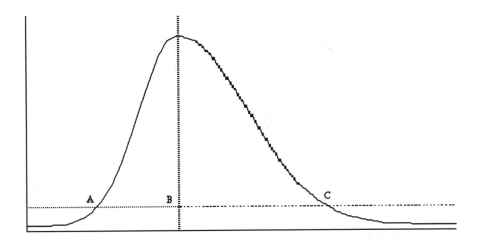

Figure 2-14.   Tailing peak.

Peak shape can be evaluated through calculation of tailing factors. With reference to Figures 2-13 and 2-14, a vertical line is dropped from the top of the peak to the baseline, and then a horizontal line across the peak at 10% of the peak height. The ratio of the distances BC/AB is calculated, which is the tailing factor. Pentachlorophenol and benzidine are the two compounds commonly used for tailing factor calculations with acceptance limits of <3.00 and and <5.00 respectively.

Another technique for evaluating peak shape is through calculation of Peak Gaussian Factors (PGF). The equation is as follows:

$$ PGF \ = \ \frac{1.83 \ x \ W_{1/2}}{W_{1/10}} $$

where: $W_{1/2}$ is the peak width at half height.
         $W_{1/10}$ is the peak width at 1/10 the height.

The PGF is normally evaluated for Bromacil and for DCPA (dacthal, 2,3,5,6-tetrachloro-1,4-benzenedicarboxcylic acid dimethyl ester) in the context of GC-MS analysis of semivolatile organic compounds in drinking water. The acceptance limits are 0.80-1.20 for Bromacil and 0.80-1.15 for DCPA.

Monitoring system performance through use of either tailing factors or PGF is an absolute measure of the inertness of the system. Breakdown checks are another absolute measure of system performance encountered in analysis of chlorinated hydrocarbon pesticides by GC. This technique depends upon the known decomposition pathways of DDT to DDD and DDE (Figure 2-15) and endrin to endrin aldehyde and endrin ketone (Figure 2-16), two of the target analytes of the methods. The degree of breakdown is related to the temperature and residence time of these compounds in the injection port of the GC and to the presence of active sites in the injection port and the column.

Measurement of the extent of the breakdown is a direct assessment of the conditions of the system.

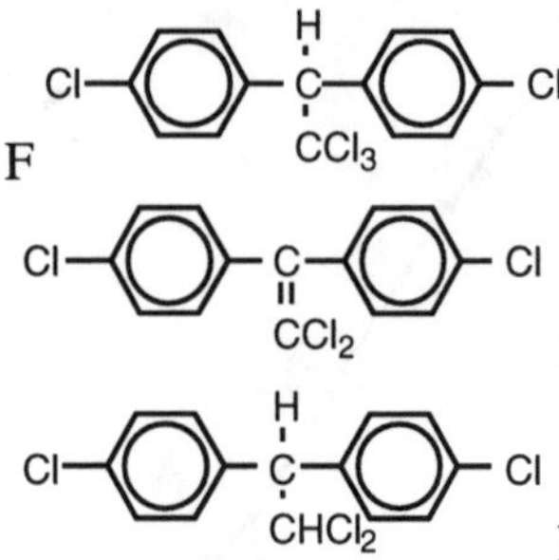

F   DDT

                                                               DDE

                                                               DDD

$$\% \text{ Breakdown} = \frac{\text{DDE} + \text{DDD}}{\text{DDT} + \text{DDE} + \text{DDD}} \times 100$$

Figure 2-15.   Breakdown check for DDT.

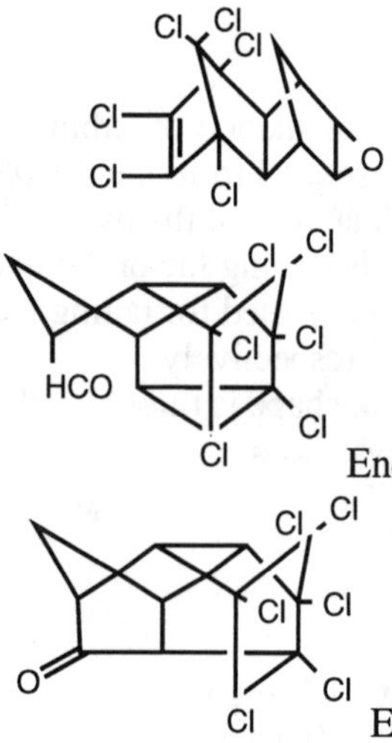

Endrin

Endrin aldehyde

Endrin ketone

$$\% \text{ breakdown} = \frac{\text{Aldehyde} + \text{Ketone}}{\text{Endrin} + \text{Aldehyde} + \text{Ketone}} \times 100$$

Figure 2-16.   Breakdown check for Endrin.

The ability to resolve (separate) two closely eluting compounds can be used as a measure of system performance. Two different approaches are taken to give a quantitative measure of resolution. The first involves calculation of the resolution.

$$\text{resolution} = \frac{\Delta t}{W_{ave}}$$

where: Δt is the difference in retention times of the two peaks.

W_{ave} is the average width of the peaks measured at the baseline in time units.

The second determination of resolution looks at the height of the valley between the two peaks and divides the valley height by the adjacent peak height or an average of the adjacent peak heights. The result is expressed as a percentage. Depending on which two peaks are specified, for example chlorothalonil-delta-BHC, atrazine-prometon, anthracene-phenanthrene, benz(a)anthracene-chrysene or others, the requirements may range from complete baseline separation to <50% valley height.

The other approach to system performance evaluation is an indirect method that examines the calibration response factors (Rf) obtained for specific target analytes during the daily continuing calibration. These specific compounds are termed System Performance Check Compounds (SPCC). The actual measurement made is the area of the quantitation ion of the analyte peak that travels from the injection port to the detector and then was ionized in the mass spectrometer. This area is compared against the area of the quantitation ion of the relevant internal standard in the calculation of the Rf. It is assumed that the internal standard is immune to the conditions of the system that the SPCC is being used to measure. Further, the conditions within the mass spectrometer contribute to the calculated Rf. The compounds monitored are listed in Table 2-12 along with the minimum response factors required.

Table 2-12. **System Performance Check Compounds (SPCC) and Minimum Response Factors**

SVO SPCC	min. Rf	VOC SPCC	min. Rf
N-Nitroso-di-n-propylamine	0.05	Chloromethane	0.10
2,4-Dinitrophenol	0.05	1,1-Dichloroethane	0.10
Hexachlorocyclopentadiene	0.05	Bromoform	0.10
4-Nitrophenol	0.05	Chlorobenzene	0.30
		1,1,2,2-Tetrachloroethane	0.30

Low results for the SVO SPCC's can be traced to problems related to standard mixture degradation, injection port contamination, contamination of the front part of the chromatography column or degradation of the liquid layer of the chromatography column. These problem areas are listed in order of increasing difficulty as far as corrective/preventative maintenance measures which should be examined and performed.

The individual SPCC's in the volatiles analysis are specific probes for conditions within the sample introduction system. Chloromethane, a gas at room temperature, is a check on the purge gas flow rate through the sparge tube and the trap. Too fast a flow rate will lead to low recoveries of the compound. Bromoform, on the other hand, is a heavy liquid at room temperature and serves as a check for too slow a purge gas flow. Low gas flows will not efficiently strip the bromoform from the sparge tube. The recovery of bromoform is also linked to the existence of cold spots and/or active sites in the transfer tubing from the trap to the injection port of the GC. 1,1-Dichloroethane and 1,1,2,2-tetrachloroethane are subject to degradation in the transfer lines and to strong adsorption to active sites in the trap. These check for contamination of the trap and transfer lines or possibly heating element failure in the trap.

14. Interference Check Samples

Interference check sample analysis is a quality control unique to metals analysis using inductively coupled plasma atomic emission spectrometry (ICP-AES). Each element when it is excited emits light of set wavelengths. The wavelengths of light emitted from a sample can be measured to provide a qualitative and a quantitative evaluation of the elemental composition of the sample. However, even the simplest element, hydrogen, emits light of several different wavelengths. Lines at 410, 434, 486 and 656 nm are characteristic of hydrogen. Other more complex elements emit light at hundreds of different wavelengths.

The photodetectors used to measure the light emitted from the sample can be constructed and situated in the ICP-AES to limit the range of wavelengths that generate a signal from the photodetector. However, in no way can they be considered as single wavelength specific, such as light emitted by a laser. The normal situation for a light signal in ICP-AES is that the photodetector is positioned to be centered on a primary element response wavelength, but light is also detected arising from other elements. A background correction point is used within the window to adjust the response of the primary element for non-specific stray light entering the photodetector. The situation is illustrated in Figures 2-17 and 2-18, where the vertical line in the windows indicates the position of the element emission for which the photodetector is intended.

Figures 2-17 and 2-18 illustrate several different types of interferences. The first is when an emitted line from a non-target element happens to coincide or overlap with the target analyte line. In the chromium wavelength scan (Figure 2-18), the major signal is due to vanadium, which provides a substantial distortion to the intensity of the chromium peak. This type of interference is normally handled by measuring the amount of vanadium in the sample at a photodetector specifically for vanadium, then multiplying the amount of vanadium by a correction factor and subtracting the result from the measured chromium response to obtain a true chromium result. Another type of interference occurs when a signal coincides with a background correction point. This results in a falsely high background correction. In comparing these two figures it should be obvious that the position of the background correction must be tailored for each photodetector.

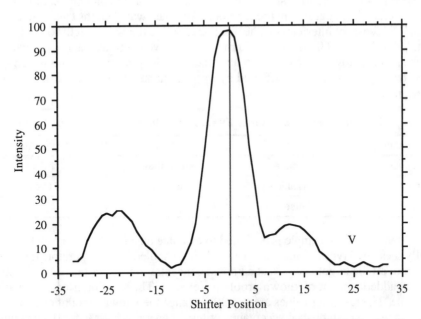

Figure 2-17. **Wavelength scan for aluminum from an ICP-AES with simultaneous design.** The background correction location is marked with a "V".

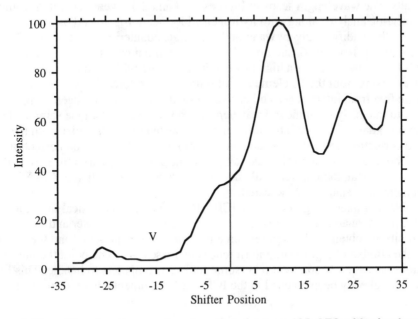

Figure 2-18. **Wavelength scan for chromium from an ICP-AES with simultaneous design.** The background correction location is marked with a "V".

The major recognized interferences from the EPA methods are listed in Table 2-13. These are specifically linked to design of an ICP-AES that has the photodetectors at the analytical wavelengths suggested in the methods. Alternate wavelengths can generate a different set of necessary interference checks. For example the wavelength for cadmium recommended in Method 6010A is 226.5 nm. At that wavelength iron and nickel are major interferences. However, a common alternate wavelength for cadmium is 228.8 nm. This wavelength is minimally affected by iron and nickel but does have arsenic as a major interference.

Table 2-13.   Major Interfering Elements Evaluated in Interference Check Samples.

Aluminum	Calcium	Iron	Magnesium
Chromium	Copper	Manganese	Nickel
Vanadium	Titanium	Beryllium	Cobalt
Zinc	Arsenic		

The interference check sample is designed to evaluate on a continuing basis how successfully these two types of interference are being handled by the operator. It consists of a solution of all the target analytes at a known concentration, for instance 1.0 or 5.0 ppm, with an added amount of known problem elements. The solution is analyzed as a regular sample. The resulting values are checked against the known amount of element in the solution with an established acceptance criteria, generally ± 20%, for determining a pass or fail. Failure to pass interference check samples translates directly into inability to generate reliable results on real samples.

The ability to pass all target analytes through ICS criteria does not guarantee reliable sample results. The wavelength scans in Figures 2-17 and 2-18 were generated from a mix of 28 metallic analytes along with hydrogen, chlorine, nitrogen, and oxygen, resulting from the acidified solvent water and the nitrate counterions. Out of the 92 naturally occurring elements, 60 are not being routinely monitored for their effects upon the ICP-AES response. There is a high probability that there will be additional interferences arising from the 60 elements not routinely monitored. To verify that ICP-AES data are free from interferences other than those that have already been corrected, it is necessary to manually examine the wavelength scans obtained from the sample. The most common situation is where an interference is detected that falls underneath the background correction point. This is remedied by moving the background correction point, re-calibrating and re-analyzing the sample. If the unknown interference coincides with the analyte signal, there is very little that can be done further with the ICP-AES, and a different method of analysis is indicated.

The problem of interfering lines in the ICP-AES also places a practical limitation on the lowest levels of analyte that can be determined in a sample. As lower and lower detection limits are obtained through refinement of the instrument optics and the plasma geometry, the number of significant interferences increases. At some point the number of corrections necessary becomes cumbersome for even computers to handle. This limit of detection has already been reached in the ICP-AES instruments that are commercially available.

15. Dual Column Confirmation

Dual column confirmation is an identification confirmation technique commonly used to bolster the confidence in qualitative results obtained from instruments that generate only retention time information. Instruments that fit this description are called two-dimensional systems, which stems from the plot of time *vs.* response, which is the output from the instrument. Examples of these instruments are gas chromatographs with the electron capture (ECD), flame ionization (FID), photoionization (PID), electrolytic conductivity (ELCD), and nitrogen-phosphorus (NPD) detectors, HPLC with single wavelength UV or refractive index detection, ion chromatography and capillary ion electrophoresis. The idea is that the analysis is performed on one column, which generates a retention time, then the analysis is repeated on a second column, which changes the elution order of the analytes or changes the relative retention times among the analytes. With the liquid chromatograph techniques of HPLC, ion chromatography and capillary ion electrophoresis, a suitable set of confirmation conditions may be possible to achieve through selection of a different mobile phase rather than replacement of the stationary column.

In analysis of organic compounds, for all results that arise from a two-dimensional instrument (2-D), there is a distinct probability that the signal obtained is the result of another compound that has the same retention time as that of the calibrated target analyte. This is true for both the analytical column and the confirmation column. The dirtier the sample, the higher the probability that this has occurred. The closer to the detection limit the analysis is being pushed, the closer to certainty that misidentification has occurred. There is also a distinct probability that instead of methyl ethyl badstuff being present in the sample and detected on both columns in the appropriate retention time window, what has actually occurred is two different non-calibrated interferents have by coincidence shown up. This is illustrated in Figure 2-19.

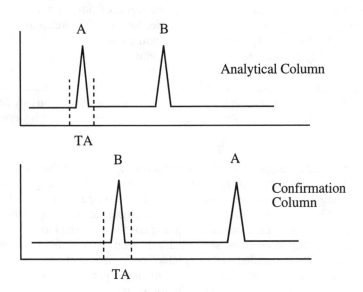

Figure 2-19.   **Fortuitous elution of two contaminants (A and B) in the retention time windows for a target analyte (TA) using a 2-D analysis.**

A very disturbing phenomenon has occurred within the last five years that is probably rooted in the proliferation of computer games that for many people occupies a unordinate portion of their relaxation time. This phenomenon is the technician who does not even glance at the picture of the chromatogram, but instead bases all interpretation upon the data print-out from the computer software. There is no computer made nor software yet designed that can replace the human operator's evaluation of the chromatogram. Many errors in data have occurred due solely to this problem. A common error that is a direct result of this problem occurs when a large amount of an analyte is injected upon the column, or the column is nearing the end of its useful life through loss-of-liquid phase. The elution of the analyte is not in a symmetrical gaussian peak but rather in a distorted peak almost in the shape of a right triangle. The peak apex moves relative to the retention time window, in some cases into an adjoining window. When this occurs the software identifies the peak as belonging to the second window. With a one-second look at the chromatogram, an analyst can recognize this problem and take steps to correct it. However, unless this visual examination is made, the analyte is merrily reported as identified, or even worse, not reported due to being misidentified on the confirmation column.

It is an appropriate question to ask, "Given these problems with the 2-D instruments, and the legal liability associated with the results of analysis of environmental samples, why would anyone choose to use 2-D instruments?" There are several factors that lead to the continued use of these methods. The first is that by-and-large these instruments have a sensitivity increase over the mass spectrometer and other 3-D instruments by a factor of up to 1000-fold. This means that if the 2-D instrument detects nothing in the sample, then the target analyte is definitely not present. The second is that the detectors used in these instruments generally respond to a limited group of compounds that have particular characteristics, such as the presence of a halogen, nitrogen, or sulfur. The 3-D systems are very general detectors and will generate a signal from virtually anything that reaches them. There tend to be thousands of background signals from the mass spectrometric analysis of samples. Screening the samples using 2-D systems allows concentration of efforts by the mass spectral operator upon a select group of possible contaminants by eliminating the presence of other compounds.

The 2-D systems find particular use for monitoring the progress of remediations of well-characterized sites. In this situation the desire is to watch the disappearance of the already conclusively identified target analytes as the work proceeds. The relatively low operational costs of the 2-D systems are also particularly attractive in this application.

16. Performance Evaluation Samples

Performance evaluation (PE) samples consist of solutions of known concentrations of target analytes sent to the laboratory to be analyzed as an unknown. They may be issued as a concentrate in an ampule, portions of which are diluted to some final volume to prepare the PE sample. Or they may come as a ready-to-analyze sample. The laboratory analyzes the samples then submits their qualitative and quantitative results to the issuing organization for evaluation. Based on either statistically derived or legislatively assigned acceptance criteria, the results are graded as "acceptable" or "non-acceptable." To generate statistically derived acceptance criteria the evaluating organization computes the mean and standard deviation of the submitted results for an analyte and prepares an acceptance interval based on the mean ± 2 or 3 standard deviations. For the PE studies the EPA issues, statistically derived limits are prepared from the data submitted by the state and EPA laboratories, and then all the rest of the participants are evaluated against this small subset. For legislatively assigned acceptance criteria, such as encountered in the Water Supply (WS) PE studies, there is a set interval around the true value for the analyte that is considered as the acceptance range. These intervals are normally found in the regulations[8]. An example would be nitrate where an acceptable result is in the $\pm 10\%$ interval around the true value.

Participation in the various PE sample studies available is a means by which the laboratory can discover analytical problems and improve performance. The PE sample studies are also one yardstick by which a potential client can gain some measure of confidence in the ability of the laboratory to generate a reliable result. Many states that have laboratory certification programs use the results from PE studies as evidence for certification or decertification of analytes and methods that the laboratory is allowed to perform and submit data.

PE samples were originally designed to be performed a single time or possibly as a duplicate by the laboratory as a regular sample, in conjunction with the normal flow of samples through the work schedule. When performed in this fashion, a statistical distribution of results can be assumed for all the tests within a PE sample study, and a good performance by the laboratory would be to get at least 80 to 85% of the individual analytes in the study correct. However, due to the emphasis placed on acceptable laboratory PE results by clients and state and Federal laboratory certification programs, the manner in which these samples are handled in the laboratory has been changed. What actually happens with them is that the laboratory technicians are alerted and ready well in advance of the arrival of the PE samples. The most capable technicians are assigned to spend an inordinate amount of time analyzing and re-analyzing the samples. Techniques, such as direct injection of the concentrate or a dilution into the analytical instrument, preparation and analysis of a variety of dilutions, matrix spikes on the samples, microextractions, use of multiple methods, and anything else the analysts can think of, are employed to insure that an acceptable result is generated. Many laboratories will share their results with other laboratories to help insure that the results are comparable. Some laboratories have been known to subcontract analysis of the PE samples to other labs. In all, the PE samples are treated as anything but what a typical sample receives. The consequence of these actions is that the evaluation is not of the average performance of the laboratory but of the best answer that the lab can possibly generate. It should not be surprising that the passing score for a good laboratory is now better than 95% of the analyte results being correct, with 100% correct being common. And just because a laboratory can generate a perfect slate of results on a PE study has very little relation to the quality of the results generated on a day-to-day basis. Still a demonstrated inability to pass PE sample studies is a sure indication that the laboratory is not capable of producing reliable results.

What a laboratory does with unacceptable PE sample results is important as a reflection of how the lab as a whole handles and corrects problems. The proper actions are to investigate the causes and circumstances for the unacceptable results. The investigation should be finalized in a written report that also indicates the corrective action taken to remedy solvable problems. These investigations commonly form the nucleus of the internal audits and inspections of the laboratory procedures and performance that are part of all quality assurance programs.

---

[8] 40 CFR 141.23 and 141.24

Laboratory clients can use PE samples as an independent measure of the lab. There are several commercial vendors[9] who prepare PE samples to meet any needs and specifications. The client can purchase one or more of these samples and submit them to the laboratory as part of a regular sample set. These constitute very useful PE samples, in that the laboratory is unaware that they are being evaluated. The treatment given the sample is no different than that received by any other sample. Further these serve as evaluations of both the qualitative and quantitative capabilities of the lab. Needless to say, it would be quite rare for a laboratory to achieve a score of 100% on one of these type evaluations. A good quality lab however will consistently perform at a success rate of 80% or better. Additionally, the results on these samples can serve as an initial point for a detailed examination of the laboratory's procedures and practices. Presenting the laboratory with the results and asking for an explanation, then sitting back and evaluating the response will give keen insight into the philosophy of the laboratory management. A no-holds barred response is the expected product of a scientifically rigorous organization while an explanation full of excuses and evasions or no explanation at all is the result of managerial fluff.

C. Batch Analysis

1. Economic and Time Considerations

Every analyst would like to apply every one of the quality controls listed in the preceeding discussions to every single sample and thereby have a definitive, quantitative answer to each of the analytical concerns about the sample. If one is involved in method development or other forms of analytical research, the end goal is to prove that the method works, and thus, no stone is left unturned in the examination of the sample and procedure. The time and costs are immaterial and are the expected dues to pay in discovering "the truth" when the ultimate goal is to describe the procedure and results in a peer-reviewed journal.

In the world of production laboratory operations, the cost and time required to perform this level of analysis on a per-sample basis becomes prohibitive. This is particularly pertinent when the goal is to provide a result on a sample submitted by a client who then will forward the result to one or another regulatory agency as part of a compliance monitoring requirement. The client has the expectation that the result is in compliance with all aspects of the agency's specifications, but at the same time there is a concern about how much cash is going to be spent to get the result. Time, capital investment, overhead, maintenance, salaries, benefits, and expendable supplies all get figured into the equation that generates the dollar figure the client needs to pay for the result.

The concept of batch analysis has its origins in the drinking water and wastewater monitoring programs, where a municipal laboratory is performing the same analysis on the same sample day after day after day. An example would be twice-weekly analysis of wastewater plant effluent for 4-nitrophenol using EPA Method 625 to verify that NPDES permit levels are not being exceeded. Quality controls specified in Method 625 include performance of a calibration, method detection limit study, and operator initial demonstration of capability prior to starting sample analysis, then on an ongoing basis perform a blank extraction with each set of samples or new lot of reagents, daily

---

9 Analytical Products Group, 1-800-272-4442; Environmental Resource Associates, 1-800-372-0122; Analytical Standards, 1-304-442-4274.

instrument tuning and calibration checks, and perform a matrix spike every 20 samples, or at least once a month. The matrix spike is tailored to meet the regulatory requirements of the NPDES permit and background content of the sample. If the matrix spike fails to meet the specified recovery objectives a quality control check sample must be successfully analyzed to demonstrate the method is in control. The idea is that the laboratory must demonstrate that it can successfully analyze the regulated analyte in the compliance sample at the specified regulatory limit. The maximun holding times for the method are 7 days from sampling until extraction, and 40 days after extraction until analysis. The 40 days maximum holding time after extraction until analysis means that all the samples extracted in a month could be saved in the refrigerator, then the GC-MS cranked up, and the extracts analyzed on one day each month. Method 625 is an approved method of testing, and all the other analytical concerns of accuracy, precision, detection limits, and laboratory contamination are met over the space of a set of 20 samples or a month. These considerations lead directly to the concept of a batch.

Key assumptions that underlie the frequency of quality control performance in Method 625 are that it is the same source for the sample being analyzed repeatedly and that the sample is not changing significantly from one analysis to the next. Thus the single matrix spike result can be generalized to predict recoveries expected on all the other repetitions analyzed in that month. The method is written with a batch procedure specifically in mind although the term is not defined in the method. If a batch is conceived with the idea in mind of meeting all the analytical concerns for a set of samples, then within the confines of this method, a batch is limited to either 20 samples, or those samples performed in a month. The batch is seen to consist of a blank, a matrix spike, possibly a quality control check, daily calibration and instrument checks, and up to 20 samples. The explicit time limitation for a batch is a month.

The batch concept has been generalized to cover almost all analytical testing protocols in the environmental laboratory. The process of generalization has been accompanied by a considerable amount of liberal individual interpretation as a result of a lack of a single comprehensive definition of what is a batch and what is not. Most of the different interpretations have been driven by strictly economic concerns instead of analytical veracity, and in some cases the interpretation can be more correctly viewed as rationalized corner cutting within a shell of seeming legitimacy.

The first consideration is determining what type of samples can go into a batch. To be scientifically valid a batch must generate quantitative results for all the analytical concerns about all the samples within the batch. The idea behind the batch is to generate specific quality control results on a few samples and then apply these results to all the samples. Thus, samples in a batch must be similar. They must be very similar. Georgia red clay, beach sand, ambient air samples, domestic sewage, and drinking water are obviously very different matrices and thus cannot be placed in a batch together. Effluent from a wastewater treatment plant, groundwater from a landfill monitoring well and drinking water from a public distribution system are all water samples, but how similar could one rationally expect them to be? Is a matrix spike performed on the drinking water at all indicative of the ability to successfully analyse the wastewater effluent?

When using the batch concept to process samples, all the samples are to be processed in exactly the same manner. Thus, the second consideration becomes whether or not it is legally possible to treat all samples in an identical fashion and meet all the requirements in the regulatory method. The details of the wastewater and drinking water regulatory methods are sufficiently different, beginning with the extraction techniques, that at least one and probably all of the samples are not being analyzed in compliance with the respective methods.

When the two considerations are combined in delineating the contents of a batch, further questions surface. How about influent and effluent samples from the same wastewater treatment plant? These are very different samples, but they both fall under the same method. How about raw source water from a reservoir and the finished drinking water the treatment plant generates? Again, different samples but the same method and regulation. Or, what about drinking water from two different treatment works? Can any of these be placed in the same batch and satisfy the assumption that a limited set of quality control results can be used to predict the behavior of all the samples? As a useful guide, batches should contain samples that are regulated under the same method, are all of the same matrix, and are from similar sources. This works well when the client sends in a lot of samples, such as a quarterly sampling event of 30 monitoring wells. However, the idea gets significantly bent when the samples are single 24-hour composites from effluent plants sent in to satisfy the once-a-month compliance analysis.

The general question of how long a period of time can be encompassed by a batch, is addressed as a maximum of a month in Method 625. Is this scientifically rational? The answer is yes, with some qualifications. The blank analysis checks for laboratory contamination, and as it is normally performed, it is a systematic check. If the solvents and other reagents are found to be clean, then as long as the same lot numbers are being used there is little rationale for continally checking the same materials. The use of a blank analysis as a random contamination indicator is not being performed with sufficient frequency to generate statistically valid predictions and thus is not a consideration. As discussed below, if effective random contamination detection is an objective, then every day the analyst prepares samples should be an occassion for inclusion of a blank. Matrix spikes and quality control samples (Laboratory Control Samples) probe the ability to generate valid data from the sample matrix. If the sample matrix is constant, then the ability to generate a result should remain constant and does not need to be redetermined on a daily basis. Once a month would seem to be sufficient for Method 625, and probably most semivolatile and metals procedures. However, the time limit must take into consideration the individual procedure. For analysis of volatile compounds, the samples, standards and reagents are easily contaminated from materials in the air, which can be significantly different from one day to the next. Thus a batch for volatiles analysis needs to be performed within a maximum of a 2-3 day period of time, and a 24-hour maximum on the batch is realistic.

There is nothing magical about a 20-sample limit to the batch. At some point in the development of the idea of a batch, a 5% frequency for blanks, duplicates and matrix spikes (as indicated in Method 625) was chosen as suitable, although some regulatory agencies, particularly on the state level, have decided that a 10% frequency is more appropriate. Batches can be increased in size over 20 samples by increasing the number of blanks, duplicates and matrix spikes so that the minimum ratio of quality controls to samples is maintained. Note that the batch size is delineated by the number of samples which are contained in the batch[10]. A batch of 20 samples contains 20 samples plus the necessary quality control samples (blank, duplicate, matrix spike, matrix spike duplicate, laboratory control sample, laboratory control sample duplicate, continuing calibration, *etc.*) added on.

---

[10] Method 1664, EPA April, 95.

2. Preparation and Instrument Batches

Batching of samples can be applied to sample preparation and to instrument analysis as two separate processes. This is necessary in situations where the instrument has time limitations for quality controls, and the analysis time for a batch of 20 samples plus quality control samples exceeds the time constraints for the instrument. An example is analysis of semivolatile compounds by GC-MS. The tune and continuing calibration performed on the GC-MS are only valid for 12 hours, while each sample requires approximately 1 hour for analysis. Thus a full preparation batch with accompanying quality controls is impossible to instrument analyse within one period of instrument quality control, and thus the preparation batch is broken into several instrument batches. If one instrument is all that is available, then the preparation batch will be broken into several instrument batches that will be performed over several days.

If more than a single instrument is used, the preparation batch may be spread over several instruments, each with a unique set of quality control results for calibration, tune and system performance. This a particularly efficient procedure if the instruments are set-up so that they are compliant with more than one method's quality control requirements. Although it is virtually impossible to use the minimum parameters for one method, say 8270B, and meet the requirements of another method like 625, or *vice versa*, it is very possible to increase the level of quality controls above the minimum and meet more than one method's needs. Thus use of a five-point calibration would meet the requirements of both methods, as will use of additional surrogate compounds and internal standards from those needed in 8270B. Continuing calibration verification performed in compliance with Method 625 with all target analytes and evaluated against the individual analyte acceptable limits in Method 8270B, while ignoring the CCC requirements, will be compliant with both. System performance evaluated with both SPCC requirements and calculation of tailing factors will satisfy both methods, as will use of the tune parameters listed in Method 625. Although the sample processing detailed in Method 3510 or 3540 will never meet the requirements of Method 625, the analysis of the extracts can be performed by a suitable hybrid procedure. But performance of the drinking water GC-MS Method 525.2 is so different that it is impossible to hybridize successfully with either or both Methods 8270B and 625.

Another example is found in the case of cyanide where sample preparation involves distillation of the cyanide from the sample. Liquid samples and solid samples would correctly be viewed as belonging in two different batches for distillation purposes. Total cyanide and reactive cyanide determinations have differences in the distillation procedure. If amenable cyanide is also considered, another procedural variation of the preparation is introduced with its own requirements for separate quality controls. However, once the samples are distilled, the distillates are identical matrices and are treated in exactly the same way in the colorimetric analysis, which is a very rapid process. Therefore separate sample preparation batches can be rolled into one analysis batch.

A problem that has been booted around for some time in the industry concerns re-analysis and re-extraction/digestion of samples due to some failure in the testing process. There is no particular reason for not assigning the reprocessed sample to the same batch in which it originally resided unless a change in reagents or solvents had occurred between the initial and repeated processing.

D. Statistical Interpretation of Quality Controls and Acceptance Limits

Mathematics is an exact science. If a problem is to be solved in mathematics there is only one correct answer. For example:

```
   15
  +17
   32
```

Figure 2-20. Mathematical problem with only one possible exact solution.

Laboratory chemisty on the other hand is an experimental science and it involves measurements. If this math problem was a chemistry analog, then the answer obtained would not be exactly 32 every time. Instead, the obtained results would be over a range of values, with the probability of obtaining any particular result decreasing the farther away from 32 the result is.

```
        15
       +17
       ___
        32
     31    33        Decreasing probability of result
   30          34
```

Figure 2-21. Chemistry analog of mathematical problem with many possible solutions

The challenge then becomes to not only determine the correctness of the result but also to characterize the spread of results. Fortunately the spread of almost all chemical measurements around a central value is controlled by completely random events in the measurement process. Thus the range of possible results from a measurement is very well described by a normal distribution. Normal distributions, or as they are also called, bell curves and Gaussian distributions, are symmetrical curves that represent the probability of the occurance of a value, as illustrated in Figure 2-22.

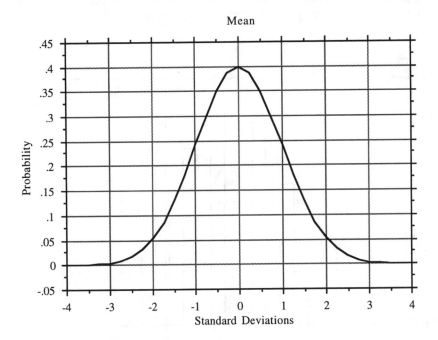

Figure 2-22. **Normal distribution curve.**

The curve is completely described by the mean value of the distribution and the numerical value of the standard deviation. Plus and minus one standard deviation encompasses 68% of the area under the curve, or as it is commonly interpreted, 68% of the observations. Plus and minus two standard deviations from the mean include 95% of the observations, while ±3 standard deviations include 99.7% of the observations.

1. Accuracy

Accuracy is a concept from quantitative analysis that attempts to address the question of how close the analytical result is to the true value of the analyte in the sample. Although some authors have attempted to define accuracy and bias as two separate terms, in the environmental industry they express the same idea and are treated as synonomous.

Accuracy is determined through the matrix spike procedure, where a known amount of the target analyte is added to a portion of the sample, then the sample and the matrix spiked sample are analyzed. The quantitative measure of accuracy is percent recovery (%R) calculated as follows.

$$\%R \;=\; \frac{\text{matrix spike result - sample result}}{\text{matrix spike true value}} \times 100 \,.$$

Each measurement performed on a sample is subject to random and systematic error. Accuracy is related to the systematic error. Attempts to assess systematic error are always complicated by the inherent random error of the measurement. With reference to Figure 2-23, the displacement of the mean of the distribution of results from the true value of the analyte is the systematic error. The true value in this instance is 100, while the mean of the distribution is 94. The systematic error for the distribution is -6.

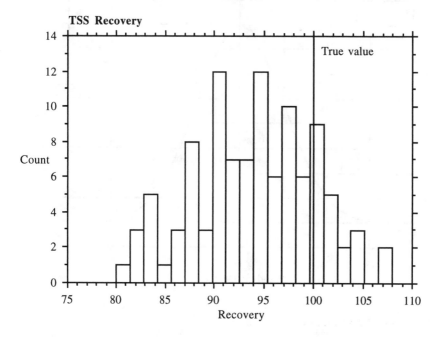

Figure 2-23. **Distribution of results obtained from 105 measurements of a Total Suspended Solids (TSS) check sample.**

A single determination of accuracy on a sample is not significant statistically, although many people will treat it as if it were. Statistics of course is the science of prediction of reality based on a limited number of observations. The more limited the number of observations, the worse the prediction is going to be. Again with reference to Figure 2-23, if a single determination of the recovery of a matrix spike is used as indicator of the systematic error, in reality there is no indication where within the distribution of results the recovery lies. Since the systematic error of a analysis depends on the mean of the distribution of results, it is impossible to obtain an estimate of the mean unless two separate determinations of recovery have been made. In practical terms this translates into a single determination of recovery on a sample being worthless. A minimum of two recovery values are needed to estimate accuracy.

2. Precision

Precision is the measurement of the ability to obtain the same value on re-analysis of a sample. The closer the results of the measurements are together, the greater is the precision. Precision has nothing to do with accuracy or true values in the sample. Instead it is focused upon the random errors inherent in the analysis that stem from the measurement process and are compounded by the sample vagaries. Precision is measured by analyzing two portions of the sample (sample and duplicate) and then comparing the results.

Unfortunately, other than simply reporting the values obtained from the sample and its duplicate (an estimate of the range), there is no good measuring stick for quantitative assessment of precision. The most commonly used measure is relative percent difference (RPD). RPD is calculated as the difference between the two measurements divided by the average of the two measurements.

$$RPD = \frac{2|A-B|}{A + B} \times 100$$

The problem with this is that it depends on the average of the two measurements and the magnitude of the calculated RPD is intimately linked to the magnitude of the results. For example, compare the calculated RPD for each set of results reported in Table 2-14. In Case 1 the results are fairly close together, and the RPD indicates that there is good relative agreement in the results. Case 2, evaluated in comparison with Case 1 gives an intuitive feeling that there is a large decrease in the repeatability of the test, which is bourne out by the calculated RPD of 100. However, Case 3 points out the problems of RPD. Comparison of the absolute differences between the results of the sample and duplicate in Case 3 with those in Case 1 gives the gut-level feeling that Case 3 represents greater repeatability than Case 1; however, the calculated RPD indicates that the results are similar to those in Case 2.

Table 2-14.   RPD Calculated for Different Pairs of Results of an Analysis.

Case	Result 1 mg/L	Result 2 mg/L	RPD
1	98	102	4
2	50	150	100
3	1	3	100

RPD as a measure of precision works very well in those cases where the same level of analyte is present in all samples; however, it fails miserably as a quantitative tool when varying levels are present. Such is the situation in environmental analysis where the normal flow of samples will include those with no detectable levels of the target analyte adjacent to samples with remarkably high levels. Analysis of sample duplicates is valuable as a qualitative measure of precision but useless as a quantitative measure in the environmental laboratory.

Because of these problems, precision is normally calculated on spiked samples as either a matrix spike (MS) and a matrix spike duplicate (MSD) or as a laboratory control sample (LCS) and laboratory control sample duplicate (LCSD). Here a constant level of analyte has been created in each sample and long and short term evaluations of RPD can be made that are applicable to the reality of the measurement. The drawback is that the precision measurement is only applicable to the particular spike level used.

3. Data Quality Objectives and Confidence Intervals

Data quality objectives (DQOs) are statements of expectations of the performance capabilities of the laboratory. (Data quality objectives as a specific part of sampling and analysis plans are discussed in the next section.) Laboratories will frequently generate a generic set of DQOs relating to their general performance, and these may be required as part of a state certification of the laboratory. A minimum set of laboratory DQOs consists of generally applicable numerical estimates for accuracy, precision, and the method detection limit. Other DQOs that can be generated include quantitative statements of ambient laboratory contamination levels of the common problems found in blank results, including methylene chloride, acetone, the various phthalates, ammonia, aluminum, iron, calcium, sodium, and magnesium. The DQOs can also be modified to meet the information needs of the particular project.

A data quality objective is prepared by first performing the quality control a number of times. Let's use the already discussed (Chapter II, 11. Surrogates) computation of a DQO for the recovery of the surrogate nitrobenzene-d5, from water samples using method 625, as an example. The distribution of the results of 791 recoveries was presented in Figure 2-4. After removal of outliers[11] from the data set (Figure 2-7), a mean of 76.2 and a standard deviation of 14.3 are obtained. DQOs are established based on confidence levels with the 95% and 99.7% levels being the most common. These correspond to ±2 standard deviations and ±3 standard deviations from the mean, respectively. The 95% confidence level, which is most commonly used for matrix spike and laboratory control sample recovery and precision estimates, means that 95% of the observations should fall within the limits. This translates into 1 out of 20 normal results being expected to fall outside the limits. And this does not include expectations for samples that present matrix interferences to the analysis, because samples that presented matrix interferences were removed from the data set as outliers. It is important to segregate samples into those that present no analytical problems from those that are distinct problem children. Inclusion of the problem samples in the data set used for calculation of the DQO generates a range useless for evaluation of normal laboratory processes controlled only by random error. The one sample out of 20 that statistically falls outside the 95% confidence range should be checked to insure that it falls within the 99.7% confidence interval (±3 standard deviations). Points outside the ±3 standard deviations need to be closely examined to determine the cause of the lack of control. If no specific cause is found, the possibility of laboratory blunder must be considered, and thus the data associated with maltreated samples are unreliable. Laboratory blunders or a botched analysis have been removed as outliers from the data sets when the DQOs were calculated in just the same manner as the results affected by matrix interference.

The 99.7% confidence level is used commonly for surrogate recoveries. This is the ±3 standard deviation interval around the mean after removal of the laboratory blunders and matrix affected results. Points outside the 99.7% confidence DQO must have a specific reason for the deviation, because all but three random events out of 1000 are included in the interval.

---

[11] Taylor, J.K. *Quality Assurance of Chemical Measurements.* 1987, Lewis Publishers, Boca Roton FL, Chapter 4.

I have frequently had clients come up to me and demand an explanation, often in a loud and belligerent tone of voice, of exactly why a result for a dissolved metal is higher than the result for a total metal analysis on the same sample. The client has an intuitive understanding that dissolved metal is a subset of total metal and therefore it is a physical impossibility that the dissolved value be higher than the total value. When the values are examined, it is most commonly found that the dissolved value is slightly higher than the total value, most commonly to the extent of about 1 to 2% higher. After assuring myself that no blunders occurred during the analysis, I then launch into my pat dissertation on confidence limits. Most clients can grasp that there is an uncertainty factor associated with any reported value of analysis of a sample, and the questions that follow the explanation of confidence limits most frequently deal with the issue of why don't laboratories include a confidence interval with the analytical result. When we get to this point I don't have a good answer. Although every single chemist involved with environmental laboratories is aware of the uncertainty associated with a reported value, there has never been a movement in the industry to provide the clients with estimates of uncertainty.

Author

The traditional approach to statistical confidence limits is based upon the formula:

$$X \pm \frac{ts}{\sqrt{n}}$$

where: X is the value of the result
t is the *t*-statistic for the desired level of confidence and the number of degrees of freedom
s is the standard deviation of the results, and
n is number of degrees of freedom.

The shortcoming of this formula is the reliance upon a standard deviation or an estimate of the standard deviation for the determination of the confidence limits. In an environmental laboratory 95% of all samples are analyzed once. The 5% of the samples that are analyzed more than once stem from the requirement to analyze at least one sample in duplicate out of a batch of 20 and at least one sample out of 20 as a matrix spiked sample and maybe a matrix spiked duplicate. The single analysis of the sample generates no information upon the standard deviation of the determinations on the sample and gives insufficient data upon which an estimate of the standard deviation can be derived.

The second best data available in the lab are derived from the collected results of the analysis of matrix spiked samples, laboratory control samples and the performance of method detection limit studies. The matrix spiked samples performed can be statistically analyzed to give a standard deviation for a single spike level performed in many different samples. The matrix spike is most frequently performed at the mid-point of the calibration curve, and standard deviations that result are applicable only to that level of analyte but will generally be applicable to a wide range of different samples. Laboratory control sample results can be used to generate standard deviations; however, again there is only one specific value of the analyte, and, for all intents and purposes, there is no contribution to the standard deviation from matrix effects.

Suppose a laboratory reports a DQO of 35-89% for recovery of a compound spiked at the 200 µg/L level into real samples. A confidence limit for this analyte can be calculated at the 200 µg/L level by determining the standard deviation of the analyte. Most DQOs are at the 95% confidence level, which is ± 2 standard deviations. Thus divide the range by 4 [(89-35)/4], which gives 13.5% of 200 or 27 µg/L. The degrees of freedom are related to the number of determinations used to generate the DQO. Say 20 in this case. Then n = 19 and the confidence interval at the 90% level is calculated as:

$$200 \pm \frac{1.725 \times 27}{4.36} = 200 \pm 10.6$$

A 95% confidence level increases the interval to:

$$200 \pm \frac{2.086 \times 27}{4.36} = 200 \pm 12.9$$

or about ± 6% of the reported value.

MDL studies involve actual determination of a standard deviation might be used to generate a confidence interval. These unfortunately are applicable to only the lowest levels of analysis and are completely insulated from any matrix effects due to the sample. However, they might be applied, given these restraints in interpretation to results up to five times the MDL. The confidence limits can be determined as follows. First divide the reported MDL by 3.14. Based on seven replicates this gives an actual laboratory-derived standard deviation. Next, multiply the MDL by five. This gives the result (X) value to which the confidence limits are applicable. "n" is equal to 6 normally, unless other numbers of replicates were used for the MDL determination. Look up the t-statistic in appropriate tables and calculate the confidence limits.

As an example, suppose the reported MDL for a test is 5.0 mg/L based on seven replicates. The confidence limits at the 90% level then become:

$$25.0 \pm \frac{1.943 \times 1.59}{2.45} = 25.0 \pm 1.3$$

to

$$10.0 \pm \frac{1.943 \times 1.59}{2.45} = 10.0 \pm 1.3$$

where   25.0 is the MDL times 5, and 10 is the MDL times 2
           1.943 is the t-statistic at the 90% confidence level for 6 degrees of freedom
           1.59 is the standard deviation, obtained by dividing the MDL by 3.14
           2.45 is the square root of the 6 degrees of freedom.

These intervals are from ± 5 to ± 13% of the reported value.

Applying these reasonings to the actual MDL study presented in Table 2-2, where the true level was 0.9 mg/L, the mean result was 0.68, a standard deviation of 0.094 was obtained in 10 trials, and a MDL of 0.27 generated, a 90% confidence interval of ±0.0545 is calculated. The calculated 90% confidence range is 0.626 to 0.734. It is instructive to note that of the actual values obtained in the study presented in Table 2-2, 7 of the 10 values lie outside this range.

As a rule of thumb without any statistical justification, for results at or close to the MDL, the 90% confidence interval is approximately ± MDL with the recognition that half the results at the MDL could be reported as below detection limit (BDL) or not-detected (ND or U). Again this would apply to samples that are totally devoid of any matrix problems or background noise. Applying this rule to the data in Table 2-2, gives a 90% confidence interval of 0.68 ± 0.27 or 0.51 to 0.95, and all the analytical results are seen to fall inside the interval. The interval is also noted to include the true value of the spike; however, this is meerly coincidence, and no significance should be attached to it.

In the general case of trying to obtain a confidence interval for a result on a specific sample, there is a way to obtain an estimate of the standard deviation based on analysis of duplicate samples. In the event of a single duplicate determination the estimate reduces to:

$$\text{standard deviation} \ \frac{|A\text{-}B|}{\sqrt{2}} = 0.7071 \ |A\text{-}B|$$

where   A and B are the sample and the duplicate results.

The estimation of the result and the 90% confidence interval then boils down to:

$$\frac{|A\text{-}B|}{2} \pm 4.46 \ |A\text{-}B|$$

where   A and B are the results of the sample and duplicate analysis.

As an application of this formula, suppose the result and duplicate are 98 and 102, then the result with 90% confidence interval becomes 100 ± 17.9 or 82 to 118. This interval includes matrix effect considerations since only data derived from the sample were used. In practical applications this interval may or may not be valid; however, it is statistically justifiable.

Application of this estimation procedure requires that each sample be performed in duplicate. Within the existing protocols in the environmental industry, duplicates are routinely processed on only 1 out of every 10 or 20 samples.

4. DQO-PRO

Data Quality Objectives are products of sampling and analysis plans within the context of remediation of hazardous waste sites. The planning process has been examined and broken down into seven distinct steps[12]:

1. State the problem to be resolved.

    Identify issues and practical restraints, help focus and clarify problem to be resolved.

2. Identify the decision.

    Provide background information and present options for potential decisions.

3. State the inputs.

---

[12] EPA 540-R-93-071, September, 1993

List factors that may contribute to the decision and technical information about environmental variables.

4. Define the boundaries of the study.

Develop a statistical description of the problem.

5. Develop a decision rule.

Develop a quantitative decision rule with a final objective or stopping point.

6. Specify the limits of uncertainty.

Identify decision errors to avoid and identify consequences of decision errors.

7. Optimize design for data collection.

Prepare the optimal data collection plan based on the decision rule and desired uncertainty limits.

In addition to the DQO statements for precision, accuracy, and method detection limit, which were discussed in the previous Section, project specific DQOs may be generated for data completeness (how much data must be of acceptable quality as a percentage of the total number of samples taken in the field or sent to the laboratory), comparability (degree to which one data set can be compared to another) and representativeness (how well the data describe the conditions of the site).

Once the first six steps of the process are completed, the 7th step becomes a mathematical exercise in applying statistics to find out how many anlytical and quality control samples are to be collected. These calculations are iterative and somewhat laborious. A computer program called DQO-PRO was developed under EPA contract to ease the burden of the calculations. It is being distributed free. Call Dr. Larry Keith at 512-454-4797 to obtain your copy.

DQO-PRO consists of three calculation modules. The Enviro-Calc module will generate the number of analytical samples that need to be collected and analyzed in order to meet a specified tolerance level or error and confidence. The Hotspot-Calc module generates an areal grid size needed to detect a hotspot of a prescribed shape and size with a specified probability. The number of analytical samples needed to be taken from the grid is also calculated. The Success-Calc module calculates the number of samples needed to detect a specified characteristic with a certain confidence level when the characteristic exists in a population of samples. Further information on these needs and application of them is contained in a recent book.[13].

It is the third module in DQO-PRO that has tremendous potential for use in environmental laboratory data evaluation. A specific application is the calculation of the number of blank samples that need to be evaluated to determine overall random laboratory contamination levels at, for instance, a 95% confidence level. Other applications will come to the reader's mind.

E. Quality Assurance Program

If quality assurance is all the things that a laboratory does to generate and verify data that meets the client's needs, then the quality assurance program must encompass all the

---

[13] Keith, L., *Principles of Environmental Sampling*, 2nd Edition, ACS Books, Washington, DC, 1996.

aspects of operations that impact the client. Normally the pricing, invoicing and financial aspects of the business are left out of the quality assurance umbrella but in a larger sense they probably need to be included.

1. Quality Assurance Manuals and Project Plans

A QA program is only as good as its documentation. Although every employee of the laboratory may have an eye toward QA, the implementation of the myrid procedures under QA is subject to individual interpretation unless there is a written standard. Which is not to say that there will not be individual interpretations even with a written standard; there is no way to get around that. The written program, however, tends to minimize the range of the deviations. Further there must be at least one person in the company who regularly examines the QA program to insure that all the little parts of it are working cooperatively toward a unified goal. Without this periodic review and revision of the written program, the individual interpretations tend to diverge from a single path into chaos.

There are many ways to document a Quality Assurance program and organizations, like ISO and ANSI have written volumes about quality systems. These pat systems are useful, but they do not go far enough to address the particular concerns and details needed to meet the legal and analytical requirements needed for successful operations within the regulatory framework that defines the environmental industry. An outline of a written QA program that addresses the needs of this market is presented in Table 2-15.

Table 2-15.   Subject Areas of an Environmental Laboratory Quality Assurance Manual

Section	Title and Description
1	Title Page with authorization signatures and dates
2	Table of Contents
3	Statement of QA Policy
4	Organizational tables and job descriptions for supervisory positions
5	Data quality objectives for accuracy, precision, and method detection limits for each test, target analyte, and sample matrix
6	Sampling procedures, field equipment lists, field decontamination protocols, and documentation, holding times, preservation and containers for each analyte group and matrix
7	Sample custody procedures and documentation
8	Analytical methods variances, glassware washing protocols, etc.
9	Equipment and instrument lists and calibration procedures along with documentation descriptions and acceptance criteria; sources of standards
10	Preventative maintenance schedules and documentation description for each analytical instrument
11	Quality control procedures and frequency for each test for determination of laboratory contamination, accuracy, precision, and method detection limits along with acceptance criteria
12	Data reduction procedures from raw instrument read-out to final reported result; data validation, review, and reporting procedures; computer system operation and maintenance procedures
13	Standard corrective action procedures and documentation for QC failures in Sections 9 and 11
14	Performance and system audit procedures and documentation
15	Frequency and content of QA reports
16	Resumés of key personnel

Table 2-15.   Subject Areas of an Environmental Laboratory Quality Assurance Manual, *continued*

Section	Title and Description
Appendices	
	References
	Glossary of terms and definitions
	Training Program and documentation
	Miscellaneous information

Most laboratories will have on hand written Standard Operating Procedures (SOP). These bridge the gap of procedure from what the analyst does on the bench to the directions given in the approved method. Most methods have general directions for conducting the analysis, with many individual decisions left up to the analyst. An example is a method that states that five calibration standards, with one at the detection limit, must be used to calibrate the instrument. The concentrations of the standards are left up to the analyst. The SOP can provide the details on the calibration, such as:

> "Prepare a stock solution of 100.0 mg/L of the standard by dissolving 321.6 mg of the solid standard in 50 mL of DI water in a 100 mL volumetric flask and diluting to volume, then dilute 1.00, 2.00, 3.00, 4.00 and 5.00 mL of the stock standard each to 100.0 mL in volumetric flasks to prepare the working calibration standards."

The SOP needs to reflect exactly what is being done by the analyst on the bench. It also must provide for procedures to be used that allow compliance with the approved method. As such the SOP becomes a key part in the Quality Assurance Program. However, inclusion of the SOPs in the Quality Assurance Manual quickly makes the manual an unwieldly large document. There is also the attitude within the industry that the SOP is a proprietary document, while the QA Manual is used as a very effective sales and marketing tool. This delineation of the two sets of documents is fully justified. If a laboratory has spent a lot of time hybridizing two GC-MS operating procedures such as discussed in general terms above for Methods 8270B and 625, so that the operation of the laboratory is more efficient while maintaining complete compliance with disparate regulatory methods, then this procedure is proprietary.

QA Project Plans (QAPjP) are versions of the QA Manual tailored for a specific project. They are normally generated by taking the computerized version of the laboratory QA Manual and chopping out those portions that do not apply to the specific project. The Data Quality Objectives section may be completely rewritten to include project specific DQO (discussed above) rather than laboratory generated values. Specific restrictions and modifications to normal operating procedures may need to be included, such as "batches will contain only project specific samples" or "MS must be performed on specified samples selected during the field sampling." Specific reporting formats or electronic deliverables for data different from the normal procedures need to be spelled out in the QAPjP. The QAPjP may be the laboratory's part of a larger scope Sampling and Analysis Plan, which may itself be a part of a overall site assessment or remediation plan prepared by the consulting engineers.

2. On-site Audits

Although it is possible to obtain an idea of a laboratory's scope and capabilities from reading the sales literature and QA Manual and by talking to the project managers on the phone, there is nothing to compare with actually visiting the laboratory. The visit may be as casual as an hour long walk-around tour to as formal as a full blown three-day, five-person detailed data and procedural audit. Regardless of the duration of the audit, it is strongly suggested that visitors prepare a list of what they want to see and discuss prior to arrival at the lab. If you come into the lab with the idea that you'll let them show you what you need to see, in actuality what will happen is that you will get shown what they want you to see, generally the best and brightest. Make a list. Then after the best and brightest have been seen, you can get down to the brass tacks of your needs.

Make a point of talking to random analysts to determine if they know their job. If you limit your talking to only the persons assigned to escort you during the visit or the managers/supervisors, you may obtain a very slanted view of the technical capabilities and training level within the lab.

Frankly discuss your needs, concerns, and observations with the laboratory staff. Their responses are often informative as to how in general they handle problems.

Be sure to write down your observations and findings from your visit to the lab. A memo or formal report of your visit sent to the lab should generate a response, particularly if you have questions about some of the lab's procedures.

There are a number of documents available that will assist visitors in determining what they need to examine in the laboratory. It is imperative however that the visitor to an environmental laboratory not be trapped by the "Quality Systems" approach to auditing. Although the presence of mounds of documented procedures covering all aspects of the lab operations is impressive, concentrating your attention on the documentation alone effectively misses half the liability inherent in the lab's data. The other half of the coin, technical competence and regulatory method compliance, can be completely missed if you look at just the paperwork. This means that you need to study the approved method and then make a determination whether or not the method is being followed, most commonly ascertained by discussing the method with the analyst.

3. Certifications, Accreditations and Validations

These are recognition that the laboratory has met minimum levels of performance or expectations under a specified program. The term "certification" is normally limited to a formal recognition by a governmental regulatory agency such as state environmental protection agency of the laboratory's allowed participation in a program.
"Accreditation" is applied to commercial third-party recognition that the laboratory has met minimum requirements under the third party's standards of performance.
"Validation" is a term used by the federal Department of Defense groups to recognize that a laboratory has met their respective sets of standards and is allowed to participate in their programs.

With the exception of the newly created Information Collection Rule - Disinfectant By-product laboratory certification, a very restricted analytical program, there is no nationwide EPA laboratory certification in any program. Instead laboratories are certified by individual state agencies for participation in certain programs. These vary from state-to-state, and there is no common standard for certification. The necessity for being certified in each particular state serves to define the market, both geographic and program-based, in which the laboratory is allowed to participate. Some states have comprehensive certification programs covering all aspects of environmental analysis, while others have very rudimentary programs, most commonly limited to drinking water.

References

1. *Handbook for Analytical Quality Control in Water and Wastewater.* EPA 600/4-79-019. March 1979. NTIS number PB-297 451.

2. *Manual for Analytical Quality Control for Pesticides and Related Compounds in Human and Environmental Samples.* EPA 600/1-79-009. 1979.

3. *Manual for the Certification of Laboratories Analyzing Drinking Water. Criteria and Procedures Quality Assurance.* EPA 570/9-90/008 April 1990. Change 1 EPA 570/9-90/008A. October 1991. Change 2 EPA 814B-92-002. September, 1992.

4. Garfield, F.M., *Quality Assurance Principles for Analytical Laboratories.* AOAC, Arlington, VA, 1984.

5. Gautier, M.A. and E.S. Gladney, "A quality assurance program for health and environmental chemistry." *American Laboratory* July, 1987.

6. Keith, L.H., *Principles of Environmental Sampling.* American Chemical Society, Washington, D.C., 1987.

7. Smith, R.-K., *Handbook of Environmental Analysis.* Second Edition, Genium Publishing, Schenectady, NY, 1995.

8. Smith, R.-K., *Water and Wastewater Laboratory Techniques.* Water Environment Federation, Alexandria, VA, 1995.

9. Taylor, J.K., *Principles of Quality Assurance of Chemical Measurements*, U.S. Department of Commerce, February, 1985.

10. Taylor, J.K., *Quality Assurance of Chemical Measurements.* Orlando Fla.: Lewis Publishers. 1987.

11. *Environmental Compliance Branch Standard Operating Procedures and Quality Assurance Manual.* U.S. EPA Region IV Environmental Services Division. February, 1991.

CHAPTER 3

Legally Admissible Data

Most sample analysis in the environmental industry is performed to fulfill:

- One of a variety of regulatory compliance monitoring requirements
- Part of a direct contract between a governmental agency and the laboratory
- Part of a contract for work with a commercial firm where the work is either directly contracted by or submitted for review to a regulatory or other governmental agency.

There are few environmental analyses that are done that do not fall under one of the above categories. For all intents and purposes, every analytical result generated on a sample is subject to being entered as evidence into court as part of a legal action to determine the facts concerning whether a regulation or contract has been fulfilled or not. This use of test results as evidence places additional requirements upon how samples are handled and the analysis documented. A common expression in environmental laboratories of the legal aspect of sample analysis is "if you didn't write it down, you didn't do it." As with most things in life, the reality is somewhat more complex than this.

My uncle was a judge in an administrative law court. I made a comment to him once about how difficult his job must be interpreting the law. In response, he told me that there was no difficulty in interpreting the law; it was all set down in a very easy to understand and unambiguous manner in the regulations and rules of the state and Federal governments. He then went on to explain that the real hard part of his job was establishing the facts of the case and whether or not the law applied in a particular situation. If the facts indicated that the law applied and that the law had been violated, then the only question was how big a penalty he should mete out as punishment. While I may, as a layman, question his use of the terms "unambiguous" and "easy to understand" in relation to the law, his point concerning the function of the judge and the court has always remained with me.

Author

A. Requirements for Legal Admissibility

The facts established in court are supported by evidence presented by the contending parties. There are two objectives of the attorneys in establishing their particular version of the facts. The first is a careful selection and presentation of evidence that supports their viewpoint. The second is to question (impeach), or better yet, prevent the presentation of the evidence used by the other party.

As evidence, scientific data must meet the criteria set forth in the Federal Rules of Evidence (FRE) if the case is being tried in Federal court. The Federal Rules of Evidence are an enactment of Congress, signed into law by the President. Many states have evidence rules covering the state courts that are either a direct copy or a modification of the Federal Rules. Aspects of the Rules that are most applicable to laboratory results include:

- Relevance
- Foundation
- Authenticity.

The first criteria for evidence is that of Relevance (FRE Section IV). To be relevant, evidence must first either support a proposition that is being established as a fact in the case or serve to make unlikely an alternate proposition. Second, the fact being established through the presentation of the evidence must have a direct bearing on the point of contention in the case.

If scientific data are being submitted as evidence and are likely to be accepted by the court as relevant, a corollary task is to present foundation evidence showing that the procedures used in generating the results were carefully performed in accordance with accepted standards. Such foundation evidence includes the condition of the equipment, operating procedures, analyst training, record-keeping procedures, and identification of the sample. The amount and thoroughness of the foundation presented will, to a large extent, depend on the level of expertise and past experiences of the contending attorneys.

Any piece of documentation submitted as evidence must be authenticated. Authentication is the identification by a witness of the sample, foundation evidence, and data results as being that which were procured from the source or instrument. A chain-of-custody record is documentation of the chain-of-custody, but it will not be admissible unless a witness is able to attest to the authenticity of the signatures upon it.

The existence of the requirements of relevance, foundation, and authenticity lead to frequent reasons for rejecting scientific evidence by the court. They are:

1. Irrelevant to case
2. Probative value (usefulness) overcome by distinct possibility of jury confusion or misuse
3. Data generated without following proper test procedures
4. Underlying scientific principle or application to present case has not received sufficient acknowledgment by scientific community.

The modern criteria for admissibility and use of scientific evidence in court have their origins in the Frye standard.

> Just when a scientific principle or discovery crosses the line
> between the experimental and demonstrable stages is difficult to
> define. Somewhere in this twilight zone the evidential force of
> the principle must be recognized and while the courts will go a
> long way in admitting expert testimony deduced from a well-
> recognized scientific principle or discovery, the thing from which
> the deduction is made must be sufficiently established to have
> gained general acceptance in the particular field to which it
> belongs.
>
> - Frye *vs.* United States, 293 F. 1013, 1014 (D.C. Cir. 1923)

The central tenet of the Frye standard is that the scientific basis of the procedure used to generate the data is generally accepted within the scientific community. Federal courts in 1993 were directed by the Supreme Court in *Daubert vs. Merrell Dow Pharmaceutical, Inc.*[1] to drop the Frye standard. The explanation was that the Frye standard was interpreted as incompatible with the Federal Rules of Evidence.

Assuming that the evidence fits the specific case and aids the jury in reaching a resolution to the dispute, the new standard for admissible evidence is the "reliability" rule, which is derived from FRE Rule 702.

> In order to qualify as "scientific knowledge" an inference or
> assertion must be derived by the scientific method. Proposed
> testimony must be supported by appropriate validation - i.e.,
> "good grounds," based on what is known. In short, the
> requirement that an expert's testimony pertain to "scientific
> knowledge" establishes a standard of evidentiary reliability.
>
> -Daubert vs. Merrill Dow Pharmaceutical, Inc, 509 U.S. 579

Reliability factors are now the key to whether data obtained from a new technique are admissible in Federal Court. There are many lists of reliability factors, the one presented below was cited in the Supreme Court ruling in *Daubert.*[2]

- Technique's general acceptance in the field including peer review and publication

- Expert's qualifications and stature

- Use that has been made of the new technique

- Potential rate of error established by testing the technique

- Existence of specialized literature

- Novelty of the new invention

- Extent to which the technique relies upon the subjective interpretation of the expert

Although courts in the current era are moving away from a strict application of the Frye standard, it is still easier to have scientific data admitted as evidence if they meet the Frye standard. Most data generated from an approved EPA method will meet the Frye standard, and the method itself becomes subject to judicial notice. Judicial notice of the method is an instruction given to the jury by the judge to accept the underlying principles

---

[1] 509 U.S. 579.

[2] Weinstein, J. and M. Berger, *Weinstein's Evidence*, 1993, 702-41 to -42.

and the method as being capable of producing data valid for scientific evidence without further discussion of the merits of the method by the attorneys. Although juries are not forced to accept a direction of judicial notice in a criminal case (they must accept judicial notice in a civil action), lack of it generally requires complete presentation of the reliability factors of the procedure as applied to the particular case at hand.

When modifications to methods or entirely novel methods have been used to generate the data, expert witnesses can spend enormous amounts of time explaining the procedure in sufficient detail so that the lay persons of the jury and the judge can understand it. This expenditure of time is distracting from the central point of the case. This task can be so daunting that the attorney may choose not to attempt to have the data admitted as evidence. If they do decide to present the data, the general procedure is first to establish the major premise that the technique or modification is valid and is accepted within the scientific community (Frye standard). The second task then is to demonstrate that the particular sample was analyzed by the described technique. This includes the identification of the sample and a detailed description of its handling. The final task, once a proper foundation has been prepared, is to present the ultimate opinion of the expert, *i.e.* the conclusions of the analysis.

Despite the emphasis placed upon format, content, and storage of the documentation of each and every step of the analysis by many Federal, state, and private laboratory auditors, the paper documentation is not of and by itself admissible as evidence. The final laboratory report is well recognized by the courts as being entirely too easy to fabricate and alter. Instead, scientific test results are presented through the testimony of analysts as expert witnesses. The analysts, through their testimony, are generally taken first through a description of the calibration, operation, and maintenance of the instrument to illustrate that it was in proper working order. This is followed by a discussion of the actual analysis to demonstrate that proper procedure was followed on the sample. The final point of testimony is to demonstrate that the analysts who used the technique were properly qualified to perform the test and then to interpret the results of the test. These functions of operation and interpretation are clearly differentiated within the eyes of the law, and although a single person may be able to perform both, in some situations it may require the testimony of two or more expert witnesses.

During their testimony, the analysts may refer to documentation generated as a part of the test procedure. The documentation may be introduced as supporting evidence. There will still be the requirement that the analyst identify the page of paper that is presented as the same or a true copy of that which was generated from the instrument. To ease this identification process, the analyst should have placed a unique mark upon the page at the time of generation. Suitable unique marks are the handwritten initials of the analyst and the date. The identification of the initials by the witness as those which they placed on the page allows for good authentication of the evidence.

Many laboratories are staffed with analysts whose employment may span a period of only 2 to 3 years on the average. The permanent staff of the lab are generally in management and supervisor positions and do not have hands-on contact with each sample or test result. In most cases, environmental laboratory data come into play in court several years after the analysis was performed. Although the records of the analysis are generally still available, the analyst who performed the work is frequently not. A problem arises in that the best witness is the analyst who actually performed the work. Although the testimony of the laboratory director or managers about the data may be factual, it can, and has been, regarded as hearsay evidence[3], and not admissible, due to the senior staff members not having had their hands upon the work. There is also the right of the criminal defendant to confront witnesses, which in this situation would be the analyst who actually performed the work. If senior staff members were actively involved in the interpretation of the data, they may be perfectly qualified to testify to the interpretation, but not the data generation.

There are some differences in the requirements for generating and admitting scientific data as evidence depending on which side of the criminal case—the defense or the prosecution—is presenting the data. Most jurisdictions allow the defense to make motions for discovery, inspection, and retesting of evidence. These are covered under Federal Criminal Rule 16, the *ABA Standards Relating to Discovery and Procedure Before Trial*, the Uniform Rules of Criminal Proceedings 421, and the modifications to these rules that have been made in the various states. The retest capability leads to the prosecution being required to archive samples that have been used to generate scientific evidence. This has been interpreted to cover all samples, even those that would normally be considered very labile.

The prosecution is required under the *Brady*[4] Supreme Court ruling to disclose evidence favorable to the defense side of the case. This reemphasizes the need for the prosecution to preserve evidence. The ruling is also interpreted as a prosecution requirement to inform the defense if perjured, falsified, or mistaken evidence or testimony has been collected. It allows the defense to obtain depositions from prosecution expert witnesses.

Different courts have different views about the quality of data presented as scientific evidence. In some jurisdictions, the evidence and foundation must meet every specific criteria of instrument performance, adherence to method procedure, and operator qualifications for the data to be accepted as evidence. In other jurisdictions, the data are accepted; however, the weight (probative value) of the evidence can be severely impacted by the inability to demonstrate compliance with test specifications.

The confidence in the certainty of the quantitative and qualitative data that the method generates can be indicated in the judicial notice issued. Techniques that generate poor qualitative data, such a gas chromatography, high pressure liquid chromatography, thin layer chromatography, immunoassay, ultraviolet absorption, and spot tests can be noticed as "nonspecific" tests. Identification conclusions based upon a procedure that is judicially noticed as nonspecific are inadmissable as evidence. This view has been upheld in criminal cases by the Supreme Court (*Jackson vs. Virginia*[5]) with relation to drug identifications where the proof of guilt beyond a reasonable doubt standard was reaffirmed. A technique that is subject to judicial notice as capable of generating specific data is gas chromatography-mass spectrometry.

The use of two nonspecific test procedures to bolster the confidence in an identification does not add up to a specific test. For example, chlorinated pesticides such as aldrin and heptachlor are commonly analyzed using a gas chromatograph equipped with an electron capture detector. The use of an analytical column and a confirmation column, even though both may generate positive results for the analytes, does not total an identification beyond a reasonable doubt. Even if a standard of "substantial" reasonable doubt is raised, gas chromatographic-based identifications will still not

---

[3] Hearsay is testimony given by a witness about what they were told about an occurrence by a second person, without the witness ever having actually observed the occurrence.
[4] Brady vs. Maryland, 373 U.S. 83 (1963).
[5] 443 U.S. 307 (1979).

provide suitable data. There will always exist a finite probability that a misidentification has occurred.

Once the method has received judicial notice and data have been accepted as evidence, it is the job of the contending attorneys to impeach the data if they can. One tactic is to show that the method was not followed exactly as written. This can render the judicial notice of the method irrelevant and places the other side in the position of having to prove that the modifications to the method constitute a scientifically valid method on their own merit. A weak point in most analytical procedures, which is very subject to this type of attack, is the holding time. Whether or not the holding time in the official method is backed up by a study that supports the number is irrelevant. The issuance of the judicial notice takes the method-specified holding time out of the arena of discussion. However, failure to meet the specified holding time is a modification of the method. Essentially no laboratories have ever performed holding time studies and thus the modification is not supportable by any hard data. The modified method is incapable of standing on its own merits, and therefore the data are impeachable.

Another tactic is to expose insufficient or non-existent training of the analysts or the sample collection personnel. The ability of the analysts to generate reliable data from the test must be demonstrated beyond any doubt. Often this can be accomplished by presentation of satisfactory results on blind performance evaluation samples, records of formal training, and performance of method detection limit studies and other initial demonstrations of capability. Lack of this evidence can lead to the presumption that the analysts had no idea what they were doing.

Official reports of required compliance monitoring, such as EPA Form 3320, are generally considered admissible evidence as a public document. Cases have occurred where the data on the forms are used as evidence of non-compliance with permit limitations on effluent pollutant loadings. In one such case[6], it was subsequently discovered by the defendant, who was the originator of the Form 3320, that the laboratory that supplied the data was not using the correct method or procedures. Based on this discovery, the defendant tried to argue that since the data he submitted on the Form 3320 were not defensible, then he should not be held accountable for a permit violation. The argument was accepted to the point that the court recognized that the data were not valid for proving whether or not the effluent limitations on the NPDES permit were exceeded. However, the court did find the defendant guilty of failure to perform compliance monitoring as required on the permit. The ruling was in essence a rejection of all data reported using unapproved methods. The reasoning was that the defendant's signature on the Form was an acceptance of the responsibility for insuring that the data reported on the Form was acquired using only accepted methods of analysis. Since the defendant was now claiming that the data were not generated in compliance with the permit, then the forms reporting compliance with the permit were not valid, and thus, the defendant failed to submit the required monthly report.

B. Sample Custody

It would never occur to the vast majority of technicians in the environmental industry to tamper with a sample by substituting one sample for another or adulterating a sample.

---

[6] Ford, L. and T.J. Warth, 1995. *Reporting S/NPDES Monitoring Data with its site-specific accuracy and precision.* Academy of Certified Hazardous Materials Managers, August 1-4, 1995 Conference, Rochester NY. Public Interest Research Group of New Jersey, Inc. *vs* Elf Atochem North America, Inc. 817 F. Supp. 1164 (D.N.J. 1993).

With the exception of the rare accident, samples pass from the point of sampling to the laboratory and through the entire analytical process without incident. However, the existence of the normal flow of sample movement is insufficient support for sample integrity within the legal arena, where, if the possibility of sample tampering could conceivably exist, then there must be definitive evidence that sample integrity was maintained. This definitive evidence is a record of the persons who had possession or custody of the sample for all periods of time, as it moved from the point of collection to the final analytical result.

Custody or control over the sample is established by the following situations[7]:

- It is in the field investigator's or the transferee's actual possession.

- It is in the field investigator's or the transferee's view, after being in his/her physical possession.

- It was in the field investigator's or the tranferee's physical possession and then he/she secured it to prevent tampering.

- It is placed in a designated secure area.

A chain-of-custody record is illustrated in Figure 3-1. Although there are any number of different ways a chain-of-custody record can be formatted, the information on the record that is relevant to the chain-of-custody must include:

- A description/listing of every sample included under the record with the time, date, number of containers and location of sampling for each sample. If a suite of different analyses are to be performed on the sample, the number of containers of the sample collected for each type of analysis should also be indicated.

- The signature with time and date of the sampling team leader who performed—or was responsible for—all aspects of the sampling.

- If samples are tracked through numbered sample tags, the tag number should also be listed for each sample.

- The field investigator and subsequent transferees must document the transfer of the samples listed on the record in the spaces provided at the bottom of the record. Each time the samples are transferred, both the person relinquishing custody and the person receiving custody must sign the record along with the time and date. The last signature is normally the receiving clerk at the laboratory.

- If the samples are shipped by commercial carrier, there is a space at the bottom of the record for listing the shipping or airbill number.

The record should be filled out with waterproof, indelible ink. The use of pencils or other erasable/alterable writing materials is to be avoided.

---

[7] *Environmental Compliance Branch Standard Operating Procedures and Quality Assurance Manual,* Environmental Protection Agency Region IV, Environmental Services Division, Athens, GA 1991, Section 3.3.

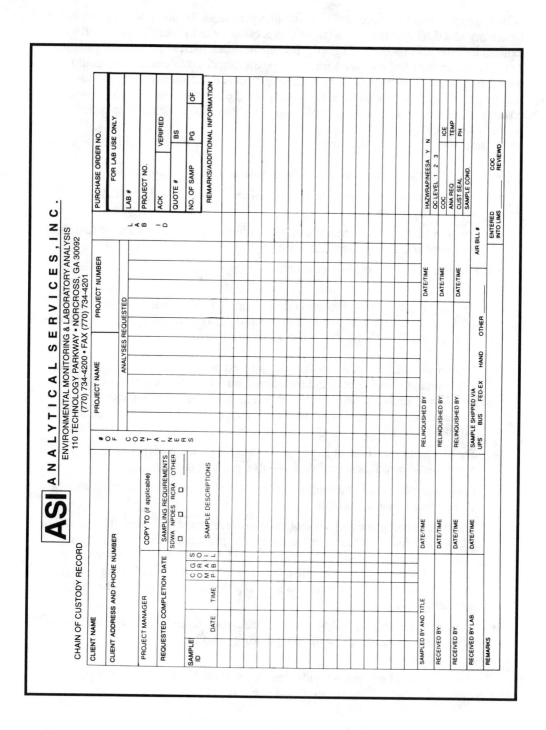

Figure 3-1.   Chain-of-Custody Record.

As a further measure of sample security, individual samples or the sample carrier are closed with custody seals (Figure 3-2). Custody seals are self-adhesive thin waterproof paper or synthetic-material strips placed over the opening of the container or carrier. The custody seals have a large number of cuts across the width of the seal, such that once the seal is applied to the container or carrier, attempted removal will tear the seal. The person originally applying the seal writes his/her name and time/date of application on the seal, then each person receiving custody of the sample should annotate on the record the condition of the seals (either intact or torn). The most common type of sample carrier is a metal or plastic cooler (ice chest). Custody seals are used to indicate that the cooler has not been opened by placing one across each opening of the lid. This includes the hinge side of the lid, so that the normal cooler would have a minimum of four custody seals on it. The liberal use of custody seals allows maintenance of chain-of-custody while the samples are shipped by commercial carriers.

NAME _____
DATE _____   TIME _____

Figure 3-2.   Custody Seal.

Once the sample reaches the laboratory, the chain-of-custody should be maintained for the sample and any extracts/digestates that are prepared from it, until analysis of the sample is completed, a final report of analysis generated, and the remaining sample is properly disposed. In practice, this rarely occurs. Received coolers are frequently opened and the samples placed on benches for cataloging and labeling, then moved to the sample storage locations. The sample receipt areas, sample storage locations, and the individual laboratory areas are often freely accessible to all employees of the company. Samples are obtained from the storage area as needed for analysis and transferred to the various laboratory areas where they are again placed on open carts or benches until portions are removed for analysis. Extracts and digestates of the samples are stored in open racks or holders on shelves or in unsecured refrigerators until the analysis is performed. The extracts and digestates frequently sit unguarded in autosampler trays until the set is processed through the instrument, then placed back on an open shelf until the data are processed. In the meantime, the analysts and clerks are leaving to find reagents and chemicals, going to the bathroom, on break, or to lunch, and the samples are left unmonitored for substantial periods of time and available to all. Although the laboratory may have a limited access policy and require all visitors to be escorted at all times while in the facility, there is generally very lax security concerning the samples within the building. Again it's the prevailing assumption that no person has a personal stake in the samples and would want to tamper with them.

Proper security measures would require a sample custodian to sign each sample in and out of the sample holding area, with all sample storage shelves and refrigerators locked at all times, accessible only by the sample custodian. Each sample would be accompanied by a chain-of-custody record. The individual samples would be inside a plastic bag tied off at the neck with a custody seal wrapped around the knot. Each time the bagged sample is transferred from one person to the next, the condition of the custody seal is noted on the record. Each time the sample is opened a new custody seal is placed around the knot. All extracts and digestates of samples would be similarly stored in locked cabinets and refrigerators, with each movement in and out of the storage logged. Autosampler trays would have locked covers. All laboratory areas would have locked doors and limited access. Analysts who sign for the custody of the samples or extracts would be required to maintain proper custody over the samples at all times.

Some jurisdictions have recognized that normal laboratory practice, although initially based on proper evidence handling procedures, is currently insufficient for withstanding rigorous examination. The Florida Department of Environmental Protection, in particular, differentiates between "normal" chain-of-custody and "evidentiary" chain-of-custody sample handling protocols.

All of this is not to say that laboratories are incapable of handling samples with strict accountability and tracking. It can be done; it's just not the normal procedure. If a user of laboratory services requires a higher level of sample security, they need to make the laboratory aware of their needs prior to the arrival of the samples at the laboratory, so that appropriate arrangements can be made.

C. Documentation

Documents are the mainstay of evidence, particularly where scientific data from an analytical laboratory are concerned. Documents are necessary to build the foundation of the evidence. Witnesses can testify that all the steps in the procedure were done correctly, but unless there exists some documentation that supports the statements of the witnesses, the testimony will always be suspect. A number of different forms of documents can be used to establish a foundation. A vitally important document, the chain-of-custody record, was discussed above. Others include the handwritten notes and records of the analyst, computer printouts from the laboratory information management system (LIMS) and from the individual instruments, and the electronic data that reside in the LIMS and the computers used to manage the instruments.

The most common physical form of documentation is paper; however, video and still pictures, audio and data recordings on tapes, hard drive disks, and CDs can also be valuable. One of the shortcomings of these alternate forms of documentation resides in the need for the jury to be able to examine the evidence. A cassette tape of data looks and feels just like any other cassette tape, whether it contains data or not. Since it is the data on the tape that are the evidence, it would be necessary to present the data for examination, frequently in the form of an alternate medium such as paper hardcopy or on a computer terminal screen.

The ease with which electronic documentation can be changed after the moment of creation is also of concern. It is much more difficult to change the contents of a handwritten page from a bound lab notebook than it is to change a computer file. This consideration also holds for the printing of data from electronic storage. Some software programs will have the original date of creation and dates of all modifications imbedded within the data file. Printouts of the data file include these dates along with the date of printing. Data from these type systems are very difficult to modify; however, it can be done. Each page of hardcopy generated from an instrument or computer needs to be annotated with the date, time, and handwritten initials of the person who generated the hardcopy. This allows authentication of the documentation through the identification of a unique mark (the initials) upon the document.

D. Traceability

The calibration of the instruments and the purity of the chemical reagents used for production of laboratory data are a key part of foundation. The results of analysis are only as good as the quality of the materials used in the procedure. There are several agencies and associations that have established criteria, acceptable in most legal jurisdictions, as standards of the purity and acceptability of specific chemical reagents. The two most commonly cited are the American Chemical Society Reagent Chemical specifications and the National Institute of Standards and Technology Standard Reference Materials. Where possible, it is desirable to use these materials in analysis. However, there is the question of who is responsible for determining that, for instance, the sodium chloride being used in a test actually meets ACS Reagent Grade specifications. The answer is that the laboratory using the chemicals does not have the time or wherewithal to make the determination, and it is the supplier of the chemical who is responsible for verifying that the specifications have been met. The supplier will prepare a certificate of analysis that attests that the cited specifications have been met for a particular lot number of the chemical or standard.

The term "traceability," as applied to laboratory data, is used to describe the ability to determine from the documentation exactly which reagents and standards were used in the analysis and where they came from. An alternate term is "paper trail." For example, if sodium sulfate is used as a drying agent in a procedure, and a requirement exists for purification of ACS Reagent Grade sodium sulfate prior to use, then there should be documentation of the purification of the sodium sulfate and that it is, in fact, ACS Reagent Grade.

Laboratories will commonly use lot numbers as an aid to establishing the paper trail. Thus, the record of the analysis may indicate that sodium sulfate lot number 015 was used in a particular analysis. One can go to the sodium sulfate preparation logbook and find a description of lot number 015 with a time, date, and initials of the person who did the purification, along with the necessary details. The logbook entry for lot number 015 will further reference when and from where the sodium sulfate was obtained.

Traceability is particularly important with regard to the standards that are used to calibrate the analytical instruments. The accuracy of the standards serves as an innate limitation on the accuracy of the sample results. Most analytical labs purchase their standards from manufacturers who specialize in the preparation and certification of calibration and other standards. These manufacturers provide a certificate of analysis for each lot of standards sold to the laboratories. Thus, each set of standards used in the lab should be traceable to the specific certificate of analysis issued by the manufacturer, which are kept in a file in the laboratory.

References

1. Giannelli, P.C. and E.J. Imwinkelried, *Scientific Evidence*, 2d Edition, The Michie Company, Charlottesville, VA 1993, and Annual updates.

2. *Environmental Compliance Branch Standard Operating Procedures and Quality Assurance Manual*, Environmental Protection Agency Region IV, Environmental Services Division, Athens GA 1991.

3. Florida Department of Environmental Regulation, Quality Assurance Section, Standard Operating Procedures for Laboratory Operations and Sample Collection Activities, DER-QA-001/92, 1992.

4. *Reagent Chemicals*, Eighth Edition, American Chemical Society, Washington, D.C. 1993.

5. Graham, M.H., *Federal Rules of Evidence,* Third Edition, West Publishing, St. Paul, Minn., 1992.

6. Lilly, G.C., *An Introduction to the Law of Evidence*, Second Edition, West Publishing, St. Paul, Minn., 1987.

CHAPTER 4

Drinking Water

Analysis of drinking water samples to verify freedom from contamination is covered under the auspices of the Safe Drinking Water Act. Regulations to enforce the Act have been promulgated by the EPA and are found in 40 CFR, Parts 141 and 142. The regulations have established Maximum Contaminant Levels (MCL) as regulatory maximums for the presence of specified analytical parameters in drinking water. If the water is found to exceed the MCL, then there is an established cascading series of governmental repercussions that are inflicted upon the provider of the water. These regulations also dictate which approved methods are to be used for which specified analytical parameters.

Enforcement of the provisions of the Act and EPA's regulations have for the most part been passed on to the individual states through grants of primacy. Each state has established its own set of drinking water rules, which almost universally are a simple reiteration of EPA's regulations.

There is no nationwide laboratory certification for drinking water analysis. However, each state is required in the primacy grant to establish either a state laboratory for performance of all drinking water analyses in the state or to establish a state drinking water laboratory certification program. EPA helps the individual states by offering training courses for drinking water certification officers and inspectors, and by suggesting the minimum standards for the laboratory certifications administered by the states. These standards are presented in an EPA publication, *Manual for the Certification of Laboratories Analyzing Drinking Water*, which is in its third edition with a fourth available in draft form.

There exist no documents or procedures that discuss the evaluation of data generated from analysis of the individual drinking water sample. The requirement for the laboratory to be certified has given rise to the industry-wide belief that if a laboratory possesses the appropriate certification and continues to meet the requirements of the certification program, then the data generated by the laboratory is acceptable.

There are two sides of this issue that need to be considered. First, there is wide variation in how the states have implemented the strictures that have been suggested by EPA as certification program standards. Some states have tried to meet both the letter and the spirit of the EPA guidelines and thus have established quite rigorous programs. Other states have established programs that can be charitably characterized as an impression of the EPA standards. Further complicating the situation is the common practice of states accepting by reciprocity the certification granted by another state without much question as to how the EPA standards are administered in the other state. This results in an uneven standard of certification and required laboratory performance as represented by the certification granted by even the single state.

The second issue concerns the actions of the laboratory after the certification has been granted. Most laboratories will maintain the standards that led to the granting of certification. However, there have been instances of laboratories "cleaning up their acts" to meet the minimum standards to obtain the necessary certification, then reverting to highly questionable practices and procedures for analysis immediately after the certification is in hand. This practice is bolstered by the highly involved and time-consuming procedures and investigations that are required by the state to revoke a granted certification from a laboratory.

From a perspective of evaluating the data from a particular sample, the questions to be answered include:

- Determination of the certification status of the laboratory
- Determination of the requirements of the particular method of analysis
- Determination of how closely the laboratory followed the method
- Evaluation of the success of the analysis on the individual sample.

Thus the following discussion looks at the particulars of the drinking water program that lead to answers to these questions.

A. Determination of the Certification Status of the Laboratory

Determination of the certification status of the laboratory can be as simple as looking up the telephone number of the drinking water laboratory certification officer in the state, calling them and asking if the laboratory at question is certified. The answer can be yes or no; however, most certification bodies further certify down to the individual parameter and method level. Thus, accompanying the fact of the certification should be a listing of approved methods and analytes. It might be assumed that the guidelines set forth by EPA in the certification officer training courses and the *Manual* are being used as standards for the granting of the certification; however, it does not hurt to spot check some of the criteria, which are discussed below. Throughout the *Manual* there are checklists that the EPA has prepared to assist the officers conducting the evaluation of the laboratory for the certification. These may be very useful to the individual reviewer of data.

1. General Considerations for Certification

a. Laboratory Quality Assurance Plan

Each laboratory performing drinking water analysis must prepare a written description of the quality assurance program and quality control procedures. While intended to be brief, an adequate discussion of the program and procedures tends to run into many pages. The topics listed in Table 4-1 are expected to be covered.

Table 4-1.   Topics Expected in a Drinking Water Laboratory Quality Assurance Plan[1].

1	Laboratory organization and responsibility
	Chart or Table showing lines of organization and authority
	Key individuals responsible for ensuring the production of valid measurements and routine assessment of measurement systems
	Description of training to keep personnel up-to-date on regulations and methods

---

[1] USEPA, Office of Groundwater and Drinking Water, *Manual for the Certification of Laboratories Analyzing Drinking Water.* Fourth Edition Draft, September 1995.

Table 4-1. **Topics Expected in a Drinking Water Laboratory Quality Assurance Plan**[2]. *Continued*

2	**Field sampling procedures**
	Holding times, preservation and container requirements for sampling
	Sample collection procedures and sampling locations
	Sample shipping and storage conditions
	Documentation of sampling
	Sample receipt procedures to verify proper preservation and containers
3	**Laboratory sample handling procedures**
	Laboratory logbooks and notebooks
	Sample storage conditions
	Procedures to track sample integrity from collection to disposal
	Chain-of-custody procedures
	Procedures for rejecting samples due to improper collection, preservation or container
	Procedures for notification of sample originator of unacceptable samples
4	**Calibration procedures**
	Frequency of calibration
	Description of calibration for each method
	Sources of calibration standards
	Calibration verification
5	**Analytical procedures**
	Sources of methods
	Standard operating procedures (references to availability and use)
	Laboratory ware cleaning procedures
6	**Data reduction, validation, verification and reporting**
	Data conversions from instrument/method output to final result
	Procedures to insure that quality control criteria have been met
	Verification of data calculation and transcription accuracy
7	**Quality control checks and frequency of use**
	Performance evaluation samples, sources and frequency of use
	Method detection limit determination and frequency
	Internal and surrogate standards
	Method and field blanks
	Replicate field sample analysis
	Matrix and reagent spikes and duplicates
	Operator initial demonstration of capability
	Control charts

2 USEPA, Office of Groundwater and Drinking Water, *Manual for the Certification of Laboratories Analyzing Drinking Water*. Fourth Edition Draft, September 1995.

Table 4-1. **Topics Expected in a Drinking Water Laboratory Quality Assurance Plan[3].** *Continued*

8	Preventative maintenance procedures and schedules
	Instrument manuals
	Instrument spare parts
	Routine equipment maintenance schedules and documentation
	Service contracts
9	Corrective action procedures
	Procedures of action when unacceptable quality control results are obtained
	Persons responsible for actions
	Documentation of corrective actions
10	Record keeping procedures
	Types of records
	Location and time duration of storage
	Security and storage of electronic records

The Quality Assurance Plan is not a one-time effort that is approved by management and then forgotten. Rather it is a living document and must be revised to keep apace of changing regulations and changing laboratory personnel and practices. In the normal laboratory, it must be revised at least once a year.

b. Performance on Routine Water Samples

EPA suggests that the certifying organization adopt one or more of the following procedures to provide on-going assessment of the laboratory's ability to successfully analyze samples:

- Blind audit samples
- Analysis of an unknown sample during the on-site audit
- Splitting samples between laboratories and than comparing results
- Data audits

c. Chain-of-custody Procedures

Chain-of-custody procedures and records are necessary to establish the authenticity of the sample. These must be initiated at the moment of sample collection and maintained through the sample transport, laboratory receipt, processing and analysis of the sample up until the moment of sample disposal. Breakdowns in the record of authenticity render the sample and results questionable for use in a legal sense, although the analytical validity of the results may be perfectly acceptable.

Minimum information that needs to be included in the chain-of-custody record includes:

- Unique sample or log number
- Date and time of sample collection

---

[3] USEPA, Office of Groundwater and Drinking Water, *Manual for the Certification of Laboratories Analyzing Drinking Water.* Fourth Edition Draft, September 1995.

- Source of sample collection (name, location and sample type)
- Preservatives used
- Analysis required
- Name of collector(s)
- Associated field data (pH, dissolved oxygen, residual chlorine, temperature, *etc.*)
- Serial numbers of seals, transportation cases, shipping manifest.

Each sample is labeled with either a self-adhesive label or tag, with data entered in waterproof ink. Identifications written directly on the container with waterproof markers are less desirable.

Suitable procedures must be in place within the laboratory to document the movement of the samples from receipt to analysis and finally disposal. Final disposal must be in accordance with local regulations and practices.

2. Specific Considerations for Certification

a. Personnel - Academic Training, Experience and Other Qualifications

Personnel within the laboratory who are responsible for generating, reviewing and/or approving results from analysis of drinking water samples must have appropriate training and experience. Five levels of analytical responsibility are recognized by the EPA as existing within the drinking water laboratory. Individuals within any particular laboratory may occupy more than one level, and in these cases they must meet the educational and experience requirements for all the levels of responsibility that they occupy. The training and educational requirements for persons working in chemical analysis are presented in Table 4-2.

Table 4-2.   Educational and Experience Requirements for Responsibility Levels in the Drinking Water Chemistry Laboratory.

Level	Education and experience requirement
Director	Academic training: Minimum bachelor's degree in science. If field is other than chemistry, individual should have chemistry credit hours equivalent to a minor in chemistry
	Experience: Minimum 2 years experience in a drinking water laboratory
Supervisor	Academic training: Minimum bachelor's degree in chemistry. If field is other than chemistry, individual should have chemistry credit hours equivalent to a major in chemistry
	Experience: Minimum 1 year experience in chemical analysis of drinking water
Data interpreter	Academic training: Minimum bachelor's degree in chemistry. If field is other than chemistry, individual should have chemistry credit hours equivalent to a major in chemistry. Must have specialized course in data interpretation in the area of responsibility.
	Experience: Minimum 1 year experience in data interpretation and evaluation.

Table 4-2. **Educational and Experience Requirements for Responsibility Levels in the Drinking Water Chemistry Laboratory.** *Continued*

Level	Education and experience requirement
Instrument operator	Academic training: Minimum bachelor's degree in chemistry or a related field or sufficient hours in chemistry equivalent to a major. May be waived if immediate Supervisor has appropriate degree.
	Specialized training: Completion of manufacturer's, professional organization, university or other qualified facility short course on the instrument (GC/MS, ICP, ICP/MS, etc.)
	Experience: Minimum 6 months on GC, AA, ICP, HPLC, ICP/MS or 1 year on GC/MS under direct supervision of experienced operator.
	Initial qualification: Documented successful completion of initial demonstration of capability on the instrument.
Other analysts	Academic training: Minimum high school diploma or equivalent.
	Experience: Successful analysis of PE or other quality control sample.

Frequently the Quality Assurance plan will include the resumes and qualifications of the key persons within the laboratory. The qualifications of other operators and analysts can be determined through examination of the training files. In states that have a laboratory analyst licensing program, evaluation of the analysts who fall in the "other" category can be as simple as verification that they have the appropriate license and that it is current.

b. Laboratory Facilities

The laboratory facility should have adequate room for analysis and preparation of reports for the samples. Lighting and environmental management should be such that comfortable working conditions are provided. Chemical fume hoods and other HVAC systems should provide for a safe working area. Easy access to water, electricity, sinks, gas and vacuum must be available.

A minimum of 150-200 square feet of floor space should be present for every analyst working. There should be at least 15 linear feet of bench space per analyst. The arrangement of the work areas must provide for separation and isolation of procedures with the potential of cross-contamination, such as volatile and semivolatile organic analyses.

c. Laboratory Equipment and Instrumentation

The laboratory must have all the equipment and instruments specified in the Methods that are performed. For example, if Method 524.2 is claimed to be performed, then there must be a GC/MS with a purge and trap present at the facility. Subcontracted analyses are only possible if the subcontract laboratory individually has the appropriate certification. In other words, certifications are not transferable.

d. General Laboratory Practices

This area looks at a variety of topics including:

- Quality of the reagents and standards that are used in the laboratory
- How reagent water is purified for use in preparing the reagent and standard solutions

- Protocols governing the cleaning of glassware and other laboratory equipment
- Laboratory safety procedures and documentation as addressed in the Chemical Hygiene Plan and Standard Operating Procedures.

e. Analytical Methodology

There are two lists of analytes under the Drinking Water Program - the Primary Drinking Water Contaminants and the Secondary Drinking Water contaminants. The primary contaminants are constant across the United States and have associated with them a Maximum Contaminant Level (MCL)(Tables 4-3 and -4). In addition to the regulated contaminants, there are a number of unregulated contaminants that are frequently requested as target analytes.

Table 4-3. **Some Approved Methods for Analysis of Drinking Water for Inorganic Contaminants[4].** The methods are not necessarily equivalent.

Contaminant	MCL mg/L	EPA	SM 18th Edition
Antimony	0.006	200.8, 200.9	3113B
Arsenic	0.05	200.7, 200.8, 200.9	3120B, 3113B
Asbestos	7 MFL	100.1, 100.2	-
Barium	2	200.7, 200.8	3120B, 3111D, 3113B
Beryllium	0.004	200.7, 200.8, 200.9	3120B, 3113B
Cadmium	0.005	200.7, 200.8, 200.9	3113B
Chromium	0.1	200.7, 200.8, 200.9	3120B, 3113B
Cyanide	0.2	335.4	4500-CN-C,E,F,G
Fluoride	4.0	300.0	4500-F-B,C,D,E
Mercury	0.002	245.1, 245.2, 200.8	3112B
Nickel	0.1	200.7, 200.8, 200.9	3120B, 3113B
Nitrate	10	300.0, 353.2	4110B, 4500-NO3-D,E,F
Nitrite	1	300.0, 353.2	4110B, 4500-NO2-B, 4500-NO3-E,F
Selenium	0.05	200.8, 200.9	3113B, 3114B
Thallium	0.002	200.8, 200.9	3113B
Lead	0.015	200.8, 200.9	3113B
Copper	1.3	200.7, 200.8, 200.9	3111B, 3120B, 3113B
pH	-	150.2	4500-H+-B
Conductivity	-	-	2510B
Calcium	-	200.7	3111B, 3120B
Alkalinity	-	-	2320B
ortho-Phosphate	-	300.0, 365.1	4110, 4500-P-E, 4500-P-F
Silica	-	200.7	3120B, 4500-Si-D,E,F
Sodium	-	200.7	3111B
Chlorine	-	-	4500-Cl-D,E,F,G,H,I
Chlorine dioxide	-	-	4500-ClO2-C,D,E
Ozone	-	-	4500-O3-B

[4] 40 CFR 141.23 and 141.74, *Federal Register* Vol 59, No. 232 Monday 5 December, 1994, pp 62455-62471.

Table 4-4. Some Approved Methods for Analysis of Drinking Water for Organic Contaminants[5]

Contaminant	MCL mg/L	EPA
Benzene	0.005	502.2, 524.2
Carbon tetrachloride	0.005	502.2, 524.2, 551
Chlorobenzene	0.1	502.2, 524.2
1,2-Dichlorobenzene	0.6	502.2, 524.2
1,4-Dichlorobenzene	0.075	502.2, 524.2
1,2-Dichloroethane	0.005	502.2, 524.2
cis-Dichloroethylene	0.07	502.2, 524.2
trans-Dichloroethylene	0.1	502.2, 524.2
Dichloromethane	0.005	502.2, 524.2
1,2-Dichloropropane	0.005	502.2, 524.2
Ethylbenzene	0.7	502.2, 524.2
Styrene	0.1	502.2, 524.2
Tetrachloroethylene	0.005	502.2, 524.2, 551
1,1,1-Trichloroethane	0.2	502.2, 524.2, 551
Trichloroethylene	0.005	502.2, 524.2, 551
Toluene	1	502.2, 524.2
1,2,4-Trichlorobenzene	0.07	502.2, 524.2
1,1-Dichloroethylene	0.007	502.2, 524.2
1,1,2-Trichloroethane	0.005	502.2, 524.2
Vinyl chloride	0.002	502.2, 524.2
Xylenes (total)	10	502.2, 524.2
Total trihalomethanes	0.10	502.2, 524.2, 551
2,3,7,8-TCDD (dioxin)	3×10^{-8}	1613
2,4-D	0.07	515.2, 555, 515.1
2,4,5-TP (Silvex)	0.05	515.2, 555, 515.1
Alachlor	0.002	505, 507, 508.1, 525.2
Atrazine	0.003	505, 507, 508.1, 525.2
Benzo(a)pyrene	0.0002	525.2, 550, 550.1
Carbofuran	0.04	531.1
Chlordane	0.002	505, 508, 508.1, 525.2
Dalapon	0.2	515.1, 552.1
Di(2-ethylhexyl)adipate	0.4	506, 525.2
Di(2-ethylhexyl)phthalate	0.006	506, 525.2
Dibromochloropropane (DBCP)	0.0002	504.1, 551
Dinoseb	0.007	515.1, 515.2, 555
Diquat	0.02	549.1
Endothall	0.1	548.1
Endrin	0.002	505, 508, 508.1, 525.2
Ethylene dibromide (EDB)	0.00005	504.1, 551
Glyphosate	0.7	547

---

[5] 40 CFR 141.24 and 141.40, *Federal Register* Vol 59, No. 232 Monday 5 December, 1994, pp 62455-62471.

Table 4-4. **Some Approved Methods for Analysis of Drinking Water for Organic Contaminants[6].** *Continued*

Contaminant	MCL mg/L	EPA
Heptachlor	0.0004	505, 508, 508.1, 525.2
Heptachlor epoxide	0.0002	505, 508, 508.1, 525.2
Hexachlorobenzene	0.001	505, 508, 508.1, 525.2
Hexachlorocyclopentadiene	0.05	505, 508, 508.1, 525.2
Lindane	0.0002	505, 508, 508.1, 525.2
Methoxychlor	0.04	505, 508, 508.1, 525.2
Oxamyl	0.2	531.1
PCB (as DCB)	0.0005	508A
Pentachlorophenol	0.001	515.1, 515.2, 525.2, 555
Picloram	0.5	515.1, 515.2, 525.2
Simazine	0.004	505, 507, 508.1, 525.2
Toxaphene	0.003	505, 508, 525.2

Drinking water analyses performed under the auspices of a state certification implies complete compliance with all procedural and quality control steps in the Method. Method variances and alternate test procedures must be reviewed and approved in writing by the certification authority. "Pre-packaged test kits other than the U.S. EPA-approved DPD and the FACTS Colorimetric Test kits are not approved for use in compliance monitoring."[7]

f. Sample Collection, Handling and Preservation

It is expected that written protocols be available that address the topics of what training the sample collector must have, how each type of sample is collected, what are the documentation procedures for the sampling process, and how, during transport, the care and security of the samples are maintained. Sampling containers, preservatives and holding times must be in accordance with the requirements as presented in Table 4-5.

The laboratory must also have protocols that address the actions taken when samples are received that do not meet the sample preservation, container, and holding time requirements. The laboratory must notify the authority requesting the analysis of the sample about the intended rejection of the sample.

The final report of analysis should identify the sample by time, date, type, and location of the sample collection. If there are non-compliant aspects of the sampling event, there must be an indication on the final analytical report that the sample results are not suitable for compliance monitoring.

---

[6] 40 CFR 141.24 and 141.40, *Federal Register* Vol 59, No. 232 Monday 5 December, 1994, pp 62455-62471.

[7] Paragraph 5.1, *Manual for the Certification of Laboratories Analyzing Drinking Water*, Third Edition USEPA Office of Water, EPA/570/9-90/008, April 1990. The paragraph is reproduced without change in the Fourth Edition (Draft).

Table 4-5. Drinking water sampling and holding time requirements from _Manual for the Certification of Laboratories Analyzing Drinking Water - Criteria and Procedures Quality Assurance_ Third Edition, Change 2 EPA-814B-92-002, September 1992

Parameter	Container[8]	Sample volume mL	Preservation	Max. Holding Time
Bacterial Tests				
Coliform, Fecal and Total	Sterile P	100	Cool 4°C, 0.1 mL of 10% $Na_2S_2O_3$	30 hours from time of collection
Inorganic Tests				
Alkalinity	P, G	200	Cool, 4°C	14 days
Antimony	P, G	500	Conc HNO_3 to pH<2	6 months
Arsenic	P, G	500	Conc HNO_3 to pH<2	6 months
Asbestos	P, G	1000	Cool, 4°C	-
Barium	P, G	500	Conc HNO_3 to pH<2	6 months
Beryllium	P, G	500	Conc HNO_3 to pH<2	6 months
Cadmium	P, G	500	Conc HNO_3 to pH<2	6 months
Calcium	P, G	500	Conc HNO_3 to pH<2	6 months
Chloride	P, G	200	None	28 days
Chromium	P, G	500	Conc HNO_3 to pH<2	6 months
Copper	P, G	500	Conc HNO_3 to pH<2	6 months
Cyanide	P, G	500	NaOH to pH>12, cool 4°C, 0.6 g ascorbic acid	14 days
Fluoride	P, G	500	None	1 month
Free Chlorine Residual	P, G	100	None	Analyze immediately
Lead	P, G	500	Conc HNO_3 to pH<2	6 months
Mercury	P, G	500	Conc HNO_3 to pH<2	28 days
Nickel	P, G	500	Conc HNO_3 to pH<2	6 months
Nitrate N	P, G	500	Cool, 4°C	28 days
Total Nitrate/Nitrite	P, G	500	Cool, 4°C, H_2SO_4 to pH<2	28 days
Nitrite N	P, G	500	Cool 4°C	48 hours
o-Phosphate	P, G	500	Filter immediately, Cool 4°C	48 hours
pH	P, G	500	None	Analyze immediately
Selenium	P, G	500	Conc HNO_3 to pH<2	6 months
Silica	P	500	Cool 4°C	28 days
Sodium	P, G	500	Conc HNO_3 to pH<2	6 months
Temperature	P, G	500	None	Analyze immediately
Thallium	P, G	500	Conc HNO_3 to pH<2	6 months
Total Filterable Residue (TDS)	P, G	500	Cool 4°C	7 days
Turbidity	P, G	500	Cool 4°C	48 hours

[8] Polyethylene (P) or Glass (G).

Table 4-5. Drinking water sampling and holding time requirements from *Manual for the Certification of Laboratories Analyzing Drinking Water - Criteria and Procedures Quality Assurance* Third Edition, Change 2 EPA-814B-92-002, September 1992. *Continued*

Parameter	Container[9]	Sample volume mL	Preservation	Max. Holding Time
Organic Tests				
EDB & DBPC (504)	40 mL glass with Teflon cap liner		3 mg sodium thiosulfate, HCl to pH <2, Cool 4°C	28 days to extraction, analyze immediately
Chlorinated pesticides (505)	40 mL glass with Teflon cap liner		3 mg sodium thiosulfate, Cool 4°C	14 days to extraction, analyze immediately
Phthalates and Adipates (506)	1L amber glass with Teflon cap liner		60 mg/L sodium thiosulfate, Cool 4°C	14 days to extraction, 14 days to analysis
NP pesticides (507)	1L amber glass with Teflon cap liner		10 mg/L mercuric chloride, 80 mg/L sodium thiosulfate, Cool 4°C	7 days to extraction, 14 days to analysis
Chlorinated pesticides (508)	1L glass with Teflon cap liner		10 mg/L mercuric chloride, 80 mg/L sodium thiosulfate, Cool 4°C	7 days to extraction, 14 days to analysis
PCB (508A)	1L glass with Teflon cap liner		Cool 4°C	14 days to extraction, 30 days to analysis
Herbicides (515.1)	1L amber glass with Teflon cap liner		10 mg/L mercuric chloride, 80 mg/L sodium thiosulfate, Cool 4°C	14 days to extraction, 28 days to analysis
BNA (525.1)	1L glass with Teflon cap liner		40-50 mg/L sodium sulfite, HCl to pH <2, Cool 4°C	7 days to extraction, 30 days to analysis
Carbamates (531.1)	1L glass with Teflon cap liner		Monochloroacetic acid to pH 3, 80 mg/L sodium thiosulfate, Cool 4°C until storage at -10°C	28 days with storage at -10°C
Glyphosate (547)	1L amber glass with Teflon cap liner		100 mg/L sodium thiosulfate, Cool 4°C	14 days
Endothall (548 and 548.1)	1L glass with Teflon cap liner		Cool 4°C	7 days to extraction, 1 day to analysis
Diquat & Paraquat (549)	1L amber high density PVC or silanized amber glass		100 mg/L sodium thiosulfate, sulfuric acid to pH <2, Cool 4°C	7 days to extraction, 21 days to analysis
PAH (550 or 550.1)	1L amber glass with Teflon cap liner		100 mg/L sodium thiosulfate, 6N HCl to pH <2, Cool 4°C	7 days to extraction, 40 days to analysis
Dioxins (1613)	1L amber glass with Teflon cap liner		80 mg/L sodium thiosulfate, Cool 4°C	40 days
TTHM (501.1 or 501.2)	40 mL glass with Teflon lined septa		3 mg sodium thiosulfate or sodium sulfite	14 days
VOC (502.1, 502.1, or 503.1)	40 mL glass with Teflon lined silicon septa		25 mg ascorbic acid or 3 mg sodium thiosulfate, 1:1 HCl to pH<2, Cool 4°C	14 days
VOC (524.1 or 524.2)	40 mL glass with Teflon lined silicon septa		25 mg ascorbic acid, 1:1 HCl to pH<2, Cool 4°C	14 days

[9] Polyethylene (P) or Glass (G).

Table 4-5. Drinking water sampling and holding time requirements from *Manual for the Certification of Laboratories Analyzing Drinking Water - Criteria and Procedures Quality Assurance* **Third Edition, Change 2 EPA-814B-92-002, September 1992.** *Continued*

Parameter	Sample volume mL Container[10]	Preservation	Max. Holding Time
Radiological Tests[11]			
Gross alpha	1L P, G	Conc. HCl or HNO_3 to pH <2	-
Gross beta	1L P, G	Conc. HCl or HNO_3 to pH <2	-
Strontium-89	1L P, G	Conc. HCl or HNO_3 to pH <2	-
Strontium-90	1L P, G	Conc. HCl or HNO_3 to pH <2	-
Radium-226	1L P, G	Conc. HCl or HNO_3 to pH <2	-
Radium-228	1L P, G	Conc. HCl or HNO_3 to pH <2	-
Cesium-134	1L P, G	Conc. HCl to pH <2	-
Iodine-131	2L P, G	None	-
Tritium	1L P, G	None	-
Uranium	1L P, G	Conc. HCl or HNO_3 to pH <2	-
Photon emitters	P, G	Conc. HCl or HNO_3 to pH <2	-

g. Quality Assurance

A general examination of the quality assurance system and performed quality controls is part of the certification process. Specific measures that are addressed include:

- Availability of quality assurance information
- Standard operating procedures
- Standard weights used for checking balance calibrations
- Color standards
- Performance evaluation samples
- Quality control samples
- Standard calibration curves
- Calibration checks
- Blanks
- Fortified samples (matrix spikes)
- Control charts
- Initial demonstration of capability
- Periodic MDL calculation
- Fortified reagent blanks (laboratory control samples).

---

[10] Polyethylene (P) or Glass (G).
[11] "Prescribed Procedures for Measurement of Radioactivity in Drinking Water," EPA-600/4-80-032 (1980).

h. Records and Data Reporting

Records and all raw data supporting the analysis of drinking water samples are required to be stored for a minimum of 10 years. Records and documentation relating to the analysis of samples performed under the monitoring requirements of the Lead and Copper Rule (40 CFR 141.91) must be maintained for a minimum of 12 years. Summary records may be maintained that include the following information:

- Date, place, and time of sampling; name of sample collector
- Classification of sample as to routine distribution system sample, check sample, raw or finished water sample, or other special purpose sample
- Date of sample receipt
- Date of sample analysis
- Laboratory and person performing analysis
- Analytical method used
- Quality control results
- Results of analysis.

3. Maintenance of Certification

Once certification is granted there are requirements that must be met on an on-going basis to maintain the certification. Failure to meet the requirements can result in a downgrading or complete loss of certification status.

a. Periodic Performance Evaluation (PE) Samples

Performance Evaluation (PE) samples come into play in two areas. First there is a requirement—on an annual basis—to successfully analyze a PE sample for each parameter for which the laboratory is certified. This, of course, assumes that a suitable PE sample is available for analysis. The PE sample must be prepared and evaluated by an impartial third party. EPA for many years has provided laboratories with PE samples in the Water Supply (WS) QA Studies. Two sets are sent to each certified laboratory each year. The acceptance ranges for results on each analyte in the PE samples is set by regulation and in many instances is based (Table 4-6) on an absolute percentage of the true value.

Table 4-6. PE Acceptance Criteria Based on True Value for Drinking Water Check Samples

Analyte	Acceptance criteria
Antimony	±30%
Barium	±15%
Beryllium	±15%
Cadmium	±20%
Chromium	±15%
Copper	±10%
Lead	±30%
Mercury	±30%
Nickel	±20%

Table 4-6.   PE Acceptance Criteria Based on True Value for Drinking Water Check Samples

Analyte	Acceptance criteria
Selenium	±20%
Thallium	±30%
Cyanide	±25%
Fluoride	±10%
Nitrate	±10%
Nitrite	±15%
Total Trihalomethanes	±20%
Regulated VOC	±20% if >10 µg/L ±40% if <10 µg/L
Alachlor	±45%
Atrazine	±45%
Carbofuran	±45%
Chlordane	±45%
2,4-D	±50%
Dalapon	2 Std. Deviations [12]
Dibromochloropropane (DBCP)	±40%
Dinoseb	2 Std. Deviations
Diquat	2 Std. Deviations
Endothall	2 Std. Deviations
Endrin	±30%
Ethylenedibromide (EDB)	±40%
Glyphosate	2 Std. Deviations
Heptachlor	±45%
Heptachlor epoxide	±45%
Lindane	±45%
Methoxychlor	±45%
Oxamyl	2 Std. Deviations
Pentachlorophenol	±50%
Picloram	2 Std. Deviations
Simazine	2 Std. Deviations
Toxaphene	±45%
2,4,5-TP (Silvex)	±50%
Hexachlorobenzene	2 Std. Deviations
Hexachlorocyclopentadiene	2 Std. Deviations
Benzo(a)pyrene	2 Std. Deviations
PCB (as DCB)	0-200%
Di(2-ethylhexyl)adipate	2 Std. Deviations
Di(2-ethylhexyl)phthalate	2 Std. Deviations

[12] Two Standard deviations based on the results of the reference laboratories used in the QA Study. The reference labs are the EPA Regional labs and selected Primacy State labs.

Persons who perform PE sample analysis must be employees of the laboratory and should be the person who would regularly perform the analysis on compliance samples. If the laboratory performs more than one method for a particular parameter a PE sample must be passed for each method. EPA will only evaluate one value per parameter per QA study, thus an alternate source of the PE sample that is acceptable to the certifying organization must be used. Several commercial sources of PE samples are available.

The other facet of the on-going performance checks is a requirement to successfully analyze a check sample at least once a quarter for each certified parameter. If the analysis is being performed regularly this is not a problem since regular analyses of check samples are part of most of the methods. However, when the procedure is performed only on an infrequent or irregular basis, this requirement can be a problem. Two of these quarterly checks are satisfied by the WS PE samples; however, the other two check samples would have to be purchased from one of the commercial sources.

b. Approved Methodology

Only methods that are approved in the appropriate regulation, or that have been approved in writing approved by the certification body as an acceptable alternate test procedure, may be used.

c. Notification of Major Changes in Laboratory Personnel

The certification authority must be notified in writing of any equipment, personnel or major facility changes within 30 days of the change. In particular, loss of qualified operators, data interpreters, or supervisors without acceptable replacements may lead to reconsideration of the certification status for affected test procedures or for the laboratory as a whole.

d. Periodic On-site Evaluations

The laboratory must be re-inspected by an on-site visit at least every three years. More frequent inspections may be required in cases of major changes in equipment, personnel, or facility. They may also be triggered by failure to maintain satisfactory PE sample results.

B. Specific Examples of Methods

When a reviewer is faced with the problem of evaluating analytical data on drinking water samples there are two issues that need to addressed. The first issue concerns how closely the laboratory complied with the technical and procedural specifications in the method. The drinking water methods are compliance monitoring methods and to be legally acceptable as fulfillment of the monitoring requirements, the methods must be followed to the letter.

The second issue concerns the usability of the numerical result of the analysis. Drinking water analyses are overshadowed by the maximum contaminant level (MCL) regulatory set-points. If the result is below the MCL there is joy. However, if the result is at or above the MCL, problems are in store for the parties responsible for the source of the sample. The questions that need to be resolved then are tied to the MCL for the particular parameter. When results indicate the MCL has not been exceeded, the question in the mind of the reviewer should be, "Is there any indication that this result is biased low or is a completely false negative and, in actuality, the sample contains the contaminant at levels exceeding the MCL?" On the other hand when a value exceeding the MCL is received, the question to be answered by the reviewer is, "Is there any indication that this result is biased high or is a completely false positive, and in reality the true value is below the MCL?" Of these two situations, the second, a false report of a contaminant in the system that exceeds the MCL, is the most damaging to the owners and operators of the water system. The complicating factor is that the MCL for individual contaminants performed in a multianalyte method vary over a wide range. For example benzene and total xylenes are both analyzed by Method 524.2; however, the respective MCLs are 0.005 and 10.00 mg/L, a factor of 2000 concentration difference. Accurate measurement of benzene concentration in the sample is going to be considerably more difficult than measurement of total xylenes. It is much more important to carefully evaluate the lab's ability to measure benzene than total xylenes. If the reviewer approaches his/her work with these two situations and the MCL in mind, the work becomes much less difficult and one is able to focus one's energy where it is most effective.

Each analytical method has unique requirements for the performance of the method and associated quality controls on the procedure. The reviewer of data must be aware of the vagaries of the specific method and this knowledge will only be acquired by a detailed examination of the method. Three of the more common analytical procedures for analysis of drinking water samples are discussed in detail below, as examples of areas to examine in verifying compliance with the method and successful analysis. These discussions should give the reviewer an idea of where a concentration of his/her efforts may be most fruitful when other method results are examined.

1. Volatile Organic Compounds (VOC) by Method 524.2

Method 524.2 is a purge and trap GC-MS procedure for determination of the identification and amount of both regulated and non-regulated volatile organic contaminants in drinking water. The most important asset of the method is the generation of the mass spectrum as an aid to correct identification of calibrated target analytes. Misidentifications of random materials in the sample as regulated analytes are very rare, thus false positives are minimal with this technique. The downside is that it takes highly trained and very skillful instrument operators and data interpreters to perform the analysis and meet all the method specifications. The following discussion is based on version 4.1 (1995) of 524.2. This version incorporates all the mandatory changes to the Method as specified in *Technical Notes*.

1.1 Initial Demonstration of Ability

The initial demonstration of ability consists of analyzing four to seven repetitions of a test solution that contains all the target analytes at a concentration of 2-5 µg/L each. The mean recovery (%R) and relative standard deviation (RSD) of the results for each analyte is computed. Acceptable results are %R within 80-120% and RSD less than 20%. This is a one-time test for each instrument operator. A copy of the raw data and a summary of the results should be placed in the operator's training file.

1.2 MDL Determinations

The MDL is performed and calculated in compliance with 40 CFR 136, Appendix B. Spike concentrations of 0.2-0.5 µg/L are normally sufficient to generate suitable data. The replicates within the MDL study should be performed over several days rather than all in one day. An MDL should be performed on each instrument by each operator at least once a year. If there are changes in the instrumentation, a new MDL needs to be performed.

It is important to verify that a proper MDL study has been performed. Check the equation for standard deviation used for the MDL calculation to insure "n-1" has been used rather than "n" in the denominator. Also check that the correct Student's t-value has been used. EPA suggests that an MDL of 0.5 µg/L for each regulated analyte must be achieved to obtain or maintain certification. The calculated MDL should be checked against the MCL for each analyte. If the MDL is at or higher than the MCL, then no data concerning that analyte, which indicates that it is present in the samples at less than the regulatory limit, are acceptable. Particular analytes to check are benzene, carbon tetra-chloride, 1,2-dichloroethane, 1,2-dichloropropane, tetrachloroethylene, trichloroethylene, 1,1,2-trichloroethane, and especially vinyl chloride and dichloromethane. Vinyl chloride has the lowest MCL of any of the regulated volatile compounds and dichloromethane is the most common laboratory contaminant encountered.

1.3 Initial Calibration Requirements

Initial calibration uses the internal standard technique. The number of calibrated points depends on the range of the calibration. Three points allow a calibration range of a factor of up to 20 in concentration, four points for a factor of up to 50 and 5 points allow up to a factor of 100. An example is the lowest standard being at 0.5 µg/L and the highest at 45 µg/L. This is a concentration factor of 90 and thus 5 calibration concentrations should be used. The calculation can either be performed using the average response factor (Rf), or a second or third order regression equation of the ratio of the area of the analyte to the area of the internal standard (A_{TA}/A_{IS}) plotted against the calculated Rf. If the average Rf is used, the %RSD of the individual Rf for the calibration standards must be less than 20%.

The lowest calibration standard must be below the MCL for the compound. It is recommended to be within a factor of 2-5 of the calculated MDL.

1.4 Continuing Calibration and Tuning Frequency and Acceptance Criteria

On a daily basis 25 ng or less 4-bromofluorobenzene (BFB) is injected and a mass spectrum acquired. The criteria the tune check must meet are presented in Table 4-7. These criteria must be met every 12 hours of operation.

Table 4-7. Acceptance Criteria for BFB Daily Tune Check in Method 524.2

m/z	Acceptance criteria	Notes
50	15-40% of mass 95	Low mass range abundance
75	30-80% of mass 95	Low mass range abundance
95	100%	Base peak
96	5-9% of mass 95	Isotopic abundance and adjacent mass resolution
173	<2% of mass 174	Adjacent mass resolution
174	>50% of mass 95	High mass range abundance
175	5-9% of mass 174	Isotopic abundance, should be 6.6%
176	>95 but <101% of mass 174	Isotopic abundance of bromine
177	5-9% of mass 176	Isotopic abundance, should be 6.6%

Continuing calibration consists of analysis of one of the calibration solutions at the beginning of each 12-hour work shift. The Rf or amount of each analyte in the solution is calculated and must be within a factor of 30% of the average Rf generated in the initial calibration or 30% of the true value of the analyte in the calibration check solution. If a compound fails to meet the acceptance criteria, all results generated since the last successful continuing calibration check must be examined closely. Based on the equation used for the calculation of the amount of analyte in the sample:

$$\text{Amount } \mu g/L = \frac{\text{Area}_{sample} \times \text{Amount}_{int. \ Std.} \times 1000}{\text{Area}_{Int. \ Std.} \times Rf \times V}$$

where: Area_{sample} is the area of the quantitation ion of the target analyte.
$\text{Amount}_{int. \ Std.}$ is the amount of the internal standard added to the sample in μg.
$\text{Area}_{Int. \ Std.}$ is the area of the quantitation ion of the internal standard.
Rf is the original Rf generated in the initial calibration.
V is the volume of the sample in mL.

If the daily Rf generated in the continuing calibration is significantly larger than the RF from the initial calibration, then falsely high amounts of analyte in the sample will be calculated. Analytes reported as lower than the MCL or not detected are probably usable. However, analytes reported as greater than the MCL may, in fact, be lower than the MCL, and a false positive situation may exist.

When the daily Rf is significantly lower than the Rf from the initial calibration, the amount of target analytes reported in the sample is going to be an underestimation. Analytes reported as not-detected may, in fact, be in the sample. Analytes reported as close in amount to the MCL may if fact exceed the MCL, a false negative situation. However, analytes reported as greater than the MCL really do exceed the MCL.

1.5 Sample Collection, Preservation, and Handling Procedures

Samples collected for VOC analysis must be dechlorinated if residual chlorine is present. The appropriate reagents are either ascorbic acid or sodium thiosulfate. After dechlorination the sample is acidified with two drops of 1:1 HCl and the VOA vial closed so as to have zero headspace (no bubbles). The sample is stored at $\leq 4°C$ until analysis. Holding time is 14 days from the moment of sample collection if the sample has been properly preserved. If the sample is not preserved with acid due to foaming action on acid addition, then the holding time is only 24 hours. If the trihalomethanes are the only analytes of interest, acid addition is not necessary and dechlorination is to be performed with sodium thiosulfate, giving a holding time of 14 days.

Samples incorrectly sampled, preserved, stored, or, if holding times are exceeded, are not acceptable for compliance monitoring. The source must be resampled.

1.6 Sample Batches and Blanks

A sample batch or sample set is defined in Method 524.2 as the number of samples that can be processed within 12 hours, and not to exceed 20 samples. Each batch must have associated with it a laboratory reagent blank (LRB) that is used to access system contamination. In light of the purpose of the blank, if two or more instruments are used to process the samples, then it follows that a blank must be performed on each instrument.

If target analyte contamination is found in the blank, analysis is to cease until the source of the contamination is found and corrected. Another blank must be analyzed to verify that the problem is corrected. Blank results are never subtracted from target analyte amounts found in samples.

When blanks are contaminated, data may still be usable if the levels of the target analytes found in the samples are less than the MCL or not-detected. However, results of analysis that exceed the MCL are not reliable and may, in fact, be a false positive.

Field blanks (trip blanks) in duplicate are prepared in the laboratory and accompany the sample containers to the sampling location and then back to the laboratory. They are analyzed when "hits" are found in the associated samples to access possible contamination of the samples arising during the transport and sampling events.

1.7 Laboratory Control Samples

Within Method 524.2 the term Laboratory Fortified Blank (LFB) is used to convey the same idea and procedure as what has been previously defined in this book as the Laboratory Control Sample (LCS). This sample, which can, in actuality, be either the continuing calibration check sample or a re-analysis of the solution used for the initial determination of capability, must be analyzed during each 12-hour work shift or once every 20 samples if more than 20 samples can be processed on a single instrument in 12 hours. The acceptance criteria for each analyte is ±30% of the true value of the analyte. Control charts are to be maintained for daily analyte recoveries from the LCS.

The LCS is the primary demonstration on a daily basis of the ability to analyze samples with good qualitative and quantitative accuracy. High recoveries of the LCS relate directly to falsely high reported values of detected analytes in samples. For those analytes that are not detected in the sample or are reported as less than the MCL, the data are usable in the sense that the MCL has, in actuality, not been exceeded. However, for analytes reported as greater than the MCL, there is a strong possibility that a false positive has been generated, and the data are not reliable.

Low recoveries in the LCS mean that target analytes are reported as lower than they actually are in the sample. Values for analytes reported as larger than the MCL reflect actual amounts in the sample that exceed the MCL. However, values reported as lower than the MCL or not detected may, in fact, be present in greater amounts in the samples, and the data are unreliable.

1.8 Matrix Spikes

It is the position of the EPA that matrix effects are not encountered in the use of Method 524.2 (Section 9.10 of the Method), and thus matrix spikes (laboratory fortified sample matrix, LFM) are not required. In the advent of possible matrix effects as demonstrated by low surrogate and/or internal standard areas for the sample, a matrix spike might be performed. Thus the LCS becomes the major quality control that demonstrates the ability to successfully analyze samples on a continuing basis.

1.9 Replicate Analysis

Replicates are defined in the beginning sections of Method 524.2 as both laboratory duplicates and field duplicates; however, they are not specifically addressed further in the Method. They are a desirable quality control that may be utilized by the laboratory.

1.10 Internal Standard and Surrogate Recoveries

The Method specified internal standard is fluorobenzene and the surrogates are 4-bromofluorobenzene and 1,2-dichlorobenzene-d$_4$. Additional surrogates and internal standards beyond these specified compounds may be used. They are added to each sample to give a 1.0 µg/L concentration if a 25.0 mL sample aliquot is analyzed—or a 5.0 µg/L concentration in the case of 5.0 mL sample aliquots. Surrogates are calibrated at a single concentration in the calibration solutions.

The area counts of the internal standard and surrogates are monitored on a per sample basis to determine possible matrix effects arising from the sample. Abrupt changes in area counts are indicative of either instrument failure or matrix effect. Area counts should be charted over time, and when a decrease of 50% from optimum values has been attained, major maintenance should be performed. Low area counts for the internal standards translates into falsely high reported values for target analytes in the samples. Compounds that are not-detected in the sample or compounds reported as less than the MCL, really do not exceed these limits, and the results are reliable. However, target analytes reported from the analysis as above the MCL may, in actuality, be less than the MCL. Any reported value for an analyte is an estimate when aberrations in the internal standards occur.

The laboratory must generate warning and control limits for surrogate recoveries as part of the control charting process. The surrogate recoveries obtained during analysis of the sample are compared against the laboratory derived acceptance limits. Low surrogate recoveries are an indication of low target analyte recoveries. Target analytes reported as not detected in the sample, or detected but less than the MCL, may, in actuality, be present in larger amounts than reported. Target analytes reported as exceeding the MCL really are present above the MCL. High surrogate recoveries suggest there may be problems with the internal standard areas.

1.11 Target Analyte Identification

Target analytes must elute from the column (retention time) within the retention time window of standards that are checked each 12-hour work shift. A simple matching of quantitation ions and retention times between the standard and the sample is insufficient for identification. There must be a match of mass spectra between the library spectrum generated by the user and the spectrum obtained for the analyte in the sample. Every peak present in the standard of greater than 10% abundance must also be present in the sample spectrum. Further, there must be an abundance match within 20% absolute abundance.

2. Semivolatile Organic Compounds (SVOC) by Method 525.2

Method 525.2 involves a sample preparation to isolate target analytes from the water matrix followed by analysis with GC-MS for identification and quantitation of both regulated and non-regulated semivolatile organic contaminants in drinking water. The most important asset of the method is the generation of the mass spectrum as an aid to correct identification of calibrated target analytes. Misidentifications of random materials in the sample as regulated analytes are very rare, thus false positives are minimal with this technique. The downside is that it takes highly trained and very skillful sample preparation chemists, instrument operators, and data interpreters to perform the analysis and meet all the method specifications.

2.1 Initial Demonstration of Ability

The initial demonstration of ability consists of analyzing four to seven repetitions of a test solution that contains all the target analytes at a concentration of 2-5 µg/L each. The mean recovery (%R) and relative standard deviation (RSD) of the results for each analyte are computed. Acceptable results are %R within 70-130% and RSD less than 30%. This is a one-time test for each instrument operator. A copy of the raw data and a summary of the results should be placed in the operator's training file.

2.2 MDL Determinations

The MDL is performed and calculated in compliance with 40 CFR 136, Appendix B. Spike concentrations of 0.5 µg/L are normally sufficient to generate suitable data. The replicates within the MDL study should be performed over several days rather than all in one day. An MDL should be performed on each instrument by each operator at least once a year. If there are changes in the instrumentation, a new MDL needs to be performed.

It is important to verify that a proper MDL study has been performed. Check the equation for standard deviation used for the MDL calculation to insure "n-1" has been used rather than "n" in the denominator. Also check that the correct Student's t-value has been used. EPA suggests that a MDL of from 1/5 to 1/10 of the MCL for each regulated analyte be achieved. The calculated MDL should be checked against the MCL for each analyte. If the MDL is at or higher than the MCL, then no data concerning that analyte (which indicate that it is present in the samples at less than the regulatory limit) are acceptable. Particular analytes to examine, which have very low MCL, are benzo(a)pyrene, di(2-ethylhexyl)phthalate, heptachlor, heptachlor epoxide, lindane, and pentachlorophenol.

2.3 Initial Calibration Requirements

A six-point initial calibration is required in Method 525.2. For single component analytes, the suggested range of concentrations in the calibration solutions is 0.1 ng/µL to 10.0 ng/µL. An internal standard calibration using average response factors (Rf) of the characteristic quantitation ion of the internal standards and the target analyte is acceptable if the %RSD of the individual response factors for a target analyte is less than 30%. An alternate to the average Rf procedure is to prepare a regression equation of the ratio of area of the target analyte quantitation ion to area of the internal standard quantitation ion (A_{TA}/A_{IS}) plotted against Rf. The regression equation may be up to third degree.

Toxaphene and Aroclors (PCB) are also target analytes of Method 525.2. These multi-peak analytes are calibrated at six levels. For toxaphene the calibration range is from 250 ng/µL to 10 µg/µL, while the Aroclors are calibrated from 25 ng/µL to 0.2 µg/µL. There are two options for the calibrations of the multi-peak analytes. The first is to calibrate against the total area of the appropriate quantitation ion for all the peaks within the elution window of the analyte. For example under this option toxaphene would be calibrated as the total area of ion 159 eluting between 13.0 and 21.0 minutes. The second option is to calculate an average response factor or linear regression using the combined area of from three to six of the most intense and characteristic peaks of the target analyte for each level of calibration.

2.4 Continuing Calibration Frequency and Acceptance Criteria

On a daily basis 25 ng or less decafluorotriphenylphosphine (DFTPP) is injected and a mass spectrum acquired. The criteria that the tune check must meet are presented in Table 4-8. These criteria must be met every 12 hours of operation.

System performance is also evaluated during the tune verification. The breakdown of 4,4'-DDT and endrin are calculated as performance parameters. The total ion current area of the compounds and their respective breakdown products, 4,4'-DDE, 4,4'-DDD, endrin aldehyde and endrin ketone, are used in the calculation.

$$\% \text{ Breakdown} = \frac{\text{DDE} + \text{DDD}}{\text{DDT} + \text{DDE} + \text{DDD}} \times 100$$

$$\% \text{ breakdown} = \frac{\text{Aldehyde} + \text{Ketone}}{\text{Endrin} + \text{Aldehyde} + \text{Ketone}} \times 100$$

Acceptable values for breakdown are less than 20%.

Table 4-8.   Acceptance Criteria for DFTPP Daily Tune Check in Method 525.2

m/z	Acceptance criteria	Notes
51	10-80% of base peak	Low mass range sensitivity
68	<2% of mass 69	Low mass resolution
70	<2% of mass 69	Low mass resolution
127	10-80% of base peak	Low-mid mass sensitivity
197	<2% of mass 198	Mid mass resolution
198	Base peak or >50% of 442	Mid mass sensitivity and resolution
199	5-9% of mass 198	Mid mass resolution and isotope check, should be 6.6%
275	10-60% of base peak	Mid-high mass sensitivity
365	>1% of base peak	Baseline threshold
441	Present and < 443	High mass resolution
442	Base peak or >50% of 198	High mass resolution and sensitivity
443	15-24% of 442	High mass resolution and isotope check, should be 19.8%

Continuing calibration verification consists of analysis of one of the calibration solutions at the beginning of each 12-hour work shift. The Rf or amount of each analyte in the solution is calculated and must be within a factor of 30% of the average Rf generated in the initial calibration or 30% of the true value of the analyte in the calibration check solution. If a compound fails to meet the acceptance criteria, and there is a substantial probability that one or more will, and the compound is detected in samples run during the ensuing 12 hours, a single point calibration of the compound is immediately performed for quantitation of the analyte hit. If the same calibrated compound fails to meet continuing calibration verification three times in a row, the problem must be corrected. If 10% or more of the calibrated compounds fail to meet acceptance criteria during a single continuing calibration verification, no sample analysis is allowed, and the problem must be fixed immediately.

Based on the equation used for the calculation of the amount of analyte in the sample:

$$\text{Amount } \mu g/L = \frac{\text{Area}_{\text{sample}} \times \text{Amount}_{\text{int. Std.}} \times 1000}{\text{Area}_{\text{Int. Std.}} \times Rf \times V}$$

where: $\text{Area}_{\text{sample}}$ is the area of the quantitation ion of the target analyte.
$\text{Amount}_{\text{int. Std.}}$ is the amount of the internal standard added to the sample in μg.
$\text{Area}_{\text{Int. Std.}}$ is the area of the quantitation ion of the internal standard.
Rf is the original Rf generated in the initial calibration.
V is the volume of the initial sample in mL.

If the daily Rf generated in the continuing calibration is significantly larger than the Rf from the initial calibration, then falsely high amounts of analyte in the sample will be calculated. Analytes reported as lower than the MCL or not detected are probably usable. However, analytes reported as greater than the MCL may, in fact, be lower than the MCL, and a false positive situation exist.

When the daily Rf is significantly lower than the Rf from the initial calibration, the amount of target analytes reported in the sample is going to be an underestimation. Analytes reported as not-detected may, in fact, be in the sample. Analytes reported as close in amount to the MCL may, in fact, exceed the MCL, a false negative situation. However, analytes reported as greater than the MCL really do exceed the MCL.

2.5 Sample Collection, Preservation and Handling Procedures

Samples of one liter in volume are collected in glass containers with a Teflon® cap liner. If residual chlorine is present it is removed by addition of 40-50 mg sodium sulfite, which may be added as a solid. The sample is then acidified to pH < 2 with 6N, hydrochloric acid. The sodium sulfite and hydrochloric acid must not be mixed prior to sampling. Samples are then held in the dark at 4°C until sample extraction. Maximum holding time from sampling to extraction is 14 days, unless carboxin, diazinon, disulfoton, disulfoton sulfoxide, fenamiphos or terbufos are target analytes. If any of these are target analytes, the sample must be extracted immediately after collection and preservation. Once the sample extract is prepared it may be stored at 4°C for up to 30 days before instrument analysis.

2.6 Sample Preparation Procedures

Sample preparation in Method 525.2 is a liquid-solid phase extraction using either a cartridge or a disk. Liquid-liquid extraction is a disallowed deviation from the method. The procedure involves addition of the internal standards and surrogate solution to an acidified sample, then passage of the sample through the solid-phase media and sequential elution with ethyl acetate and methylene chloride. The extract is concentrated to 0.5 to 1.0 mL, a recovery standard is added and the extract analyzed by GC-MS.

The cleanliness and efficiency of the solid-phase media is determined by analysis of blanks and laboratory control samples initially when new lots of the media are obtained and periodically during the use of the lot. Phthalate contamination is of great concern due to frequent findings of the material in certain lots of media.

2.7 Blanks

Sample preparation blanks and field blanks are performed with every set of 20 or fewer samples processed within a 12-hour work shift. Blanks must be examined closely for phthalate and other laboratory created contamination. Blank results are never subtracted from analyte results in samples. If blank contamination is found, samples need to be closely examined for the same contaminants. If the contaminants are not detected in the samples, the data are probably reliable. If the contaminants are found in the samples at significantly higher concentration (>10 times) than the amount in the blank, the results may be usable. However, when the blank and sample results are within a factor of 10 of each other, laboratory contamination is the only appropriate conclusion, and the sample results are unusable.

Field blanks are used to monitor the sample acquisition process. If samples are found to have non-detected levels of target analytes, the field blank is not of much use. However, when target analytes are detected in the samples, the field blanks should be examined to see if the analytes are artifacts of the sampling procedure or if they are indicative of contamination in the water source.

2.8 Laboratory Control Samples

Method 525.2 refers to laboratory fortified blanks (LFB) as fulfilling the same purpose as laboratory control samples (LCS). These quality control samples are of the same composition as those used in the initial demonstration of ability (Section 2.1). They are processed exactly like samples at a rate of one every group of up to 20 samples prepared within a 12-hour work shift. If toxaphene is to be determined in the set of samples, then a separate LCS with toxaphene must be performed every 24 hours. When Aroclors are included as target analytes, the recoveries of the single PCB congeners included in the calibration solutions and LCS are sufficient to demonstrate ongoing ability. If the single PCB congeners are not in the LCS solution, then a single multicomponent LCS containing toxaphene or the Aroclors is analyzed with each sample set, with a different analyte chosen each day. This allows the laboratory to generate recoveries on all the target analytes over a period of time.

The results on the LCS are evaluated as individual target analyte recoveries with the acceptance limits 70-130%. Control charts are to be maintained on the recoveries with precision evaluated over time as %RSD. Acceptable %RSD are <30%.

The LCS is the primary demonstration on a daily basis of the ability to analyze samples with good qualitative and quantitative accuracy. High recoveries of the LCS relate directly to falsely high reported values of detected analytes in samples. For those analytes that are not detected in the sample or are reported as less than the MCL, the data are usable in the sense that the MCL has, in actuality, not been exceeded. However, for analytes reported as greater than the MCL, there is a strong possibility that a false positive has been generated, and the data are not reliable.

Low recoveries in the LCS means that target analytes are reported as lower than they actually are in the sample. Values for analytes reported as larger than the MCL reflect actual amounts in the sample that exceed the MCL. However, values reported as lower than the MCL or not detected may, in fact, be present in greater amounts in the samples, and the data are unreliable.

2.9 Matrix Spikes

Laboratory fortified matrix samples (LFM) and replicates are used to determine the effect of the sample on method performance. These are performed at a rate of one per 20 samples processed in a 12-hour work shift. Acceptance criteria include recoveries within 70-130% for each target analyte and %RSD <30.

When matrix spike recoveries are outside the acceptance limits and the LCS recoveries are acceptable, this is an indication of matrix effects from the sampling source, and the evaluation should be documented. The sample results can be interpreted similar to those presented in the preceding discussion (Section 2.8).

2.10 Replicate Analysis

Replicate analysis is a required quality control with regards to matrix spiked samples. However, other than a definition of laboratory duplicates presented in the definitions section of Method 525.2, replicate analyses are not expressly addressed as a required quality control. It still makes good analytical sense for the laboratory to perform sample duplicates.

2.11 Internal Standard and Surrogate Recoveries

The internal standards specified in Method 525.2 are acenaphthene-D_{10}, phenanthrene-D_{10}, and Chrysene-D_{12}. Additional internal standards may be used. The specified surrogates are 1,3-dimethyl-2-nitrobenzene, perylene-D_{12} and triphenylphosphine. An additional suggested surrogate is pyrene-D_{10}. A recovery standard, terphenyl-D_{14}, is used to determine recovery of the internal standards and surrogates. Recoveries should be greater than 70%. Internal standard and surrogate quantitation ion areas should be within ±30% of the last daily continuing calibration verification and within ±50% of the initial calibration.

Method 525.2 requires addition of the internal standards to the sample prior to any sample processing. Thus recoveries of target analytes are designed to be internally compensated by the recoveries of the internal standards, which correct for final volume variances and sample preparation vagaries. However, in the case of low internal standard recoveries (<70%) there is the problem of the lowered instrument response to the analyte. This can result in required quantitations, to meet very low MCLs, approaching instrument signal-to-noise or IDL limits and their inherent inaccuracies. This means that the values reported as non-detected or as very low level detects are actually estimates rather than reproducible results.

2.12 Target Analyte Identification

Target analytes must elute from the column (retention time) within the retention time window of standards that are checked each 12-hour work shift. A simple matching of quantitation ions and retention times between the standard and the sample is insufficient for identification. There must be a match of mass spectra between the library spectrum generated by the user and the spectrum obtained for the analyte in the sample. Every peak present in the standard of greater than 10% abundance must also be present in the sample spectrum. Further there must be an abundance match within 20% absolute abundance.

3. Metals by Method 200.7

Method 200.7 is an inductively coupled plasma-atomic emission spectrometry (ICP-AES) procedure for determination of up to 28 or more elements per analysis. Sample preparation involves digestion of an aliquot of the sample in strong mineral acid with heating to obtain a solution suitable for introduction into the instrument. The ICP-AES provides both qualitative and quantitative analysis of the elements in the sample. However, the many spectral interferences that can be generated from non-target elements in samples can give erroneous results, both negative and positive. It takes trained personnel to perform successful digestions of the samples without loss of analytes and introduction of laboratory contamination and highly skilled instrument operators/data interpreters to provide reliable results. The following discussion is based upon EPA Method 200.7, Revision 4.4, May 1994.

3.1 Initial Demonstration of Performance and MDL Determinations

Initial demonstration of performance consists of evaluation of the linear dynamic range of the instrument for each target analyte. The evaluation is performed by analysis of successively higher concentrations of analytes until deviation (<10%) from the linear calibration curve is obtained. The procedure must be repeated at least once a year.

A quality control sample (QCS) consisting of target analytes at a level of ≥1.0 mg/L (silver is at 0.50 mg/L) is prepared from a source different than those used to prepare the calibration standards. The quality control sample must be analyzed three times, and the mean result of the three determinations calculated. The acceptance range is within ±5% of the true value. This serves as a check of the calibration standards and the set-up of the instrument. The QCS analysis must be repeated at least once a quarter.

The method detection limit (MDL) is performed and calculated in compliance with 40 CFR 136, Appendix B. Spike concentrations of two to three times the estimated instrument detection limit are normally sufficient to generate suitable data. The replicates within the MDL study should be performed over several days rather than all in one day. An MDL should be performed on each instrument by each operator at least once a year. If there are changes in the instrumentation, a new MDL needs to be performed.

It is important to verify that a proper MDL study has been performed. Check the equation for standard deviation used for the MDL calculation to insure "n-1" has been used rather than "n" in the denominator. Also check that the correct Student's t-value has been used. EPA suggests that a MDL of from 1/5 to 1/10 of the MCL for each regulated analyte be achieved. The calculated MDL should be checked against the MCL for each analyte. If the MDL is at or higher than the MCL, then no data are acceptable that indicate that the analyte is present in the samples at less than the regulatory limit. Particular analytes to examine are antimony, beryllium, cadmium, thallium and lead, which all have very low MCL.

3.2 Initial Calibration Requirements

The ICP-AES must be calibrated at least daily, and more frequent calibration may be required. Minimum requirements for Method 200.7 calibration consist of analysis of a blank and a high concentration standard. More calibration points are recommended, including at least a calibrated point at the MDL or at the reporting limit. Some state programs specifically require the addition of a calibration point at the reporting limit. All calibrations are linear, and the calibration range must reside within the determined linear dynamic range. The calibration must be checked by immediate analysis of at least four exposures of the IPC (Section 3.3). The results of the IPC must lie within ±5% of the true value and the %RSD of the exposures <3%. As a practical note it has been discovered by many laboratories that the number of calibration levels used in an initial calibration relates directly to the stability of the calibration. A four level calibration is normally observed to last two to three times as long as the blank and single standard calibration. In the long run the laboratory saves time and effort by performing a calibration that exceeds the minimum requirements of the Method.

Results reported from instruments that are not calibrated daily are not reliable. The sample introduction system of the ICP is very sensitive to environmental conditions of temperature, barometric pressure and humidity. Even climate-controlled facilities exhibit minor day-to-day and hour-to-hour fluctuations that are sufficient to disturb an ICP calibration. The calibration must be frequently (see Section 3.3) checked and as soon as the check fails, the instrument must be recalibrated.

3.3 Continuing Calibration Frequency and Acceptance Criteria

Continuing calibration verification consists of analysis of a calibration blank followed immediately by the Instrument Performance Check (IPC, or continuing calibration verification) solution. The IPC is prepared from the same standards used in the initial calibration solutions and consists of silver at <0.50 mg/L, potassium, phosphorus and silica at 10.0 mg/L and the rest of the target analytes at 2.0 mg/L. The calibration blank and IPC must be performed every 10 samples, and as the last analyses of the day.

The calibration blank should always read less than the reporting limit for each target analyte. The IPC results for each target analyte must lie within ±10% of the true value of the solution.

Sample results must be bracketed by successful IPC analyses. If an IPC fails to meet the acceptance criteria, all sample results since the last successful IPC are invalidated, the instrument must be recalibrated and the samples must be rerun.

3.4 Sample Collection, Preservation and Handling Procedures

Samples must be collected in contaminant-free sampling containers. The best containers are made of high density polyethylene (HDPE) for drinking water target analytes. Samples may be preserved at the moment of collection by the addition of 1:2 nitric acid to achieve a pH of <2. Method 200.7 suggests that field preservation may lead to sample contamination. To avoid these problems and increasing transportation regulations, it is suggested that samples be brought to the laboratory within two weeks of sample collection and preserved there with acid.

Once acid is added to the sample, it is allowed to sit for at least 16 hours, then the pH is determined. If greater than pH 2, more acid must be added and the sample again allowed to sit for 16 hours. If the pH is <2 then the sample is ready for processing and analysis. The procedure and pH readings are documented. Samples after acidification may be held for up to six months.

3.5 Sample Preparation Procedures

Most drinking water samples are particulate free and exhibit turbidities less than 1.0 NTU. These samples are prepared by addition of nitric acid to achieve a 1% nitric acid concentration and are suitable to analyze without further sample preparation.

Samples with turbidities greater than 1.0 NTU must be digested as are samples that produce a precipitate upon acidification. A 100 mL portion of the sample is heated with nitric and hydrochloric acids and concentrated to about 20 mL. After cooling the sample is filtered and diluted to 50.0 mL, and is ready for analysis. The digestion procedure achieves a two-fold concentration of the sample. Other concentration factors can be performed in a similar fashion.

3.6 Blanks

There are a number of blanks associated with Method 200.7. These include field blanks, sample preparation blanks and instrument rinse blanks (calibration blanks). All blanks should be checked closely as an indication of sample contamination.

Sample preparation blanks must be prepared at a rate of one for every 20 samples processed within a 12-hour work shift. If contamination is detected in the sample preparation blank at levels exceeding the MDL by a factor of 2.2 or greater, or if analytes are found in samples at less than ten times the blank level, the samples and blanks should be reprepared for analysis. Sample results are never corrected for contamination found in any blank.

Instrument rinse blanks are for the purpose of monitoring sample carryover in the sample introduction part of the ICP. When high levels of analytes are detected in samples, calibration blanks are performed to verify that the instrument has been rinsed clean. If the instrument is determined to still have contamination, rinsing is continued until a calibration blank is obtained that is clean. Every set of ten sample results must be bracketed by clean calibration blanks.

If analytes are detected in samples, the field blank is examined to determine possible contamination introduced during the sampling process. The same guidelines used for interpretation of sample preparation blanks apply to field blanks. If the field blank is discovered to be contaminated, it may be due to the sample containers, the preservative acid, or the sampling technique. All need to be examined closely, the problem discovered and corrected, and the sampling event repeated.

3.7 Laboratory Control Samples

Laboratory fortified blanks (LFB, or laboratory control samples) are performed at a rate of one per 20 samples processed within a batch (batch is not further defined in Method 200.7). Recovery limits for analytes in the LCS are 85-115%. Control charts are to be maintained for each analyte and limits updated every five to 10 points. Control chart limits are based only on the most recent 20 to 30 data points. The laboratory may establish their own control limits for the LCS recoveries based on mean ±3 standard deviations; however, the limits may be no wider than 85-115%.

The LCS is the primary demonstration on a daily basis of the ability to analyze samples with good qualitative and quantitative accuracy. High recoveries of the LCS relate directly to falsely high reported values of detected analytes in samples. For those analytes not detected in the sample or reported as less than the MCL, the data are usable in the sense that the MCL has, in actuality, not been exceeded. However, for analytes reported as greater than the MCL, there is a strong possibility that a false positive has been generated, and the data are not reliable.

Low recoveries in the LCS means that target analytes are reported as lower than they actually are in the sample. Values for analytes reported as larger than the MCL, reflect actual amounts in the sample that exceed the MCL. However, values reported as lower than the MCL or not detected may, in fact, be present in greater amounts in the samples and the data are unreliable.

3.8 Matrix Spikes

Laboratory fortified matrix samples (LFM, matrix spikes) are present in Method 200.7 in two different types. The first is the spike added to the samples prior to any sample preparation. This must be performed at a rate of at least one for every ten samples processed. The other matrix spike performed is added after the digestion procedure, a post-digestion spike (PDS). The recovery limits for each element in the matrix spike are 70-130%, while the PDS recovery expectations are 85-115%.

If matrix spike recoveries are not within expectations, but the laboratory control samples are acceptable, then matrix effects inherent to the sample may be present. If an element is present in the sample at background levels greater than three times the matrix spike level, the poor recovery of the element should be discounted. Possible interpretations for poor recoveries other than high background are presented in the previous Section (3.7). However, it should be recognized that there is also the distinct problem of uncorrected spectral interference being present in the sample, as discussed in Chapter 2 of this book.

3.9 Replicate Analysis

Replicates are defined in the beginning sections of Method 200.7 as both laboratory duplicates and field duplicates; however, they are not specifically addressed further in the Method. Replicates are a desirable quality control that may be utilized by the laboratory.

References

1. *Manual for the Certification of Laboratories Analyzing Drinking Water*, Third Edition USEPA Office of Water, EPA/570/9-90/008, April 1990.

2. *Manual for the Certification of Laboratories Analyzing Drinking Water*. Fourth Edition Draft U.S. EPA Office of Water, September 1995.

3. *Methods for the Determination of Organic Compounds in Drinking Water*, U.S. EPA Office of Water, PB91-231480, December, 1988, revised July 1991.

4. *Methods for the Determination of Organic Compounds in Drinking Water*, Supplement 1 U.S. EPA Office of Water, PB91-146027, July 1990.

5. *Methods for the Determination of Organic Compounds in Drinking Water*, Supplement 2, U.S. EPA Office of Water, PB92-207703, August, 1992.

6. *Methods for the Determination of Organic Compounds in Drinking Water*, Supplement III, U.S. EPA Office of Water, EPA-600/R-95/131, PB95-261616, August, 1995.

7. *Technical Notes on Drinking Water Methods,* U.S. EPA Office of Water, EPA/600/R-94/173, PB95-104766, October, 1994.

8. *Methods for the Determination of Metals in Environmental Samples,* U.S. EPA Office of Water, EPA/600/4-91/010, June, 1991

9. *Methods for the Determination of Metals in Environmental Samples,* Supplement 1, U.S. EPA Office of Water, PB945-125472, May 1994

CHAPTER 5

Clean Water Act

With the passage of the Federal Water Pollution Control Act in 1972 and later amended as the Clean Water Act (CWA), EPA began the long process of attempting to return the surface waters of the United States to "fishable and swimmable" condition. The process involves regulating discharges of wastewaters through the National Pollutant Discharge Elimination System (NPDES). Facilities that discharge wastewater must do so under a permit issued by the state or EPA that places numerical limits on the concentrations of various pollutants in the wastewater. In return for a permit to discharge wastewater, the facility must implement a compliance monitoring program that may include daily, weekly, monthly, quarterly, and annual sampling and analysis efforts.

The numerical limits in an NPDES permit or state-issued equivalent permit are driven by three considerations. First, the CWA defines a series of "conventional pollutants" in the Act itself. These pollutants are regulated at all facilities, regardless of the industry, and are designed to ensure that some basic level of wastewater treatment is practiced. They include "pollutants" such as total suspended solids (TSS), biological oxygen demand (BOD), and oil and grease. When first promulgated into law, the CWA included considerable funds for a grant program to assist municipalities with the construction of wastewater treatment plants that could meet the NPDES limits for these conventional pollutants, thus attempting to ensure that all publicly-owned treatment works (POTWs) met some minimum standards. In later years, these grant funds were scaled back.

The second set of limits is imposed at the national level when EPA establishes "effluent guidelines" for categories of industries. The guidelines contain the effluent limits for that industry that EPA has demonstrated can be achieved by the "best available technology" (BAT) for wastewater treatment employed across members of that industry. The pollutants that are regulated under an effluent guideline are those that EPA has shown are likely to be present in the industry wastewater and that are not covered under the conventional pollutants. These often include specific organic compounds and metals, but may also regulate non-specific parameters such as color.

The third level of regulation is imposed most often by states with primacy for their wastewater program. It involves *lower* limits for certain pollutants or limits for additional pollutants designed to protect the water quality of a specific receiving water. These latter limits are often derived from health-based or risk-based calculations of the effects of a potential discharge on the aquatic life in the receiving water or on humans who use the receiving water, such as subsistence fishermen. One difficulty with this third type of regulation is that in many cases, the numerical limitations have not been demonstrated to be achievable by a specific wastewater treatment technology. An even greater difficulty is that the health-based or risk-based limits may be well below the capabilities of existing analytical methods that might be used to monitor compliance with the limits. In this latter instance, the role of the data validator may be reduced to pointing out that validation is not possible.

A. Approved Methods

Not long after the CWA was passed, the Natural Resources Defense Council (NRDC) filed a lawsuit in Federal Court against Russell Train, the EPA Administrator, for failing to enforce the provisions of the CWA that were designed to eliminate pollutant discharges. The suit, known as *NRDC v. Train* was settled in 1976 by a consent decree, under which EPA agreed to establish a list of "priority pollutants" that would be subject to monitoring. Through a process that combined both science and legal negotiations, EPA established a list of 129 priority pollutants. In order to be placed on this list, a pollutant had to meet three criteria:

- The pollutant had to have been found in the wastewater of at least one industry during surveys conducted by EPA.

- There had to be an analytical method that could measure the compound in wastewater effluents.

- There had to be an authentic standard available for the pollutant.

Thus, in order to meet the terms of the consent decree, EPA had to have in place a series of analytical methods that applied to the priority pollutants. Section 304(h) of the CWA granted authority to the EPA Administrator to *"promulgate guidelines establishing test procedures for the analysis of pollutants."* It was under this authority that EPA developed the now extensive series of analytical methods for wastewater compliance monitoring, including the familiar 200 and 600 Series methods.

In order to demonstrate compliance with a wastewater discharge permit, the discharger or its contract laboratory *must* employ an "approved" analytical method specified in Section 304(h) of the CWA. EPA has approved methods from other sources such as APHA (Standard Methods), ASTM, and USGS. The list of all methods approved under Section 304(h) is published in 40 *CFR* Part 136, and some are reproduced in Tables 5-1 and 5-2. The lists of approved methods are not static, and the most recent copy of the regulations must be consulted. The requirement for the use of approved methods is similar to that in place under the Safe Drinking Water Act (SDWA) and a significant difference from the approach employed under the Resource Conservation and Recovery Act (RCRA), where, with a few specific exceptions, Federal statutes allow the use of any appropriate method. With the requirement to use specific approved methods, data validation can focus on whether the laboratory applied the appropriate method and met the quality control specifications in it. This eliminates the need to rely on a quality assurance project plan (QAPP) for the QC specifications.

Table 5-1. **Some Approved Methods for NPDES Permit Compliance Monitoring of Inorganic Analytes.**

Inorganic Parameters	EPA			SM[1]	Other
Acidity (as Calcium Carbonate)		305.1		2310 B(4a)	
Alkalinity (as Calcium Carbonate)	310.2	310.1		2320 B	
Aluminum (total, digested)					
AA Direct Aspiration		202.1		3111 D	
AA Furnace		202.2		3113 B	
ICP/AES		200.7		3120 B	
Colorimetric				3500-Al D	
Ammonia (as N)					
Manual distillation followed by:		350.2		4500-NH3 B	
Nesslerization		350.2		4500-NH3 C	
Titration		350.2		4500-NH3 E	
Electrode		350.3		4500-NH3 F or G	
Automated Phenate		350.1		4500-NH3 H	
Biochemical oxygen demand		405.1		5210 B	
Chemical oxygen demand					
Titrimetric	410.1	410.2	410.3	5220 C	
Spectrophotometric		410.4		5220 D	2
Chloride					
Titrimetric (silver nitrate)				4500-Cl⁻ B	
Titrimetric (mercuric nitrate)		325.3		4500-Cl⁻ C	
Colorimetric, automated	325.2	325.1		4500-Cl⁻ E	
Chlorine, total residual					
Amperometric direct titration		330.1		4500-Cl D	
Iodometric direct titration		330.3		4500-Cl B	
Back titration, either end-point		330.2		4500-Cl C	
DPD-FAS titration		330.4		4500-Cl F	
DPD spectrophotometric		330.5		4500-Cl G	
Electrode					3
Copper (Total, digested)					
AA direct aspiration		220.1		3111 B or C	
AA furnace		220.2		3113 B	
ICP/AES		200.7		3120 B	
Colorimetric (Neocuproine)				3500-Cu D	

[1] *Standard Methods for the Examination of Water and Wastewater*, 18th Edition, 1993, APHA, AWWA, WEF Washngton, D.C.

[2] OIC Chemical oxygen demand method, Oceanography International Corporation, 512 West Loop, PO Box 2980, College Station, TX 77840; Chemical oxygen demand method 8000, *Hach Handbook of Water Analysis*, Hach Chemical Company, PO Box 389, Loveland, CO 80537.

[3] *Orion Research Instruction Manual*, Residual chlorine electrode model 97-70, Orion Research, 840 Memorial Dr., Cambridge, MA 02138. The calibration graph must be derived using a reagent blank and three standard solutions containing 0.2, 1.0 and 5.0 mL 0.00281 N potassium iodate/100 mL solution.

Table 5-1. Some Approved Methods for NPDES Permit Compliance Monitoring of Inorganic Analytes. *Continued*

Inorganic Parameters	EPA	SM[4]	Other
Copper (Total, digested), *continued*			
Colorimetric (Bicinchoninate)		3500-Cu E	5
Cyanide (Total, distilled)		4500-CN C	
Titrimetric		4500-CN D	
Spectrophotometric manual	335.3	4500-CN E	
Spectrophotometric automated	335.3		
Fluoride (total, distilled)		4500-F⁻ B	
Electrode manual	340.2	4500-F⁻ C	
Colorimetric (SPADNS)	340.1	4500-F⁻ D	
Automated Complexone	340.3	4500-F⁻ E	
Hardness (as calcium carbonate)			
Automated colorimetric	130.1		
Titrimetric or calculated from ICP	130.2	2340 C	
Hydrogen ion (pH)			
Electrometric	150.1	4500-H⁺ B	
Iron (Total, digested)			
AA direct aspiration	236.1	3111 B or C	
AA furnace	236.2	3113 B	
ICP/AES	200.7	3120 B	
Colorimetric (phenanthroline)		3500-Fe D	6
Kjeldahl nitrogen (Total as N)			
Digestion and distillation followed by	351.3	4500-NH3 B or C	
Titration	351.3	4500-NH3 E	
Nesslerization	351.3	4500-NH3 C	
Electrode	351.3	4500-NH3 F or G	
Automated phenate	351.1		
Block digester colorimetric	351.2		
Manual or block digester potentiometric	351.4		
Nitrate			
Colorimetric (Brucine sulfate)	352.1		
Nitrate-Nitrite (N) minus Nitrite (N)	352.1		
Nitrate-Nitrite (N)			
Manual cadmium reduction	353.3	4500-NO3 E	
Automated cadmium reduction	353.2	4500-NO3 F	

[4]*Standard Methods for the Examination of Water and Wastewater*, 18th Edition, 1993, APHA, AWWA, WEF Washngton, D.C.

[5] Method 8506, Hach Handbook of Water Analysis, Hach Chemical Company, PO Box 389 Loveland CO 80537.

[6] Method 8008, *Hach Handbook of Water Analysis*, Hach Chemical Company, PO Box 389, Loveland, CO 80537.

Table 5-1. **Some Approved Methods for NPDES Permit Compliance Monitoring of Inorganic Analytes.** *Continued*

Inorganic Parameters	EPA	SM[7]	Other
Nitrate-Nitrite (N), *continued*			
Automated hydrazine	353.1	4500-NO3 H	
Nitrite (N)			
Manual spectrophotometric	354.1		8
Oil and Grease			
Gravimetric total recoverable	413.1[9]	5520 B	
Orthophosphate			
Automated ascorbic acid	365.1	4500-P F	
Manual single reagent	365.2	4500-P E	
Manual two reagent	365.3		
Oxygen dissolved			
Winkler (azide modification)	360.2	4500-O C	
Electrode	360.1	4500-O G	
Phenols (manual distillation)			
Colorimetric 4AAP	420.1		
Automated 4AAP	420.2		
Residue, total	160.3	2540 B	
Residue, filterable	160.1	2540 C	
Residue, nonfilterable	160.2	2540 D	
Residue, settleable	160.5	2540 F	
Residue, volatile	160.4		
Sulfate			
Automated colorimetric	375.1		
Gravimetric	375.3	$4500\text{-}SO_4^{-2}$ C or D	
Turbidimetric	375.4		
Sulfide			
Titrimetric	376.1	$4500\text{-}S^{-2}$ E	
Colorimetric	376.2	$4500\text{-}S^{-2}$ D	
Temperature	170.1	2550 B	
Turbidity, Nephelometric	180.1	2130 B	
Zinc (Total, digested followed by)			
AA direct aspiration	289.1	3111 B or C	
AA furnace	289.2		
ICP/AES	200.7	3120 B	
Dithizone colorimetric		3500-Zn E	
Zincon colorimetric		3500-Zn F	10

[7] *Standard Methods for the Examination of Water and Wastewater*, 18th Edition, 1993, APHA, AWWA, WEF Washngton, D.C.
[8] Method 8507, *Hach Handbook of Water Analysis*, Hach Chemical Company, PO Box 389, Loveland, CO 80537.
[9] EPA method 1664 is to be promulgated for this parameter by the end of 1994.
[10] Method 8009, *Hach Handbook of Water Analysis*, Hach Chemical Company, PO Box 389, Loveland, CO 80537.

Table 5-2.   Some Approved Methods for Analysis of NPDES Compliance Monitoring Organic Analytes.

Organic Parameters	EPA GC	EPA GC/MS	EPA HPLC	SM[11]
Volatile Organic Compounds (VOC)				
Acrolein	603	624, 1624		
Acrylonitrile	603	624, 1624		
Benzene	602	624, 1624		6210B, 6220B
Bromodichloromethane	601	624, 1624		6210B, 6230B
Bromoform	601	624, 1624		6210B, 6230B
Bromomethane	601	624, 1624		6210B, 6230B
Carbon tetrachloride	601	624, 1624		6210B, 6230B
Chlorobenzene	601, 602	624, 1624		6210B, 6230B
Chloroethane	601	624, 1624		6210B, 6230B
2-Chloroethylvinylether	601	624, 1624		6210B, 6230B
Chloroform	601	624, 1624		6210B, 6230B
Chloromethane	601	624, 1624		6210B, 6230B
Dibromochloromethane	601	624, 1624		6210B, 6230B
1,2-Dichlorobenzene	601, 602	624, 625		6210B, 6220B
1,3-Dichlorobenzene	601, 602	624, 625		6210B, 6220B
1,4-Dichlorobenzene	601, 602	624, 625		6210B, 6220B
Dichlorodifluoromethane	601	624, 1624		6210B, 6230B
1,1-Dichloroethane	601	624, 1624		6210B, 6230B
1,2-Dichloroethane	601	624, 1624		6210B, 6230B
1,1-Dichloroethene	601	624, 1624		6210B, 6230B
trans-1,2-Dichloroethene	601	624, 1624		6210B, 6230B
1,2-Dichloropropane	601	624, 1624		6210B, 6230B
cis-1,3-Dichloropropene	601	624, 1624		6210B, 6230B
trans-1,3-Dichloropropene	601	624, 1624		6210B, 6230B
Ethylbenzene	602	624, 1624		6210B, 6220B
Methylene chloride	601	624, 1624		6210B, 6230B
1,1,2,2-Tetrachloroethane	601	624, 1624		6210B, 6230B
Tetrachloroethene	601	624, 1624		6210B, 6230B
Toluene	602	624, 1624		6210B, 6220B
1,1,1-Trichloroethane	601	624, 1624		6210B, 6230B
1,1,2-Trichloroethane	601	624, 1624		6210B, 6230B
Trichloroethene	601	624, 1624		6210B, 6230B
Trichlorofluoromethane	601	624, 1624		6210B, 6230B
Vinyl chloride	601	624, 1624		6210B, 6230B
Semivolatile Organic Compounds (BNA)				
Acid Fraction				
4-Chloro-3-methylphenol	604	625, 1625		6410B, 6420B
2-Chlorophenol	604	625, 1625		6410B, 6420B

---

[11] *Standard Methods for the Examination of Water and Wastewater*, 18th Edition, 1993, APHA, AWWA, WEF Washngton, D.C.

Table 5-2. **Some Approved Methods for Analysis of NPDES Compliance Monitoring Organic Analytes.** *Continued*

Organic Parameters	EPA			SM[12]
	GC	GC/MS	HPLC	
Semivolatile Organic Compounds (BNA), *continued*				
Acid Fraction				
2,4-Dichlorophenol	604	625, 1625		6410B, 6420B
2,4-Dimethylphenol	604	625, 1625		6410B, 6420B
2,3-Dinitrophenol	604	625, 1625		6410B, 6420B
2-Methyl-2,4-dinitrophenol	604	625, 1625		6410B, 6420B
2-Nitrophenol	604	625, 1625		6410B, 6420B
4-Nitrophenol	604	625, 1625		6410B, 6420B
Pentachlorophenol	604	625, 1625		6410B, 6420B
Phenol	604	625, 1625		6410B, 6420B
2,4,6-Trichlorophenol	604	625, 1625		6410B, 6420B
Base/Neutral Fraction				
Acenaphthene	610	625, 1625	610	6410B, 6440B
Acenaphthylene	610	625, 1625	610	6410B, 6440B
Anthracene	610	625, 1625	610	6410B, 6440B
Benzidine		625, 1625	605	6410B
Benzo(a)anthracene	610	625, 1625	610	6410B, 6440B
Benzo(a)pyrene	610	625, 1625	610	6410B, 6440B
Benzo(b)fluoranthene	610	625, 1625	610	6410B, 6440B
Benzo(g,h,i)perylene	610	625, 1625	610	6410B, 6440B
Benzo(k)fluoranthene	610	625, 1625	610	6410B, 6440B
Benzyl butyl phthalate	606	625, 1625		6410B
Bis(2-chloroethoxy)methane	611	625, 1625		6410B
Bis(2-chloroethyl)ether	611	625, 1625		6410B
Bis(2-ethylhexyl)phthalate	606	625, 1625		6410B
4-Bromophenylphenyl ether	611	625, 1625		6410B
2-Chloronaphthalene	612	625, 1625		6410B
4-Chlorophenylphenylether	611	625, 1625		6410B
Chrysene	610	625, 1625	610	6410B, 6440B
Dibenzo(a,h)anthracene	610	625, 1625	610	6410B, 6440B
3,3'-Dichlorobenzidine		625, 1625	605	6410B
Diethyl phthalate	606	625, 1625		6410B
Dimethyl phthalate	606	625, 1625		6410B
Di-n-butyl phthalate	606	625, 1625		6410B
Di-n-octyl phthalate	606	625, 1625		6410B
2,4-Dinitrotoluene	609	625, 1625		6410B
2,6-Dinitrotoluene	609	625, 1625		6410B
Fluoranthene	610	625, 1625	610	6410B, 6440B
Fluorene	610	625, 1625	610	6410B, 6440B

---

[12] *Standard Methods for the Examination of Water and Wastewater*, 18th Edition, 1993, APHA, AWWA, WEF Washngton, D.C.

Table 5-2. **Some Approved Methods for Analysis of NPDES Compliance Monitoring Organic Analytes.** *Continued*

Organic Parameters	EPA			SM[13]
	GC	GC/MS	HPLC	
Semivolatile Organic Compounds (BNA), *continued*				
Base/Neutral Fraction				
Hexachlorobenzene	612	625, 1625		6410B
Hexachlorobutadiene	612	625, 1625		6410B
Hexachlorocyclopentadiene	612	625, 1625		6410B
Hexachloroethane	616	625, 1625		6410B
Indeno(1,2,3-cd)pyrene	610	625, 1625	610	6410B, 6440B
Isophorone	609	625, 1625		6410B
Naphthalene	610	625, 1625	610	6410B, 6440B
Nitrobenzene	609	625, 1625		6410B
N-Nitrosodimethylamine	607	625, 1625		6410B
N-Nitrosodi-n-propylamine	607	625, 1625		6410B
N-Nitrosodiphenylamine	607	625, 1625		6410B
2,2-Oxybis(1-chloropropane)	611	625, 1625		6410B
Phenanthrene	610	625, 1625	610	6410B, 6440B
Pyrene	610	625, 1625	610	6410B, 6440B
1,2,4-Trichlorobenzene	612	625, 1625		6410B
Pesticides/PCB				
PCB-1016	608	625		6410B, 6431B
PCB-1221	608	625		6410B, 6431B
PCB-1232	608	625		6410B, 6431B
PCB-1242	608	625		6410B, 6431B
PCB-1248	608	625		6410B, 6431B
PCB-1254	608	625		6410B, 6431B
PCB-1260	608	625		6410B, 6431B
Aldrin	608	625		6410B, 6630B
α-BHC	608	625		6410B, 6630B
β-BHC	608	625		6410B, 6630B
δBHC	608	625		6410B, 6630B
γBHC (Lindane)	608	625		6410B, 6630B
Chlordane	608	625		6410B, 6630B
4,4'-DDD	608	625		6410B, 6630B
4,4'-DDE	608	625		6410B, 6630B
4,4'-DDT	608	625		6410B, 6630B
Dieldrin	608	625		6410B, 6630B
Endosulfan I	608	625		6410B, 6630B
Endosulfan II	608	625		6410B, 6630B
Endosulfan sulfate	608	625		6410B, 6630B
Endrin	608	625		6410B, 6630B

---

[13] *Standard Methods for the Examination of Water and Wastewater*, 18th Edition, 1993, APHA, AWWA, WEF Washngton, D.C.

Table 5-2. **Some Approved Methods for Analysis of NPDES Compliance Monitoring Organic Analytes.** *Continued*

Organic Parameters	EPA			SM[14]
	GC	GC/MS	HPLC	
Pesticides/PCB				
Endrin aldehyde	608	625		6410B, 6630B
Heptachlor	608	625		6410B, 6630B
Heptachlor epoxide	608	625		6410B, 6630B
Toxaphene	608	625		6410B, 6630B

B. Data Validation Guidance

EPA does not require regular submission of extensive documentation of NPDES compliance monitoring results. The basic reporting approach includes the Discharge Monitoring Report (DMR, EPA Form 3320) submitted by the permitted facility to EPA or the authorized state. The DMR is a high level summary of the results of all the compliance monitoring analyses, providing a concentration or detection limit (for analytes not detected) for each pollutant listed in a permit. While some authorized states may require additional information, in total, the data do not begin to approach the level of detail typical of a CLP-type data package. However, the Form 3320 stipulates that the approving (signing) official certifies (takes legal responsiblity) that all analytical results reported on the Form were obtained in accordance with regulations. This responsibility serves as a motivation for the certifying officials to examine the data in some depth to establish in themselves some level of comfort that what they have just signed is not going to come back at them with serious legal repercussions (See Chapter 3 for an example.).

Unfortunately, there has been very little guidance from EPA or states regarding validation of NPDES compliance monitoring results. Two documents can be used to provide a basic framework for independent validation efforts. The first is the *NPDES Compliance Inspection Manual*, from the Office of Water Enforcement and Permits Division, dated May, 1988. Chapter Eight of the manual describes an approach to evaluating laboratory quality assurance programs and laboratory analysis techniques. The approach is relatively generic and focuses on verifying that the facilities, instrumentation, procedures, and documentation are in place to perform compliance monitoring. As written, the approach is best suited for an on-site evaluation of a permittee's laboratory facility, but it also describes the evaluation of contract laboratories performing analyses for the permittee. The end of the chapter includes a two-page checklist that may be employed for such as evaluation. The checklist includes "yes," "no," and "not applicable" answers regarding:

- A written QA manual

- The use of EPA-approved analytical methods and availability of copies of the methods in the lab

- Instrument calibration and maintenance

- Use and adequacy of laboratory QC procedures

---

[14] *Standard Methods for the Examination of Water and Wastewater*, 18th Edition, 1993, APHA, AWWA, WEF Washngton, D.C.

- Frequencies of duplicate analyses and matrix spike analyses

- Availability and quality of facilities, equipment, and reagents, such as reagent water, compressed gases, fume hoods, lighting, power, glassware, standards, written operating instructions and troubleshooting procedures

- laboratory precision, accuracy, and quality control procedures and records

- Data handling and reporting practices, including rounding, significant figures, reporting formats and units, laboratory notebooks, and record keeping practices

- Numbers of analysts and analyst training.

Obviously, while much of this information might be reviewed by a data validator from hard copy records, there are still substantial portions that could only be meaningfully confirmed during an on-site inspection. The discussion in the manual and the checklist focus on the laboratory's ability to follow a specific process, have the facilities, and produce and maintain the appropriate records. While a laboratory that meets all of these inspection criteria ought to be able to produce useful compliance monitoring results, the criteria offer no specific means of evaluating the results of an individual analysis. As with the SDWA laboratory certification concept, it *assumes* that the data are acceptable if the laboratory passes such as inspection.

The second useful guidance document from the Office of Water is *Guidance on Evaluation, Resolution, and Documentation of Analytical Problems Associated with Compliance Monitoring,* June, 1993, EPA 821/B/93/001. This document is called The "pumpkin book" due to the color of the cover in the original issue. This document was prepared in response to numerous reports of analytical difficulties associated with compliance monitoring requirements for the organic chemicals, plastics, and synthetic fibers (OCPSF) regulations, but contains a relatively comprehensive discussion of data validation that is applicable to any NPDES compliance monitoring scenario.

The approach to data validation described in that document is the one that EPA uses to validate data that it collects in developing an effluent guideline. The focus is on establishing the useability of the results relative to regulatory development. The difference between developing regulations and monitoring compliance with those regulations is that compliance monitoring seeks to prove the negative, that the sample has *not* violated a compliance limit, and in developing regulations, EPA attempts to demonstrate that a pollutant is present in the sample.

Validation of NPDES compliance monitoring data should address nine general areas:

- Purity and traceability of reference standards

- Number of calibration points

- Linearity of calibration

- Calibration verification

- Method Detection Limit (MDL)

- Initial demonstration of capability

- Analysis of blanks

- Recovery of analyte spikes into the sample matrix

- Analysis of QC check samples.

1. Purity and Traceability of Reference Standards

The accuracy of the analytical instrumentation must be established through the use of reference standards. EPA methods require that the standards used for calibration and other purposes be of known purity and traceable to a reliable reference source. While EPA and the National Institute for Standards and Technology (NIST, formerly NBS) have provided administered repositories for standards in the past, the current budgetary considerations at EPA have virtually eliminated such programs, and laboratories generally rely on commercial vendors for standards. Those commercially-available materials can generally be traced to reference standards maintained by either EPA or NIST, and virtually all vendors provide *some* documentation of the purity and traceability of the materials that they supply.

Given this situation, verifying the purity and traceability of a laboratory's standards is essentially a *pro forma* process. The necessary documentation is not generally provided with each data package, but should be maintained on file at the laboratory and be available to validators and auditors alike, upon request.

2. Number of Calibration Points

Although all analytical instruments require calibration using the standards discussed above, the number of standards that are required varies with the instrumentation. In general, instruments used for organic analyses under the 600 Series or 1600 Series methods require a minimum of three calibration standards. The concentrations of the standards may be specified in some methods and not in others. The lowest standard is generally at a concentration within five times the method detection limit (MDL), and the highest standard should be near the upper limit of the working range of the instrument.

Some of the methods for trace metals rely on a single-point calibration during routine analyses. The use of a single-point calibration is reasonable for such methods because the measurements depend on the absorption of light of specific wavelengths, and this absorption closely follows Lambert-Beer's Law, whereby absorption is directly proportional to concentration. However, even when a single point is used for routine calibration, it remains important to establish the upper end of the working range of the instrument through the analysis of additional standards.

The point in reviewing the number of calibration points is first to determine that an initial multipoint calibration was performed, thereby defining the working range of the instrument. The second step is to determine what the upper and lower limits of the range are, so that the validator can ensure that samples with analyte concentrations *above* that range have been appropriately diluted and reanalyzed. The diluted sample results need only apply to those analytes that were out of the calibration range in the initial analysis. It is acceptable to use data for different analytes from different levels of dilution within the same sample. The final step is to ensure that the calibration range includes the regulatory limit of concern for the samples, e.g., the NPDES permit limit for the pollutant.

If the validator cannot determine the number of points or their concentrations, then the data cannot be thoroughly validated and the validator must contact the laboratory to obtain the necessary information. If all of the calibration range is above the regulatory limit of concern, and the analyte is not detected, then the validator cannot verify that the laboratory could have detected the analyte at the regulatory limit and the results are not valid for monitoring compliance with such a limit.

3. Calibration Linearity

The calibration of an analytical instrument involves determining the relationship between the response of the instrument to the concentration or amount of an analyte introduced into the system. For many instruments and methods that involve the absorption of light by a solution, the relationship can be described by Lambert-Beer's Law and approximates a straight line. For some methods and instruments other calibration relationships may be more appropriate, including quadratic equations or higher order mathematical functions. To be a useful quantitative method, the instrument need only produce a unique result (concentration) for any given instrument response. However, given that many early analytical methods were based on Lambert-Beer's Law and the fact that linear models are easy for people to understand and simplify calculations, the use of a linear calibration is a common and convenient convention. Virtually all EPA analytical methods under CWA and other programs can be modelled by a linear relationship, if only over a relatively narrow concentration range.

The response factor (GC/MS methods) or calibration factor (GC, HPLC methods) is the ratio of the response of the instrument to the concentration (or amount) of analyte introduced into the instrument. The advantage of the linear calibration is that the response factor or calibration factor represents the slope of the calibration "curve," and is relatively constant, simplifying the calculations and the interpretation of the data.

All of the 600 and 1600 Series methods specify some criterion for determining the linearity of the calibration "curve." When this criterion is met, the calibration "curve" is sufficiently linear to permit the laboratory to use an average response factor or calibration factor, and it is assumed that the calibration "curve" is a straight line that passes through the zero/zero calibration point. Linearity is determined by calculating the RSD of the response factor or calibration factor for each analyte and comparing this RSD to the limit specified in the method. If the RSD does not exceed the specification, linearity is assumed.

In the 600 and 1600 Series methods, the linearity specification varies from method to method, depending on the quantitation technique. The typical limits on the RSD are:

- 15% for the gas chromatography (GC) and high performance liquid chromatography (HPLC) methods

- 35% for analytes determined by the internal standard technique in the gas chromatography/mass spectrometry (GC/MS) methods (e.g., 624, 625, 1624, and 1625)

If the calibration is not linear, as determined by the RSD of the response factor or calibration factor, the 600 and 1600 Series methods allow the analyst to "employ the entire calibration curve." While ill-defined, this often means that a regression line or other mathematical function may be employed to relate the instrument response to the concentration. At worst, it means that the calibration data have been plotted and the analyst "eyeballs" the concentration that corresponds to the instrument response.

For determination of nearly all of the organic analytes using the 600 and 1600 Series methods, the calibration curves are linear over a concentration range of 20-100 fold, depending on the detector being employed. Whatever calibration range is used, the laboratory must provide the RSD results by which one can judge linearity, even in instances where the laboratory is using a calibration curve. In instances where the laboratory employs a curve rather than an average response factor or calibration, the data reviewer should review each calibration point to assure that the response increases as the concentration increases. If it does not, the instrument is not operating properly, and the data are not considered valid. Ideally, the laboratory will provide the equation used to fit a non-linear curve and the validator should be able to independently calculate the results reported by the laboratory.

As noted earlier, the 200 Series methods for metals may involve a single-point calibration for ICP analyses and a three-point calibration for atomic absorption and graphite furnace analyses. As a result, there are no specific QC limits associated with the linearity of the calibration line.

If the calibration does not meet the linearity specifications of the method, and the laboratory used the response factor or calibration factor approach anyway, then the quantitative results for those analytes that did not meet the QC specifications are in question. It is not uncommon for a laboratory to have one or more compounds in a lengthy target compound list fail the QC specifications. If this occurs, the validator's job is to determine if there is any detrimental effect on the specific sample results. If, for instance, the analyte that fails the QC specification is *not* an analyte listed in a facility's NPDES permit, then there is no real concern relative to compliance monitoring. If the analyte is listed in the permit, but was reported as not detected, then the validator's job is to determine the likelihood that the calibration problem could have resulted in a false negative result. This would only be the case if the lowest calibration standard had a response much lower than expected *and* the regulatory limit for the analyte was near the concentration of that standard.

In cases where the purpose of the analysis is not compliance monitoring, but characterization of an effluent, it may even be useful to list some analytes with calibration problems as "detected" without a specific concentration result. This harks back to EPA's approach in developing the original priority pollutant list. Knowing that an analyte was detected in some wastewater may be more important in that case than the specific numerical result, and calibration problems rarely cause false *positive* results.

4. Calibration Verification

Calibration verification involves the analysis of a single standard, typically in the middle of the calibration range, at the beginning of each analytical shift. The concentration of each analyte in this standard is determined using the initial calibration data and is compared to specifications in the method. If the results are within the specifications, the laboratory is allowed to proceed with analysis without recalibrating and use the initial calibration data to quantify sample results.

Calibration verification differs in concept and practice from "continuing calibration" that is described in the CLP methods. In this latter technique, a standard is analyzed and new response factors or calibration factors are calculated on the basis of that analysis. If the new factors are close to the average from the initial calibration, all subsequent sample analyses are conducted using these "updated" response or calibration factors. The degree of "closeness" is generally measured as the percent difference between the old and new factors. The problem with "continuing calibration" is that it amounts to a daily single point calibration. Information about the behavior of the instrument at concentrations above and below that of this single standard can only be inferred from the initial multiple point calibration.

Specifications for calibration verification are often given as a percentage difference from the test concentration, and vary with the specific method, depending on the quantitation technique. For the 600 and 1600 Series GC and HPLC methods, the difference must be within ± 20%. For GC/MS methods such as 1624 and 1625, the acceptance criteria are given as ranges of concentration of each analyte, based on an interlaboratory study.

If the calibration cannot be verified, then the laboratory may either recalibrate the instrument, or prepare a fresh calibration verification standard and make a second attempt to verify calibration. If calibration cannot be verified with a fresh calibration standard, the instrument *must* be recalibrated. If calibration is not verified, subsequent data are not considered valid until the instrument is recalibrated.

In instances where the laboratory has employed some non-linear calibration relationship, there are no explicit acceptance criteria for calibration verification. While some laboratories still use a single-point verification and a percent difference criterion, that approach tells one very little about whether the shape of the calibration curve has remained sufficiently close to that of the initial calibration. The use of at least two verification standards would be a better approach, but again, no specifications are given in the CWA methods.

5. Method Detection Limits

While there are various approaches to specifying method sensitivity, the CWA methods were the first EPA methods to formalize the use of the method detection limit (MDL) concept that is based on the standard deviation of replicate analyses. The MDL procedure is specified in 40 CFR Part 136, Appendix B, and the citation there is used by other EPA Programs. In short, a laboratory prepares a minimum of seven aliquots of reagent water, spiking the analytes of interest at some approximation of the detection limit, analyzing all the aliquots, determining the mean concentration and the standard deviation of the concentration of each analyte, and multiplying the standard deviation by the Student's *t*-statistic for the number of replicates (3.143 for seven aliquots).

Determined in this fashion, the MDL is a snapshot of the method performance at the time that measurements were made. If repeated, the MDLs will most likely be different, though the differences are generally small. The MDL procedure is sensitive to differences in analysts and instruments as well.

Whatever faults may be ascribed to the MDL procedure, it does represent some demonstration of method performance and sensitivity in a given laboratory. While the CWA methods do not specify a frequency at which MDLs must be determined, a laboratory ought to be able to provide MDL data specific to the instrument(s) used to generate NPDES compliance monitoring data. The validator should make two specific checks of the MDL data if possible, First, verify that the reported MDLs are lower than the regulatory limits of concern for the analytes in the permit. Secondly, if the data for all the MDL replicates are provided, confirm that the calculations were performed correctly. A very common mistake is to use the wrong number of degrees of freedom to calculate the standard deviation or to choose Student's *t*-value. From a purely statistical point of view, when fewer than 30 replicate measurements are made, the number of degrees of freedom used to calculate the standard deviation is $n-1$, not n, where n is the total number of measurements.

Unfortunately, when health-based or risk-based permit limits are established in some permits, the permit limitations are actually below the detection capabilities of the CWA methods. In these instances, it is critical to check the MDLs reported by the laboratory and to consult the permit for the specific reporting practices that may be specified. For instance, in the case of 2,3,7,8-tetrachlorodibenzo-*p*-dioxin (2,3,7,8-TCDD), permit limits for some facilities are being established at the water-quality-based effluent limitation (WQBEL) of 13 parts per *quintillion* (ppqt), while the approved monitoring

only achieve a quantitation limit of ten parts per quadrillion (ppq), three
agnitude higher than the WQBEL. In these instances, the permits generally
icit information regarding how compliance will be monitored in the absence
capable of meeting the WQBEL. Why has this situation occurred? In part
evel of concern over dioxins and the desire by the regulators to be able to
WQBEL if a more sensitive method becomes available during the life of the
rmit.

6. Initial Demonstration of Capability

The quality control sections of the CWA methods specify that each laboratory wishing to
perform the method must make an initial demonstration of its capability to do so.
Sometimes called the initial precision and accuracy tests, or the start-up test, this
demonstration is accomplished through the analysis of four aliquots of reagents water
spiked with the analytes of interest at concentrations specified in the individual methods.
The mean concentration and standard deviation are calculated for each analyte and
compared to acceptance criteria in the methods.

Like the MDL, the initial demonstration is performed in reagent water, a matrix that
should provide the best results. Thus, the start-up test provides a slightly optimistic view
of laboratory capabilities. However, it is some baseline of laboratory performance, and it
is surprising how many laboratories have difficulties with the demonstration the first
time they try it for a method new to their laboratory.

It is also important to remember that if a change is made to a method, the start-up
test must be repeated with the change as an integral part of the method. Such changes
may involve alternative extraction, concentration, or cleanup processes, alternative GC
columns, GC conditions, or detectors, or other steps designed to address a particular
matrix problem. If the start-up test is not repeated when these steps are modified or
added, any data produced by the modified method are considered not valid.

Performing the start-up test "after the fact" is not acceptable, and may not be used to
validate data that have been considered not valid because the start-up test was not
performed.

Also like the MDL, the initial demonstration data are not generally provided with the
results for specific compliance monitoring results. They certainly should be on file in the
laboratory and available on request. The demonstration should be performed at least once
by each analyst in the laboratory for each method that the analyst will employ for routine
sample analyses. If the data cannot be provided, or the results indicate that the laboratory
did not meet the performance specifications of the particular method, then the validator
may need to dig much deeper to evaluate the compliance monitoring results.

7. Analysis of Blanks

The analysis of method blanks is an important requirement of the CWA methods.
Method blanks are required on a routine basis, when any part of the analytical process
has been changed and whenever contamination of the laboratory is suspected. The
methods require that a blank be prepared and analyzed with each batch of samples. The
size of a batch is generally defined as a maximum of 20 environmental samples started
through the analytical process within a period of time. It is common practice that each
day that a laboratory prepares samples, they will also prepare a blank, even if fewer than
20 samples are prepared. The purpose of analyzing a blank with each set of samples is to
determine the extent of possible contamination of the samples while in the laboratory. If
the blank is handled by the same analysts in the same way as the samples, and the blank

shows no contamination, then it is likely that the samples will not have been contaminated. Requiring that a blank be analyzed after the analytical process has been changed is consistent with requiring that the start-up test be repeated, because the change to the analytical process presents the possibility that samples can be contaminated by the use of the new procedures.

Contamination in the laboratory is a common problem, though there are many opinions on what constitutes contamination. In the CWA methods, *any* concentration of a compound above the detection limit of the method in question is a potential cause for concern. In reality, it is not unusual to find low levels of common laboratory solvents, phthalates, and other ubiquitous compounds in laboratory blanks. The problem is most critical for the analysis of volatile organic contaminants, where the solvents in use in other parts of the laboratory may limit the ultimate sensitivity of the volatile analysis. For trace metal methods, iron, zinc, copper, and mercury are often found in method blanks at levels that raise concern, and most metals will be found from time to time.

Controlling laboratory contamination is an important aspect of each laboratory's quality assurance plan. The laboratory should maintain records, typically in the form of control charts, of blank contaminants. These records should prompt corrective action by the laboratory, including re-analysis of any affected samples. Such control charts may be requested by the reviewer in evaluating sample results; however, they are not routinely submitted with sample data.

Unfortunately, by the time that the data are submitted, it is usually too late for corrective action. Therefore, the reviewer has several options in making use of the sample data. First, if a contaminant is present in a blank, but *not* present in a sample, then there is little need for concern about the sample result.

The second approach deals with instances where the blank contaminant is also reported in a sample. A useful rule of thumb for organic analytes is that:

- If the sample result is at least ten times that in the blank, then the likely contribution to the sample from the laboratory environment is at most 10%. Because most of the methods in question are no more accurate than that level, the possible contamination is negligible.

- If the sample result is at least five times but less than ten times the blank result, the compound is probably present in the sample, but the numerical result should be considered an upper limit of the true concentration

- If the sample result is below five times the level in the blank, there is no adequate means by which to judge whether or not the sample result is attributable to laboratory contamination. The results for that compound in that sample then become unacceptable for monitoring compliance.

There are two difficulties in evaluating sample results relative to blank contamination. First, the reviewer must be able to associate the samples with the correct blanks. For analysis of volatiles by purge-and-trap techniques, where no sample extraction is required, the blanks and samples are associated by the date and time of analysis, and the results of the blanks are specific to the instrument as well. For methods involving the extraction of organic compounds from the samples, the blanks and samples are primarily associated by the date on which they were *extracted*.

The second difficulty involves samples that have been diluted. The dilution of the sample with reagent water or the dilution of the extract with solvent represent additional potential sources of contamination that will not be reflected in the results for the blank unless the blank was similarly diluted. Therefore, in applying the ten-times rule, the concentration of the sample is compared to the blank result multiplied by the dilution factor of the sample or sample extract.

Some laboratories would have the reviewer believe that subtracting the concentration of the analyte in the blank from the concentration of the analyte in the sample is a reliable method of determining the true concentration of the analyte in the sample. Unfortunately, experience indicates that this practice is not reliable. Further, most methods specifically prohibit blank correction of the results, for example, in Sections 8.1.3 and 13.2 of Method 624. The obvious problem occurs when the blank concentration is higher than that in the sample, and subtraction would yield a negative concentration value. Using the ten-times rule above provides a more appropriate means of evaluating the results, and does not require that the reviewer alter the results reported by the laboratory.

As with most of the other aspects of data validation, if an analyte found in the blank is not of specific concern for the NPDES permit, then it may not warrant much attention from the validator, unless the purpose of the analysis was to provide broad survey results and not to monitor compliance.

8. Recoveries of Surrogates and Matrix Spike Compounds

The 600 Series methods require each sample be spiked with surrogate compounds to monitor the efficiency of the entire analytical process. These surrogates are usually isotopically-labeled or fluorinated analogs of the target analytes that are not expected to be found in environmental samples. The appropriate surrogates are listed in each method along with the spiking concentration. In addition, the 600 Series and the 200 Series methods describe the analysis of spiked samples to provide information on the accuracy of the determination of the target analytes. A matrix spike (MS) sample is a second aliquot of the original sample spiked with some or all of the target analytes prior to extraction and carried through the entire analytical process. The recovery of the spiked compound is used to assess the accuracy of the analysis. When a third aliquot of the sample is also spiked and analyzed, it constitutes a matrix spike duplicate (MSD). The measured concentrations of the spiked analytes are compared, and the relative percent difference (RPD) of the concentrations is a measure of the precision of the analytical process. Spiked samples are used to ensure that the analytes of interest are actually present in the samples (the accuracy and precision of "not detected" results cannot be calculated). Generally, the methods require that samples be spiked at a frequency of 5% (one out of every 20 field samples) or once per batch of samples started through the extraction process within a period of time. To be most useful, the spiking concentrations should be:

- At the regulatory limit for the analyte
- One to five times any background concentration of the analyte. This may require *a priori* knowledge of the background concentration, and hence, is not always accomplished
- At the default level specified in a particular method.

For the trace metals methods, spiking is useful to assess accuracy, and precision may be calculated from simple duplicate analyses, as the majority of the common metals will be present at some level in most samples. The spiking of the samples is performed both prior to—and after—the digestion of the sample, so that the efficiency of the entire process can be assessed. So-called "post-digestion spikes" are of value, as they can indicate problems due to both direct and re-combinatorial spectral interferences in the sample, which are independent of any digestion specific interferences. Again, the frequency for spiked samples is 5%.

The 600 and 200 Series methods generally provide QC acceptance criteria for matrix spike recoveries and RPDs. If the recovery of the matrix spike is within the limits specified in the method, then the method is judged to be applicable to that sample matrix. If, however, the recovery of the spike is not within the recovery range specified, either the method does not work on the sample, or the analytical process is out of control.

The evaluation of surrogate recoveries and matrix spike recoveries proceed in similar fashions. Surrogate recoveries are often expressed as percent recovery, i.e., the concentration found in the sample divided by the concentration that resulted from spiking, times 100. Some methods have surrogate recovery ranges that are based on interlaboratory validation studies, and data from a single laboratory should generally fall within these limits. Other methods use consensus limits. The latter are easily identified by the fact that they are nice round numbers, often equally distributed around 100%, such as 80-120% or 50-150%. The advantage of the consensus limits is that they are easy to work with for reviewers. The disadvantages include the fact that they are often not founded in the reality of real-world wastewater samples. When the limits are obviously based on a consensus, the validator may need to employ professional judgment to determine if falling outside of such limits represents a real performance problem or an overly optimistic consensus. The validator may need to request that the laboratory submit control charts or other internal records that demonstrate the typical performance that the laboratory can achieve in real-world wastewater matrices.

If surrogate recoveries are below the acceptance limits, the efficiency of the extraction and analysis may be subject to question, and the target analyte results may be biased low. For methods that employ multiple surrogates, it is not often possible to associate specific target analytes with each surrogate compound. Thus, it is not always possible to make much use of compliance monitoring results with low surrogate recoveries. As a result, most of the 600 Series methods specify that samples with low surrogate recoveries be re-extracted and re-analyzed, in an attempt to determine if the surrogate recoveries can be improved. If a re-extraction is not performed or the recoveries did not improve, then the sample results may be considered as minimum concentrations. If these minimum concentrations exceed any permit limits, then it is highly likely that the concentrations in a sample with acceptable surrogate recovery would also have exceeded the limits.

If all the surrogate recoveries are low, then perhaps a dilution of the original sample should have been attempted prior to the re-extraction. Some methods that use multiple surrogates also employ a pH change during extraction. Thus, if the base/neutral surrogates in Method 625 are low but the acid surrogates are not, then the acid fraction data may be usable as is while the base/neutral results may be minimum values.

There are several possible causes for surrogate recoveries above the acceptance limits. These include spiking errors and calculation errors, which will often affect all of the surrogates similarly, and in GC methods with non-MS detectors, co-elution of an interference or a target analyte with one or more surrogates that increases the area of the peak thought to represent the surrogate. Errors associated with internal standard quantitation can also increase the surrogate recoveries in those methods that employ internal standards.

To evaluate the matrix spike results, the data reviewer must determine that:

- The unspiked sample has been analyzed.
- The spiked sample has been analyzed.
- The recovery of the spike is within the range specified.

In instances where matrix spike recoveries are not within the specifications, it still may be possible to use the sample results for compliance monitoring purposes. In particular, if the recovery of the spiked compound is *above* the method specifications *and* the compound is *not* detected in the sample analysis, it is unlikely that the compound is present in the sample. This is because the factors that caused the analysis to overestimate the concentration in the spiked sample would not likely have resulted in an *under*estimate in the unspiked sample. For samples in which the compound *is* detected, but the matrix spike recovery is above the method specifications, the concentration reported in the unspiked sample is likely an upper limit of the true concentration.

As with low surrogate recoveries, if the analyte concentration exceeds the permit limit, and the matrix spike recovery is low, it is likely that the actual analyte concentration would also have exceeded the limit had the matrix spike recovery been within the acceptance limits. In such situations, EPA or a state might use the data to demonstrate a permit violation, despite the low matrix spike recovery.

In an ideal situation, the analytes spiked into the MS aliquot will be those that are regulated under the wastewater permit. When a large number of analytes are regulated, this may not always be possible. Likewise, if an outside laboratory does not ask the permittee which analytes are regulated, then the matrix spike compounds may not reflect the regulated analytes or their regulatory limits. Thus, the data validator must use professional judgment to associate analytes with matrix spike compounds based on chemical similarities, if any use is to be made of sample results with poor matrix spike recoveries.

Many of the 1600 Series wastewater methods employ some form of isotope dilution quantitation, whereby labeled analogs of the target analytes are spiked into the original sample prior to extraction. The results of these labeled compounds are used to correct the results for their unlabeled counterparts for the inherent losses during the analytical process. The result is that the sample data are generally more accurate and precise than when a similar 600 Series method is employed. In addition, because the labeled analog recoveries can be measured relative to an internal standard that is added to the sample extract just prior to injection into the GC/MS, each sample serves as its own matrix spike analysis. Thus, the isotope dilution methods do not require the use of surrogates or separate matrix spike aliquots. These methods contain acceptance criteria for the recovery of each labeled compound. These ranges are often quite wide, and are generally derived from interlaboratory method validation studies. Because the results for the target analytes are recovery-corrected, it is often easier to use them even when the labeled analog recovery is below the acceptance limits. This is because the recovery correction accounts for much of the difference already.

9. QC Check Samples

The 600 and 200 Series methods often specify the analysis of a QC check sample. The QC check sample is generally prepared in reagent water to avoid problems with the sample matrix. The purpose of this sample is to separate issues of method performance from issues of laboratory performance, and it is used in conjunction with the matrix spike analyses when the matrix spike results are outside of the acceptance criteria.

The laboratory should obtain and analyze a QC check sample from an external source. If such samples are not available, the laboratory should prepare and analyze a spike of the analytes in reagent water. This spiked reagent water aliquot is often called a laboratory control sample (LCS). If the results for the QC check sample are not within the range specified, then the analytical system must be repaired and the sample and spiked sample analyses repeated. If the recovery of this spike is within the range specified, then the analytical process is judged to be in control. However, the results of the sample analysis cannot be accepted for regulatory compliance purposes because the matrix spike results indicate that the method is not applicable to the sample.

10. Other QC Criteria

Many of the 1600 Series and 600 Series methods discuss "statements of data quality" that should be generated by the laboratory on a routine basis. These statements are derived from spiked sample analyses, and estimate a 95% confidence interval around the mean recovery of each spiked analyte. The methods specify that such statements of data quality be updated after every five spiked sample analyses.

The data are rarely provided with individual sample results, and while they may be useful, there are other approaches to quality control, including control charting, that may be valuable to the laboratory and the reviewer. From a practical standpoint, the statements of data quality, control charts, or other internal QC checks may only need to be requested from the laboratory when the sample-specific QC data indicate serious problems with the laboratory or when irreplaceable samples must be utilized to support a decision.

C. Method Compliance Issues

There are two opposing forces in existence for any samples analyzed under compliance monitoring requirements of NPDES permits. The first is the legal issue of exact method compliance, which was described in Chapter 3. The second force is the requirement implicit in most of the methods for the laboratory to demonstrate that they can successfully determine the permitted target analytes at the regulatory level in the sample. The implicit nature of the second force lies in the method-specified acceptance ranges for recoveries of regulatory level matrix spikes performed on each sample source each month.

Many times the sample is not amenable to providing acceptable matrix spike recoveries using the specified procedure in the method. Most of the methods will include specific alternate techniques that the analyst may employ to successfully analyze the sample. Examples of these include, the use of continuous liquid-liquid extractors rather than separatory funnels in the sample preparation of Method 625, the use of calibration plots instead of average response factor for calibration of GC/MS instruments, and the use of additional internal standards and/or surrogates in Methods 624 and 625. Exercising these choices is a part of the method and compliance is still maintained.

Another aspect of this problem is that analytical techniques and instruments are constantly evolving, with new and improved procedures being frequently introduced. The majority of the EPA wastewater methods, particularly the organic methods (600 series), have not been reviewed or revised since 1983. That was an eternity ago as far as the current technological state of analysis is concerned. EPA recently published a proposed regulation that will drop from approval many out-dated and technically inferior methods[15]. Final rule publication has not been made at the time of this writing; however, the methods most in need of revision, the organic methods, were not included in the proposed deletion list.

On occasion, a sample will arrive at the laboratory that is impossible to analyze within the confines of the method-specified alternative procedures. New techniques may make the analysis possible, but their application is not compliant with the method. EPA has a specific protocol in place to allow use of alternate testing methods. This involves first, preparation, by the requesting laboratory, of reams of comparative data concerning the performance of the approved method and the proposed alternate test procedure covering all aspects of quality control. Second, the data package is submitted for approval to either the state NPDES permitting agency, or to the local EPA Regional Office. Either of these approving authorities will issue to the requesting laboratory a formal written approval of the alternate test procedure if it is acceptable. The laboratory that made the application is then able to use the alternate test procedure for compliance monitoring. But, the approval is limited to that single laboratory. Without specific written approval, other labs using the alternate test procedure are performing non-compliant analyses. Further, what is approved as an alternate test procedure in one state or EPA Region may be specifically disallowed in another state or EPA Region[16].

D. Specific Method Examples

1. Volatile Organic Compounds (VOC) by Method 624

Method 624 is a purge and trap GC/MS procedure for determination of the identification and amount of volatile organic contaminants in wastewater for NPDES permit compliance monitoring. The most important asset of the method is the generation of the mass spectrum as an aid to correct identification of calibrated target analytes. Misidentifications of random materials in the sample as target analytes are very rare, thus false positives are minimal with this technique. The downside is that it takes highly trained and very skillful instrument operators and data interpreters to perform the analysis and meet all the method specifications.

1.1 Initial Demonstration of Ability

The initial demonstration of ability consists of analyzing four repetitions of a test solution that contains all the target analytes at a concentration of 20 µg/L each. The mean recovery (%R) and relative standard deviation (RSD) of the results for each analyte is computed. Acceptable results will meet the criteria listed in Table 5 of Method 624. This is a one-time test for each instrument operator. A copy of the raw data and a summary of the results should be placed in the operator's training file.

---

[15] Guidelines establishing test procedures for the analysis of pollutants: New Methods; Proposed Rule. *Federal Register*, Vol. 60, No. 201, pp 53987-54006, Wednesday, 18 October, 1995.

[16] This was made abundantly clear in a recent report to the Ranking Minority Member Committee on Environment and Public Works, Max S. Baucus, U.S. Senate, by the G.A.O. *Water Pollution: Differences among the States in issuing permits limiting the discharge of pollutants*. USGAO, GAO/RCED-96-42, January, 1996. Another example revolves around pre-promulgation approval of Method 1664. EPA Region IV allowed any laboratory that so wished, to use the new protocol, while Region VI required each laboratory to individually petition the Region for permission.

1.2 MDL Determinations

The MDL is performed and calculated in compliance with 40 CFR 136, Appendix B. The replicates within the MDL study may be performed over several days rather than all in one day. An MDL should be performed on each instrument by each operator at least once a year. If there are changes in the instrumentation, a new MDL needs to be performed.

It is important to verify that a proper MDL study has been performed. Check the equation for standard deviation used for the MDL calculation to insure "n-1" has been used rather than "n" in the denominator. Also check that the correct Student's t-value has been used.

The calculated MDL should be checked against the regulatory limit for each analyte. If the MDL is at—or higher than—the regulatory limit, then no data concerning that analyte that indicate that it is present in the samples at less than the regulatory limit are acceptable. In many instances the regulatory authority will interpret the result of a reported non-detect of the target analyte with a detection limit above the effluent limit as evidence of a permit violation.

MDLs performed on reagent water may not be very applicable to the actual samples. For particularly intractable samples, it is probably worthwhile to perform an MDL in the sample itself. If the permittee is submitting an application to a regulatory agency for a variance on either permit regulatory levels or monitoring requirements, inclusion of a sample-specific MDL study can go far toward assuring approval of the variance.

1.3 Initial Calibration Requirements

Initial calibration uses the internal standard technique. A minimum of three calibration standards must be used with one near, but above the MDL. The calculation can either be performed using the average response factor (Rf) or a plot of the ratio of the area of the analyte to the area of the internal standard (A_{TA}/A_{IS}) plotted against the calculated Rf. If the average Rf is used, the %RSD of the individual Rf for the calibration standards must be less than 35%.

1.4 Continuing Calibration and Tuning Frequency and Acceptance Criteria

Each day, prior to analysis of samples or calibration, 50 ng 4-bromofluorobenzene (BFB) is either directly injected or purged into the GC/MS and a mass spectrum acquired. The criteria that the tune check must meet are presented in Table 5-3. These criteria must be met every day of operation.

Table 5-3.   Acceptance Criteria for BFB Daily Tune Check in Method 624.

m/z	Acceptance criteria
50	15-40% of mass 95
75	30-60% of mass 95
95	100%
96	5-9% of mass 95
173	<2% of mass 174
174	>50% of mass 95
175	5-9% of mass 174
176	>95 but <101% of mass 174
177	5-9% of mass 176

Continuing calibration consists of analysis of the quality control check standard, with each analyte of interest at 20 µg/L, at the beginning of each day. The amount of each analyte in the solution is calculated and must be within the ranges listed in Table 5 of Method 624. If a compound of interest fails to meet the acceptance criteria on repeat analysis of a check standard, the instrument must be recalibrated. Based on the equation used for the calculation of the amount of analyte in the sample:

$$\text{Amount µg/L} = \frac{\text{Area}_{sample} \times \text{Amount}_{int.\ Std.} \times 1000}{\text{Area}_{Int.\ Std.} \times Rf \times V}$$

where: Area_{sample} is the area of the quantitation ion of the target analyte.
$\text{Amount}_{int.\ Std.}$ is the amount of the internal standard added to the sample in µg.
$\text{Area}_{Int.\ Std.}$ is the area of the quantitation ion of the internal standard.
Rf is the original Rf generated in the initial calibration.
V is the volume of the sample in mL.

If the daily recovery of the analyte in the continuing calibration is significantly larger than 20 µg/L, then falsely high amounts of analyte in the sample will be calculated. Analytes reported as not detected are probably usable. However, analytes reported as greater than the MDL or the regulatory limit may, in fact, be lower than the MDL or the regulatory limit, and a false positive situation exists.

When the daily recovery of the analyte is significantly lower than 20 µg/L, the amount of target analytes reported in the sample is going to be an underestimation. Analytes reported as not-detected may, in fact, be in the sample. Analytes reported as close in amount to the MDL may if fact exceed the MDL, a false negative situation. However, analytes reported as greater than the regulatory limit really do exceed the regulatory limit.

1.5 Sample Collection, Preservation and Handling Procedures

Samples collected for VOC analysis must be dechlorinated if residual chlorine is present. The appropriate reagent is sodium thiosulfate. After dechlorination, the VOA vial is closed so as to have zero headspace (no bubbles). If aromatic analytes are of interest the sample is acidified to pH about 2 with 1+1 hydrochloric acid. The sample is stored on ice or refrigerated until analysis. Holding time is 14 days from the moment of sample collection.

Samples incorrectly sampled, preserved, stored, or, if holding times are exceeded, are not acceptable for compliance monitoring. The source must be resampled.

1.6 Sample Batches and Blanks

A sample batch or sample set is defined in Method 624 as the number of samples processed within a month, not to exceed 20 samples. On each day that analysis is performed, a reagent blank must be analyzed, which is used to access system contamination. In light of the purpose of the blank, if two or more instruments are used to process the samples, then it follows that a blank must be performed on each instrument.

If target analyte contamination is found in the blank, analysis is to cease until the source of the contamination is found and corrected. Another blank must be analyzed to verify that the problem is corrected. Blank results are never subtracted from target analyte amounts found in samples.

When blanks are contaminated, data may still be usable if the levels of the target analytes found in the samples are less than the regulatory limit or not-detected. However, when blank contamination is substantial, results of analysis that are less than ten times the amount of contamination in the blank and still exceed the regulatory limit, are not reliable and may, in fact, be a false positive.

Field blanks (trip blanks) in duplicate are prepared in the laboratory and accompany the sample containers to the sampling location and then back to the laboratory. They are analyzed when "hits" are found in the associated samples to access possible contamination of the samples arising during the transport and sampling events.

1.7 Laboratory Control Samples

Within Method 624 the term Quality Control (QC) check sample is used to convey the same idea and procedure as what has been previously defined in this book as the laboratory control sample (LCS). This sample, which contains the target analytes at 20 µg/L each, is used to check the calibration on a daily basis and as a back-up analysis when matrix spiked samples fail to meet the acceptance limits in Table 5 of Method 624. The source of the QC check standard should be different than that of the calibration standards.

High recoveries of the LCS relate directly to falsely high reported values of detected analytes in samples. For those analytes not detected in the sample or reported as less than the regulatory limit, the data are usable in the sense that the regulatory limit has, in actuality, not been exceeded. However, for analytes reported as greater than the regulatory limit, there is a strong possibility that a false positive has been generated, and the data are not reliable.

Low recoveries in the LCS means that target analytes are reported as lower than they actually are in the sample. Values for analytes reported as larger than the regulatory limit reflect actual amounts in the sample that exceed the regulatory limit. However, values reported as lower than the regulatory limit or not detected may, in fact, be present in greater amounts in the samples, and the data are unreliable.

1.8 Matrix Spikes

Matrix spikes (MS) are the primary indication that successful analysis of the compliance monitoring parameters is achieved on a regular basis. Matrix spikes must be performed for each sampling point at a rate of 5% of the samples analyzed from the site or at least one per month, whichever is more frequent. The matrix spike level depends on the background level of the target analyte in the sample and the regulatory limit for the analyte. The level of the matrix spike should be at the regulatory limit or one-to-five-times higher than the background level in the sample, whichever is greater. If there is no regulatory limit, a level of 20 µg/L or one-to-five-times higher than the background level, whichever is greater, is appropriate. Recoveries of the matrix spike are calculated and compared to the acceptance limits in Table 5 of Method 624. If recoveries are outside the criteria, a QC check sample is immediately analyzed to verify that the analytical system is in control.

High recoveries of the MS relate directly to falsely high reported values of detected analytes in samples. For those analytes, that are not detected in the sample or are reported as less than the regulatory limit, the data are usable in the sense that the regulatory limit has, in actuality, not been exceeded. However, for analytes reported as greater than the regulatory limit, there is a strong possibility that a false positive has been generated, and the data are not reliable.

Low recoveries in the MS means that target analytes are reported as lower than they actually are in the sample. Values for analytes reported as larger than the regulatory limit, reflect actual amounts in the sample that exceed the regulatory limit. However, values reported as lower than the regulatory limit or not detected may, in fact, be present in greater amounts in the samples and the data are unreliable.

1.9 Replicate Analysis

Replicates are not specifically addressed in Method 624. Precision is evaluated based on repeated measurements of the matrix spikes and QC check standards as results are collected over time. Replicates are a desirable quality control that may be utilized by the laboratory.

1.10 Internal Standard and Surrogate Recoveries

The Method states that a minimum of three internal standards and three surrogate compounds from those suggested in Table 5-4 are to be used in the analysis. Additional surrogates and internal standards beyond these suggested compounds may be used. Surrogates are calibrated just like target analytes at a minimum of three concentration levels.

Table 5-4.   Suggested Surrogates and Internal Standards of Method 624.

Benzene-D_6	4-Bromofluorobenzene	1,2-Dichloroethane-D_4
1,4-Difluorobenzene	Ethylbenzene-D_5	Ethylbenzene-D_{10}
Fluorobenzene	Pentafluorobenzene	Bromochloromethane
2-Bromo-1-chloropropane	1,4-Dichlorobutane	

The area counts of the internal standards should be monitored on a per-sample basis to determine possible matrix effects arising from the sample. Abrupt changes in area counts are indicative of either instrument failure or matrix effect. The laboratory should develop internal guidelines for evaluation of internal standard areas with an indication of when internal standard areas are out of control, and major maintenance should be performed. Suggested ranges are a factor of two (50% to 200%) based on the daily calibration check. Low area counts for the internal standards translates into artificially high reported values for target analytes in the samples. Compounds that are not detected in the sample or compounds reported as less than the regulatory limit really do not exceed these limits, and the results are reliable. However, target analytes reported from the analysis as above the regulatory limit may, in actuality, be less than the regulatory limit. High area counts for the internal standards result in falsely low values for target analytes. Any reported value for an analyte is an estimate when aberrations in the internal standards occur.

The laboratory must generate warning and control limits for surrogate recoveries as part of the control charting process. The surrogate recoveries obtained during analysis of the sample are compared against the laboratory derived acceptance limits. Low surrogate recoveries are an indication of low target analyte recoveries. Target analytes reported as not detected in the sample or detected—but less than the regulatory limit—may, in actuality, be present in larger amounts than reported. Target analytes reported as exceeding the regulatory limit really are present above the regulatory limit. High surrogate recoveries suggest there may be problems with the internal standard areas.

1.11 Target Analyte Identification

Target analytes must elute from the column (retention time) within ±30 seconds of authentic standards. For each candidate target analyte the three characteristic ions must maximize within one scan of each other. There must be a match of the abundance of the three characteristics ions within ±20% between the library (reference or user generated) spectrum of the target analyte and the spectrum obtained for the analyte in the sample.

2. Semivolatile Organic Compounds by Method 625

Method 625 involves a sample preparation to isolate target analytes from the water matrix through extraction with an organic solvent (methylene chloride) followed by analysis with GC-MS for identification and quantitation of target analyte semivolatile organic contaminants in effluent wastewater. The most important asset of the method is the generation of the mass spectrum as an aid to correct identification of calibrated target analytes. Misidentifications of random materials in the sample as regulated analytes are very rare, thus false positives are minimal with this technique. The downside is that it takes highly trained and very skillful sample preparation chemists, instrument operators and data interpreters to perform the analysis and meet all the method specifications.

2.1. Initial Demonstration of Ability

The initial demonstration of ability consists of analyzing four repetitions of a test solution that contains all the target analytes at a concentration of 100 µg/L each. The mean recovery (%R) and relative standard deviation (RSD) of the results for each analyte is computed. Acceptable results will meet the criteria listed in Table 6 of Method 625. This is a one-time test for each instrument operator. A copy of the raw data and a summary of the results should be placed in the operator's training file.

2.2 MDL Determinations

The MDL is performed and calculated in compliance with 40 CFR 136, Appendix B. The replicates within the MDL study may be performed over several days rather than all in one day. An MDL should be performed on each instrument by each operator at least once a year. If there are changes in the instrumentation, a new MDL needs to be performed.

It is important to verify that a proper MDL study has been performed. Check the equation for standard deviation used for the MDL calculation to insure "n-1" has been used rather than "n" in the denominator. Also check that the correct Student's t-value has been used.

The calculated MDL should be checked against the regulatory limit for each analyte. If the MDL is at—or higher than—the regulatory limit, then no data concerning that analyte, which indicate that it is present in the samples at less than the regulatory limit, are acceptable. In many instances the regulatory authority will interpret the result of a reported non-detect of the target analyte with a detection limit above the effluent limit as evidence of a permit violation.

MDLs performed on reagent water may not be very applicable to the actual samples. For particularly intractable samples, it is probably worthwhile to perform an MDL in the sample itself. If the permittee is submitting an application to a regulatory agency for a variance on either permit regulatory levels or monitoring requirements, inclusion of a sample-specific MDL study can go far toward assuring approval of the variance.

2.3 Initial Calibration Requirements

A minimum three-point initial calibration is required in Method 625. One of the calibration levels must be near but above the MDL, with the rest of the standard concentrations defining the calibrated range. An internal standard calibration using average response factors (Rf) of the characteristic quantitation ion of the internal standards and the target analyte is acceptable if the %RSD of the individual response factors for a target analyte is less than 35%. An alternate to the average Rf procedure is to prepare a plot of area of the target analyte quantitation ion to area of the internal standard quantitation ion (A_{TA}/A_{IS}) against Rf. A regression equation may be used to describe the calibration curve.

2.4 Continuing Calibration Frequency and Acceptance Criteria

On a daily basis 50 ng decafluorotriphenylphosphine (DFTPP) is injected and a mass spectrum acquired. The criteria that the tune check must meet are presented in Table 5-5. These criteria must be met every day of operation.

Table 5-5. **Acceptance Criteria for DFTPP Daily Tune Check in Method 625.**

m/z	Acceptance criteria
51	30-60% of base peak
68	<2% of mass 69
70	<2% of mass 69
127	40-60% of base peak
197	<1% of mass 198
198	Base peak
199	5-9% of mass 198
275	10-30% of base peak
365	>1% of base peak
441	Present and < 443
442	>40% of 198
443	17-23% of 442

System performance is also evaluated during the tune verification. It consists of tailing factor calculations of 100 ng benzidine for the base/neutral fraction analysis and 50 ng pentachlorophenol for the acid fraction analysis. The benzidine tailing factor must be less than 3.0, and the pentachlorophenol value < 5.0. If these evaluations can not be passed, the analyst is instructed to correct the situation.

Continuing calibration verification consists of analysis of one of the calibration solutions at the beginning of each day. The Rf or amount of each analyte in the solution is calculated and must be within a factor of ±20% of the average Rf generated in the initial calibration or ±20% of the true value of the analyte in the calibration check solution.

Based on the equation used for the calculation of the amount of analyte in the sample:

$$\text{Amount } \mu g/L = \frac{\text{Area}_{sample} \times \text{Amount}_{int.\ Std.} \times 1000}{\text{Area}_{Int.\ Std.} \times Rf \times V}$$

where: Area$_{sample}$ is the area of the quantitation ion of the target analyte.
Amount$_{int. Std.}$ is the amount of the internal standard added to the sample in μg.
Area$_{Int. Std.}$ is the area of the quantitation ion of the internal standard.
Rf is the original Rf generated in the initial calibration.
V is the volume of the initial sample in mL.

If the daily Rf generated in the continuing calibration is significantly larger (>20%) than the RF from the initial calibration, then falsely high amounts of analyte in the sample will be calculated. Analytes reported as lower than the regulatory limit or not detected are probably usable. However, analytes reported as greater than the regulatory limit may, in fact, be lower than the regulatory limit, and a false positive situation exists.

When the daily Rf is significantly lower (more than 20%) than the Rf from the initial calibration, the amount of target analytes reported in the sample is going to be an underestimation. Analytes reported as not-detected may, in fact, be in the sample. Analytes reported as close in amount to the regulatory limit may, in fact, exceed the regulatory limit, a false negative situation. However, analytes reported as greater than the regulatory limit really do exceed the regulatory limit.

2.5 Sample Collection, Preservation and Handling Procedures

Samples of one liter in volume are collected in glass containers with a Teflon® cap liner. If residual chlorine is present it is removed by addition of 80 mg sodium thiosulfate. Samples are then held at 4°C until sample extraction. Maximum holding time from sampling to extraction is 7 days. Once the sample extract is prepared it may be stored refrigerated for up to 40 days before instrument analysis.

2.6 Sample Preparation Procedures

Sample preparation in Method 625 is a liquid-liquid extraction using either separatory funnel or continuous liquid-liquid extraction glassware. The procedure involves addition of the surrogate solution to 1 L of sample, pH adjustment to pH >12 with sodium hydroxide solution and extraction with methylene chloride. This fraction is termed the base/neutral fraction. The pH of the sample is next adjusted with sulfuric acid to pH >2 and again extracted with methylene chloride. The second extract is termed the acid fraction. The extracts are not to be mixed together, and must be analyzed separately. The extracts are individually concentrated to no less than 1.0 mL, internal standards added, and the extracts analyzed by GC/MS.

The cleanliness and efficiency of the sample processing is assessed by daily performance of blanks. Phthalate contamination is of great concern due to frequent findings of the material in many reagents and laboratory apparatus, particularly plasticware. Plasticware may be used if it is proven free of contamination through analysis of methylene chloride rinses.

2.7 Blanks

Sample preparation blanks and field blanks are performed with every set of 20 or fewer samples processed within a one-month period. Blanks must be examined closely for phthalate and other laboratory created contamination. Blank results are never subtracted from analyte results in samples. If blank contamination is found, samples need to be closely examined for the same contaminants. If the contaminants are not detected in the samples, or if they are found in the samples, but are less than the regulatory limit, the data are probably usable. Also, if the contaminants are found in the samples at significantly higher concentration (>ten times) than the amount in the blank, the results may be usable. However, when the blank and sample results are within a factor of ten of each other, laboratory contamination is the only appropriate conclusion, and the sample results are unusable.

Field blanks are used to monitor the sample acquisition process. If samples are found to have non-detected levels of target analytes, the field blank is not of much use. However, when target analytes are detected in the samples, the field blanks should be examined to see if the analytes are artifacts of the sampling procedure or if they are indicative of contamination in the sample source.

2.8 Laboratory Control Samples

Method 625 refers to quality control (QC) check standards as fulfilling the same purpose as laboratory control samples (LCS). These quality control samples are of the same composition as those used in the initial demonstration of ability (Section 2.1), *i.e.* 100 µg/L of each target analyte. They are processed exactly like samples every time a matrix spike sample is prepared. This translates to a rate of once each group of up to 20 samples prepared within a month. The QC check sample is used to verify that the analytical system is in control whenever a failing result is obtained on a matrix spike sample.

The results on the LCS are evaluated as individual target analyte recoveries with the acceptance limits given in Table 6 of Method 625. Control charts are to be maintained on the recoveries of the QC check standards and the matrix spike samples with precision evaluated over time as %RSD.

High recoveries of the QC check standard relate directly to falsely high reported values of detected analytes in samples. For those analytes not detected in the sample or are reported as less than the regulatory limit, the sample data are usable in the sense that the regulatory limit has, in actuality, not been exceeded. However, for analytes reported as greater than the regulatory limit, there is a strong possibility that a false positive has been generated, and the data are not reliable.

Low recoveries in the LCS means that target analytes are reported as lower than they actually are in the sample. Values for analytes reported as larger than the regulatory limit, reflect actual amounts in the sample that exceed the regulatory limit. However, values reported as lower than the regulatory limit or not detected may, in fact, be present in greater amounts in the samples, and the data are unreliable.

2.9 Matrix Spikes

Matrix spikes are the primary assessment of the laboratory's ability to analyze the sample for the regulated compounds at the regulatory level. The matrix spike must be tailored to the individual permit for the sample. The matrix spike is prepared by adding each target analyte to the sample at either the regulatory limit or at one-to-five-times the background concentration of the target analyte in the sample, whichever is the higher value. If there is no set regulatory limit, the addition of target analyte is made at 100 µg/L or at one to five times the background concentration of the target analyte in the sample, whichever is the higher value. Matrix spikes are performed at a rate of one per 20 samples processed in a one month period. Acceptance criteria that must be met are listed in Table 6 of Method 625.

When matrix spike recoveries are outside the acceptance limits, and the LCS recoveries are acceptable, this is an indication of matrix effects from the sampling source, and the evaluation should be documented. The sample results can be interpreted similar to those presented in the preceding discussion (Section 2.8).

2.10 Replicate Analysis

Replicate analysis is not expressly addressed as a required quality control in Method 625. It still makes good analytical sense for the laboratory to perform sample, matrix spike, and laboratory control sample duplicates.

2.11 Internal Standard and Surrogate Recoveries

The Method states that a minimum of three internal standards and three surrogate compounds from those suggested in Table 5-6 are to be used in the analysis. Additional surrogates and internal standards beyond these suggested compounds may be used. Surrogates are calibrated just like target analytes at a minimum of three concentration levels.

Table 5-6. Suggested Surrogates and Internal Standards of Method 625.

Base/Neutral Fraction		
Aniline-D_5	Anthracene-D_{10}	Benzo(a)anthracene-D_{12}
4,4'-Dibromobiphenyl	4,4'-Dibromooctafluorobiphenyl	Decafluorobiphenyl
2,2'-Difluorobiphenyl	4-Fluoroaniline	1-Fluoronaphthalene
2-Fluoronaphthalene	Naphthalene-D_8	Nitrobenzene-D_5
Pentafluorobiphenyl	Phenanthrene-D_{10}	Pyridine-D_5
Acid Fraction		
2-Fluorophenol	Pentafluorophenol	Phenol-D_5
	Perfluoro-2-methylphenol	

The area counts of the internal standards should be monitored on a per-sample basis to determine possible matrix effects arising from the sample. Abrupt changes in area counts are indicative of either instrument failure or matrix effect. The laboratory should develop internal guidelines for evaluation of internal standard areas with an indication of when internal standard areas are out of control, and major maintenance should be performed. Suggested ranges are a factor of two (50% to 200%) based on the daily calibration check. Low area counts for the internal standards translates into artificially high reported values for target analytes in the samples. Compounds that are not-detected in the sample or compounds reported as less than the regulatory limit really do not exceed these limits, and the results are reliable. However, target analytes reported from the analysis as above the regulatory limit may, in actuality, be less than the regulatory limit. High area counts for the internal standards result in falsely low values for target analytes. Any reported value for an analyte is an estimate when aberrations in the internal standards occur.

The laboratory must generate warning and control limits for surrogate recoveries as part of the control charting process. The surrogate recoveries obtained during analysis of the sample are compared against the laboratory derived acceptance limits. Low surrogate recoveries are an indication of low target analyte recoveries. Target analytes reported as not detected in the sample, or detected—but less than the regulatory limit—may, in actuality, be present in larger amounts than reported. Target analytes reported as exceeding the regulatory limit really are present above the regulatory limit. High surrogate recoveries suggest there may be problems with the internal standard areas.

2.12 Target Analyte Identification

Target analytes must elute from the column (retention time) within ±30 seconds of authentic standards. For each candidate target analyte the three characteristic ions must maximize within one scan of each other. There must be a match of the abundance of the three characteristics ions within ±20% between the library (reference or user generated) spectrum of the target analyte and the spectrum obtained for the analyte in the sample.

3. Oil and Grease by Method 1664 (Proposed)

Method 1664 is a replacement for Oil & Grease determinations and other related procedures that use Freon as the extraction solvent. Method 1664 is titled, "N-Hexane extractable material (HEM) and silica gel treated n-hexane extractable material (SGT-HEM) by extraction and gravimetry (Oil and Grease and Total Petroleum Hydrocarbons.") Method 1664 is written in the Environmental Methods Monitoring Council (EMMC) format and is what is termed a performance-based method. Performance-based methods are procedures that contain a prescriptive set of directions for performing the method, but also include required acceptance criteria for accuracy, precision, method detection limit that must be met should the analyst wish to change the procedure. In Section 9.1.2.2 of Method 1664 there is a list of procedures and required documentation needed to exercise a performance-based modification:

- The names, titles, addresses, and telephone numbers of the analyst(s) who performed the analyses and modification, and of the quality control officer who witnessed and will verify the analyses and modification

- A list of the pollutants measured

- A narrative stating the reason for the modification

- Results from all quality control tests comparing the modified method to this method, including calibration, calibration verification, initial precision and recovery, analyses of blanks, accuracy assessment, and ongoing precision and recovery

- Data that will allow an independent reviewer to validate each determination by tracing the instrument output (weight or other signal) to the final result. These data include sample numbers and other identifiers, extraction dates, analysis dates and times, analysis sequence/run chronology, sample weight or volume, extract volume for SGT-HEM, make and model of analytical balance and weights traceable to NIST, copies of logbooks, printer tapes, and other recordings of raw data, and finally, data system outputs, and other data to link the raw data to the reported results.

In so far as data evaluation is concerned, as long as the performance criteria are met, changes to the procedure should not affect the data quality.

The base procedure consists of extraction of an acidified 1 L sample with three portions of hexane in a separatory funnel. The extracts are combined and dried over sodium sulfate, then concentrated to dryness. The weighed residue is the HEM.

3.1. Initial Demonstration of Ability

The initial demonstration of ability (initial demonstration of precision and recovery, IPR) consists of analyzing four repetitions of a test solution that contains hexadecane and stearic acid, as oil and grease standards, at 40 mg/L each. The mean recovery (%R) and relative standard deviation (RSD) of the results is computed. Acceptable results will meet the criteria of 83-101% for the recovery and < 10% for the RSD. This is a one-time test for each analyst and for each modification made to the procedure. A copy of the raw data and a summary of the results should be placed in the analyst's training file.

3.2 MDL Determinations

The MDL is performed and calculated in compliance with 40 CFR 136, Appendix B. The replicates within the MDL study may be performed over several days rather than all in one day. An MDL should be performed by each analyst at least once a year. If there are changes in the procedure, a new MDL needs to be performed. Method 1664 specifies that an MDL of no more than 1.4 mg/L is acceptable. If this MDL is achieved, then a Minimum Level (ML) of 5.0 mg/L is to be used for reporting sample results.

It is important to verify that a proper MDL study has been performed. Check the equation for standard deviation used for the MDL calculation to insure "n-1" has been used rather than "n" in the denominator. Also check that the correct Student's t-value has been used.

The calculated ML should be checked against the regulatory limit for each analyte. If the ML is at or higher than the regulatory limit, then no data concerning that analyte, which indicate that it is present in the samples at less than the regulatory limit, are acceptable. In many instances the regulatory authority will interpret the result of a reported non-detect of the target analyte with a detection limit above the effluent limit as evidence of a permit violation.

MDLs performed on reagent water may not be very applicable to the actual samples. For particularly intractable samples, it is probably worthwhile to perform an MDL in the sample itself. If the permittee is submitting an application to a regulatory agency for a variance on either permit regulatory levels or monitoring requirements, inclusion of a sample-specific MDL study can go far toward assuring approval of the variance.

3.3 Calibration Requirements

Calibration in Method 1664 consists of using certified weights to check the calibration of the analytical balance used for weighing the residue. Weights of 2 mg and 1000 mg are required to check the balance accuracy before and after the residue determinations on each day of analysis. Lack of balance check weights or a lack of balance calibration checking on a daily basis invalidates the results.

3.4 Sample Collection, Preservation and Handling Procedures

Samples of one liter in volume are collected in glass containers with a Teflon cap liner. Unless samples are extracted immediately, samples are acidified with hydrochloric or sulfuric acid to pH <2. Samples are then held at 0-4°C until sample extraction. Maximum holding time from sampling to extraction is 28 days.

3.5 Sample Preparation and Batch Procedures

Sample preparation in Method 1664 is a liquid-liquid extraction using a separatory funnel. The method defines a batch as consisting of a blank, a matrix spike and matrix spike duplicate, an OPR sample and up to ten analytical samples. The time limit of a batch is defined as "extracted at the same time." This should be interpreted as within a single work shift (8-12 hours).

3.6 Blanks

Sample preparation blanks and field blanks are performed with every set of ten or fewer samples processed within a batch. Blanks must be examined closely for laboratory created contamination. Blank results are never subtracted from analyte results in samples. If blank contamination is found, samples need to be closely examined. If oil & grease are not detected in the samples, or if it is found in the samples, but less than the regulatory limit, the data are probably usable. Also, if the pollutants are found in the samples at significantly higher concentration (>10 times) than the amount in the blank, the results may be usable. However, when the blank and sample results are within a factor of ten of each other, laboratory contamination is the only appropriate conclusion, and the sample results are questionable.

Field blanks are used to monitor the sample acquisition process. If samples are found to have non-detected levels of target analytes, the field blank is not of much use. However, when target analytes are detected in the samples exceeding the regulatory limit, the field blanks should be examined to see if the high levels are artifacts of the sampling procedure or if they are indicative of non-compliance in the sample source.

3.7 Laboratory Control Samples

Method 1664 refers to ongoing precision and recovery samples (OPR) as fulfilling the same purpose as laboratory control samples (LCS). The OPR samples are identical to the IPR samples. They are processed exactly like samples every time a batch is prepared. The OPR sample is used to verify that the analytical system is in control.

The results on the OPR are evaluated on recovery, with 79-114% being the method specified acceptance range. Control charts are to be maintained on the recoveries of the OPR and the matrix spike samples.

High recoveries of the LCS relate directly to falsely high reported values of detected analytes in samples. For those analytes, which are not detected in the sample or are reported as less than the regulatory limit, the sample data are usable in the sense that the regulatory limit has, in actuality, not been exceeded. However, for analytes reported as greater than the regulatory limit, there is a strong possibility that a false positive has been generated, and the data are not reliable.

Low recoveries in the LCS means that target analytes are reported as lower than they actually are in the sample. Values for analytes reported as larger than the regulatory limit reflect actual amounts in the sample that exceed the regulatory limit. However, values reported as lower than the regulatory limit or not detected may, in fact, be present in greater amounts in the samples, and the data are unreliable.

3.8 Matrix Spikes

Matrix spikes are the primary assessment of the laboratory's ability to analyze the sample for the regulated analytes at the regulatory level. The matrix spike must be tailored to the individual permit for the sample. The matrix spike is prepared by adding a solution of hexadecane and stearic acid to the sample at either the regulatory limit or at one to five times the background concentration of the target analyte in the sample, whichever is the higher value. If there is no set regulatory limit, the addition of target analyte is made at the same level as the OPR sample (40 mg/L each component) or at one-to-five-times the background concentration of the target analyte in the sample, whichever is the higher value. Matrix spikes are performed in duplicate at a rate of one per ten samples processed in a batch. Acceptance criteria that must be met are 79-114% for recovery and <18 for RPD.

When matrix spike recoveries are outside the acceptance limits, and the OPR recoveries are acceptable, this is an indication of matrix effects from the sampling source, and the evaluation should be documented. The sample results can be interpreted similar to those presented in the preceding discussion (Section 3.7).

3.10 Replicate analysis

Replicate analysis is not expressly addressed as a required quality control in Method 1664. It still makes good analytical sense for the laboratory to perform sample, matrix spike and laboratory control sample duplicates.

References

1. *Guidance on Evaluation, Resolution, and Documentation of Analytical Problems Associated with Compliance Monitoring,* U.S. EPA Office of Water, June, 1993, EPA 821/B/93/001.

2. *NPDES Compliance Inspection Manual,* U.S. EPA Office of Water, May 1988.

3. *Handbook for Analytical Quality Control in Water and Wastewater Laboratories,* U.S. EPA Office of Research and Development, EPA-600/4-79-019, PB 297451, March, 1979.

4. *Guidelines establishing test procedures for the analysis of pollutants,* U.S. EPA Office of Water, 40 Code of Federal Regulations, Part 136, 1995.

CHAPTER 6

Resource Conservation and Recovery Act (RCRA)

It is not a mere coincidence that the CERCLA Contract Laboratory Program (CLP) has spawned a large and thriving data validation business, and the RCRA program has not. It is the result of fundamental differences between the intents and execution of the CERCLA and RCRA programs. The most basic difference is in the data quality objectives (DQOs) of the two programs. CERCLA, through the CLP, has established a uniform set of DQOs for most projects. By specifying the CLP analytical methods, the data user is defining the DQOs as "data of known and defensible quality." Moreover, the user is stipulating that using the CLP methods and meeting the letter of their QC requirements is enough to meet the DQOs. The result is likely data of known quality for the approximately 125 target organic analytes or 27 metals and cyanide included in the CLP SOWs. Those results are often enough to demonstrate that uncontrolled hazardous wastes may exist at a site and may be in need of remediation. Since the waste site may be abandoned, the government's responsibility is to "prove the positive," that a hazard may exist.

The goals of analyses under the RCRA program may be significantly different. The data may be used to determine if a waste meets the characteristics of a toxic or hazardous waste, that a waste treatment procedure has been effective, or that a release of potentially hazardous materials from a solid waste management unit (SWMU) has occurred. Since many analyses under RCRA are carried out by or for a member of a regulated industry or disposal contractor, the job is often to "prove the negative," that the waste is not hazardous or that a release has not occurred. The RCRA program philosophy is that the methods used need only be "appropriate" for the analytes of interest in the matrix of interest at the regulatory levels of interest. Thus, a waste may be deemed to exhibit the characteristic of toxicity if after the application of the toxicity characteristic leaching procedure (TCLP), the level of benzene in the leachate is greater than 300 ppb. Conversely, a SWMU may pose a threat to ground water supplies if the concentration of benzene exceeds the maximum contaminant level (MCL) established by the Safe Drinking Water Act of 5 ppb. It should not come as a surprise that measuring these two concentrations of benzene might not be best accomplished by a single analytical method.

A. SW-846 as Guidance

Thus, the Office of Solid Waste (OSW) has issued the SW-846 methods manual primarily as a guidance document, with the few exceptions noted earlier in Chapter 1 where SW-846 methods are required for use. Further, SW-846 is divided into a variety of types of methods, notably sample preparation methods, cleanup methods, and determinative methods, which should be combined together to address the specific analytes, matrices, and regulatory levels of interest. Given the diversity of uses to which these methods may be put, the methods do not contain the degree of specific QC criteria and specifications that are characteristic of the CLP methods. Rather, the QC criteria should grow out of the DQOs for a specific project, and should be specified in the Quality Assurance Project Plan (QAPP, formerly QAPjP) specific to the project. This approach is described in detail in Chapters One and Two of SW-846. Even the target analyte lists in the various methods are not intended as required lists of analytes. Rather, they are analytes that may be amenable to the analysis.

For each type of method, there is a so-called "base method" that draws together information common to methods of each type into a single location (see Table 6-1 for a listing of the SW-846 methods). Thus, Method 3500 is the base method for all organic sample extraction procedures, and it contains recommended sample sizes, surrogates, etc. Similarly Method 3600 contains information common to the sample cleanup procedures, and Method 8000 contains a wide variety of information common to both the gas and liquid chromatographic determination procedures. These base methods often bring together the minimum QC criteria that should be met for the analytes of interest.

It is imperative that all parties involved in a RCRA data collection activity recognize the intent of the SW-846 manual and take appropriate steps to utilize the diversity of methods to meet the DQOs of a given project. It is unconscionable for a regulator to specify that all the analytes listed in Method 8270 must be analyzed in all samples without regard to the likelihood that they could be present at a site. It is equally unconscionable for an analyst to perform the analyses without having consulted Chapters One and Two of the manual and the various base methods. In addition, for any large project, the analyst should have a copy of the QAPP to review. The owner/operator has a responsibility to empower the analyst with knowledge of the analytes of interest or subject to regulatory requirements and to ensure that the laboratory staff have read and agreed to the specifications of the QAPP. Finally, the data reviewer should have copies of all these materials at hand and understand the DQOs for the project before attempting to validate the results to the standards of the project.

Having said that, we recognize many laboratories analyze a few samples here and there for a given client and that neither the laboratory nor the client may feel that a QAPP is necessary. While this may be true, we hope that if a project isn't important enough to prepare a QAPP, then the data may not warrant validation either. One cannot make up for lack of a plan at the beginning of a project by attempting to validate the data at the end of the project. To do so virtually guarantees problems, as no one can say for certain what the "requirements" were, what data quality objectives were to be employed, what was the appropriate format for the final report, and what supporting data were to accompany the final results. To have the data validator call a month after the submission of the final reports and complain to the lab that they can't do their job because the QC data were not provided in "CLP-like" format is a result of poor planning and a lack of communication on the front end of the project. It's also going to be very costly to generate the requested formats after the fact of the analysis. Many laboratories have prepared a Comprehensive Quality Assurance Manual, which covers all aspects of the lab's work, in an attempt to address the all-too-frequent lack of a QAPP. The data can be evaluated based on the lab's own standards of performance expectations and the decisions the chemists and staff made during the analyses. However, project specificity is entirely absent.

There are several implications to the guidance nature of the SW-846 methods. The guidance is absolutely essential with respect to allowing the analyst to combine the most appropriate series of sample digestion, extraction, clean-up, and determinative methods to give a procedure that is best suited to the sample matrix and the data needs. There is also guidance built into the various methods themselves. For example, in Method 8270C, the determinative method for analysis of semivolatile compounds by GC/MS, there is a requirement for performing a tune of the instrument to DFTPP standards on a daily basis. One particular set of tuning criteria is presented in the method; however, a footnote mentions that alternate tuning criteria, such as those in the CLP-SOW, Method 525 or manufacturer's instructions may be used, provided that method performance is not adversely affected. Overall, changes may be made to the methods in SW-846 as long as method performance, as measured by accuracy, precision, and detection limits, and data quality are not decreased. It is to be expected that any method modifications be documented in some detail by the laboratory and that quantitative performance characteristics obtained during use of the modification be included in the documentation.

Modifications may include using alternate internal standards and surrogates, and at different fortification levels than those suggested by the methods. Other modifications that have notably increased method performance include use of Turbo-Vap® evaporators[1] rather than K-D concentrators for solvent removal and use of the Accelerated One-Step® continuous liquid-liquid extractor[2] in Method 3520A. These are minor changes and in general result in increased method performance at reduced cost. It has been our experience, however, that the most frequent modifications to the methods made by laboratories and analysts, under the guise of guidance, are more correctly characterized as unwarranted corner-cutting through deletion of significant portions of the quality control procedures. These short-cuts invariably result in a marked deterioration in method performance and data quality and can frequently be recognized by a paucity of documentation.

Table 6-1.   SW-846 Methods

0010	Modified method 5 sampling train
0011	Sampling for formaldehyde emissions from stationary sources
0020	Source assessment sampling system (SASS)
0023A	Sampling method for dioxins and furans from stationary sources
0030	Volatile organic sampling train (VOST)
0031	Sampling method for volatile organic compounds (SMVOC)
0040	Sampling of principal organic hazardous constituents from combustion sources using Tedlar bags
0050	Isokenetic HCl/Cl_2 emission sampling train
0051	Midget impinger HCl/Cl_2 emission sampling train
0060	Determination of metals in stack emissions
0061	Determination of hexavalent chromium emissions from stationary sources
0100	Sampling for formaldehyde and other carbonyl compounds in indoor air
1010	Pensky-Martins closed sup method for determining ignitability
1020A	Setaflash closed cup method for determining ignitability
1030	Ignitability of solids
1110	Corrosivity toward steel
1120	Dermal corrosion
1310A	Extraction procedure (EP) toxicity test method and structural integrity test
1311	Toxic characteristic leaching procedure
1312	Synthetic precipitation leaching procedure
1320	Multiple extraction procedure

---

[1] Zymark Corporation.
[2] Corning, Inc.

Table 6-1.   SW-846 Methods, *continued*

1330A	Extraction procedure for oily wastes
3005A	Acid digestion of waters for total recoverable or dissolved metals by FLAA or ICP
3010A	Acid digestion of aqueous samples and extracts for total metals for analysis by FLAA or ICP
3015	Microwave assisted acid digestion of aqueous samples and extracts
3020A	Acid digestion of aqueous samples and extracts for total metals for analysis by GFAA
3031	Acid digestion of oils for metals analysis by FLAA or ICP
3040A	Dissolution procedure for oils, greases or waxes
3050B	Acid digestion of sediments, sludges, or soils
3051	Microwave assisted acid digestion of sediments, sludges, soils and oils
3052	Microwave assisted acid digestion of siliceous and organically based matrices
3060A	Alkaline digestion for hexavalent chromium
3500B	Organic extraction and sample preparation
3510C	Separatory funnel liquid-liquid extraction
3520C	Continuous liquid-liquid extraction
3535	Solid phase extraction (SPE)
3540C	Soxhlet extraction
3541	Automated soxhlet extraction
3542	Extraction of semivolatile analytes collected using modified method 5 (Method 0010) sampling train
3545	Accelerated solvent extraction (ASE)
3550B	Ultrasonic extraction
3560	Supercritical fluid extraction of total recoverable petroleum hydrocarbons (TRPH)
3561	Supercritical fluid extraction of polynuclear aromatic hydrocarbons
3580A	Waste dilution
3585	Waste dilution for volatile organics
3600C	Cleanup
3610B	Alumina cleanup
3611B	Alumina column cleanup and separation of petroleum wastes
3620B	Florisil cleanup
3630C	Silica gel cleanup
3640A	Gel-permeation cleanup
3650B	Acid-base partition cleanup
3660B	Sulfur cleanup
3665A	Sulfuric acid/permanganate cleanup
3810	Headspace
3820	Hexadecane extraction and screening of purgeable organics
4000	Immunoassay
4010A	Screening for pentachlorophenol by immunoassay
4015	Screening for 2,4-D by immunoassay
4020	Screening for PCBs by immunoassay
4030	Soil screening for petroleum hydrocarbons by immunoassay
4035	Soil screening for PAH by immunoassay
4040	Soil screening for toxaphene by immunoassay
4041	Soil screening for chlordane by immunoassay

Table 6-1.   SW-846 Methods, *continued*

4042	Soil screening for DDT by immunoassay
4050	TNT explosives in water and soils by immunoassay
4051	RDX in soil and water by immunoassay
5000	Sample preparation for volatile organic compounds
5021	Volatile organic compounds in soils and other solid matrices using equilibrium headspace
5030B	Purge and trap for aqueous samples
5031	Volatile, nonpurgeable, water-soluble compounds by azeotropic distillation
5032	Volatile organic compounds by vacuum distillation
5035	Closed system purge and trap and extraction for volatile organics in soil and waste samples
5041A	Analysis for desorption of sorbent cartridges from volatile organic sampling train (VOST): capillary GC/MS technique
5050	Bomb preparation method for solid waste
6010B	ICP-AES
6020	ICP-MS
7000A	AA Methods
7020	Aluminum FLAA
7040	Antimony FLAA
7041	Antimony GFAA
7060A	Arsenic GFAA
7061A	Arsenic Hydride AA
7062	Antimony and arsenic (Borohydride reduction AA)
7063	Arsenic by anodic stripping voltammetry (ASV)
7080A	Barium FLAA
7081	Barium GFAA
7090	Beryllium FLAA
7091	Beryllium GFAA
7130	Cadmium FLAA
7131A	Cadmium GFAA
7140	Calcium FLAA
7190	Chromium FLAA
7191	Chromium GFAA
7195	Chromium, hexavalent (Coprecipitation)
7196A	Chromium, hexavalent (Colorimetric)
7197	Chromium, hexavalent (Chelation/extraction)
7198	Chromium, hexavalent (Differential pulse polarography)
7199	Determination of hexavalent chromium in drinking water, groundwater, and industrial wastewater effluents by ion chromatography
7200	Cobalt FLAA
7201	Cobalt GFAA
7210	Copper FLAA
7211	Copper GFAA
7380	Iron FLAA
7381	Iron GFAA
7420	Lead FLAA

Table 6-1. SW-846 Methods, *continued*

7421	Lead GFAA
7430	Lithium FLAA
7450	Magnesium FLAA
7460	Manganese FLAA
7461	Manganese GFAA
7470A	Mercury in liquid waste CVAA
7471A	Mercury in solid or semisolid waste CVAA
7472	Mercury in aqueous samples and extracts by anodic stripping voltammetry (ASV)
7480	Molybdenum FLAA
7481	Molybdenum GFAA
7520	Nickel FLAA
7521	Nickel GFAA
7550	Osmium FLAA
7580	White phosphorus by solvent extraction and gas chromatography
7610	Potassium FLAA
7740	Selenium GFAA
7741A	Selenium Hydride AA
7742	Selenium Borohydride reduction AA
7760A	Silver FLAA
7761	Silver GFAA
7770	Sodium FLAA
7780	Strontium FLAA
7840	Thallium FLAA
7841	Thallium GFAA
7870	Tin FLAA
7910	Vanadium FLAA
7911	Vanadium GFAA
7950	Zinc FLAA
7951	Zinc GFAA
8000B	Determinative chromatographic separations
8011	EDB and DBCP by microextraction and GC
8015B	Nonhalogenated organics using GC/FID
8021B	Halogenated volatiles by GC using PID and ECD in series; capillary column technique
8031	Acrylonitrile by GC
8032A	Acrylamide by GC
8033	Acetonitrile by GC-NPD
8041	Phenols by GC: capillary column technique
8061A	Phthalate esters by capillary GC-ECD
8070A	Nitrosamines by GC
8081A	Organochlorine pesticides by capillary column GC
8082	PCB by capillary GC
8091	Nitroaromatics and cyclic ketones: capillary column technique
8100	Polynuclear aromatic hydrocarbons
8111	Haloethers: capillary column technique
8121	Chlorinated hydrocarbons by GC: capillary column technique

Table 6-1. **SW-846 Methods,** *continued*

8131	Aniline and selected derivatives by GC: capillary column technique
8141A	Organophosphorus compounds by GC: capillary column technique
8151A	Chlorinated herbicides by GC using methylation or pentafluorobenzylation derivatization
8260B	Volatile organic compounds by GC/MS
8270C	Semivolatile organic compounds by GC/MS
8275A	Semivolatile organic compounds (PAH and PCB) in soils/sludges and solid wastes using TE/GC/MS
8280A	Dioxins and furans by HRGC/LRMS
8290	Dioxins and furans by HRGC/HRMS
8310	Polynuclear aromatic hydrocarbons
8315A	Determination of carbonyl compounds by HPLC
8316	Acrylamide, acrylonitrile, and acrolein by HPLC
8321A	Solvent extractable non-volatile compounds by HPLC/TS/MS or UV
8325	Solvent extractable non-volatile compounds by HPLC/PB/MS
8330	Nitoaromatics and nitramines by HPLC
8331	Tetrazene by HPLC
8332	Nitroglycerine by HPLC
8410	GC/FTIR for semivolatile organics
8430	Analysis of bis(2-chloroethyl)ether hydrolysis products by direct aqueous injection GC/FTIR
8440	TRPH by IR
8515	Colorimetric screening method for TNT in soil
8520	Continuous measurement of formaldehyde in ambient air
9010A	Total and amenable cyanide (colorimetric manual)
9012A	Total and amenable cyanide (colorimetric automated UV)
9013	Cyanide extraction procedure for solids and oils
9020B	Total organic halides (TOX)
9021	Purgeable organic halides
9022	TOX by neutron activation analysis
9023	Extractable organic halides (EOX) in solids
9030A	Acid-soluble and acid-insoluble sulfides
9031	Extractable sulfides
9035	Sulfate (colorimetric, automated chloranilate)
9036	Sulfate (colorimetric, automated methylthymol blue)
9038	Sulfate (turbidimetric)
9040B	pH electrometric measurement
9041A	pH paper method
9045C	Soil and waste pH
9050A	Specific conductance
9056	Determination of inorganic anions by ion chromatography
9057	Determination of chloride from HCl/Cl_2 emissions sampling train (Methods 0050 and 0051) by anion chromatography
9060	Total organic carbon (TOC)
9065	Phenolics (spectrophotometric 4AAP manual)
9066	Phenolics (colorimetric, automated 4AAP)
9067	Phenolics (spectrophotometric, MBTH)

Table 6-1.   SW-846 Methods, *continued*

9070	Total recoverable oil & grease
9071A	Oil & grease extraction method for sludge and sediment samples
9075	Test method for total chlorine in new and used petroleum products by XRF
9076	Test method for total chlorine in new and used petroleum products by oxidative combustion and microcoulometry
9077	Test methods for total chlorine in new and used petroleum products (field test kit methods)
9078	Screening test method for PCB in soil
9079	Screening test method for PCB in transformer oil
9080	Cation exchange capacity of soils (ammonium acetate)
9081	Cation exchange capacity of soils (sodium acetate)
9090A	Compatibility test for wastes and membrane liners
9095A	Paint filter liquids test
9096	Liquid release test
9100	Saturated hydraulic conductivity, saturated leachate conductivity and intrinsic permeability
9131	Total coliform MPN
9132	Total coliform MF
9210	Nitrate ISE
9211	Bromide ISE
9212	Chloride ISE
9213	Cyanide ISE
9214	Fluoride ISE
9215	Sulfide ISE
9250	Chloride (automated ferricyanide AAI)
9251	Chloride (automated ferricyanide AAII)
9253	Chloride (titrimetric, silver nitrate)
9310	Gross alpha and gross beta
9315	Alpha-emitting radium isotopes
9320	Radium-228

B. Validation of Data from SW-846 Methods

While the CLP has established formal data validation procedures, such as providing the QC acceptance limits, OSW leaves the specifics of data validation to the QAPP. Chapter One of SW-846 describes six aspects of laboratory data that should be reviewed:

- **Completeness of laboratory records** - This is the simplest form of review, ensuring that all the samples sent to the laboratory were analyzed for the appropriate analytes and that the relevant results have been reported, including the quality control results.

- **Evaluation of detection limits and quantitation limits** - The results are reviewed to ensure that the sensitivity of the methods was adequate to meet the regulatory limits, action levels, or target concentrations specified in the QAPP.

- **Evaluation of QC results** - The results of all QC samples, calibration checks, etc., are compared to the QC criteria established in the QAPP or developed in the laboratory.

- **Holding times** - Sample holding times are reviewed relative to the specifications in the QAPP. These may be significantly different from the variety of holding times presented in the multitude of Holding Time, Preservation and Container Tables strewn through out the environmental regulations. SW-846 has three sets of Tables (Chapter 2, Chapter 4 and Chapter 11), which are not uniform.

- **Performance evaluation data** - Results from PE studies may be reviewed.

- **Correlation between related results** - Where possible, the results obtained from related laboratory tests are compared. For example, if 1,2-dichlorobenzene was detected in both the volatile and semivolatile GC-MS analyses, are the results similar? Other correlations include reconciliation of VOC and pesticide/PCB results with total organic halogen (TOX) values. Correlation between historical data, knowledge of the site, and present data can be important.

Reviewing these six aspects of the data must be done while keeping in mind the basic premise of the RCRA Methods Program - to determine the analytes of concern in the matrix of concern at the regulatory limits of concern. Thus, the first step in the data validation process is to determine the analytes, matrices, and regulatory limits. Whether that information is contained in a formal QAPP or gleaned from discussions with the responsible parties, the data validation process proceeds in a similar fashion. This information will allow the review to evaluate completeness and detection and quantitation limits.

The next step is to determine what data are available. Another significant difference between the CLP approach and that of SW-846 is that there are no formal data reporting requirements in SW-846. Yes, the 1985 vintage CLP data reporting forms were included in the original 3rd Edition of SW-846. However, they covered only a limited suite of analytes (from the CLP SOWs of that time), and they were withdrawn from the manual several years later, in part because of their limitations. Many vendors now provide software that allow a laboratory to produce high quality data reports that meet or exceed the specifications of the CLP SOWs. Most of those software packages also allow the user to customize the reports to address non-CLP analytes and methods. As a result, the extent and format of the data reported from a given analysis is typically a function of asking the laboratory to provide the data and paying them for the effort.

Because different instruments provide different data (e.g., GC/MS procedures produce plots of mass intensities while GC procedures do not), the specific form of the data will differ according to the method. In the case of SW-846 screening methods, whether performed in the field or a fixed laboratory, the results for a given sample may simply be a positive or negative response from the screening test recorded in a field or laboratory notebook. The analytical approach employed should be specified in the QAPP as well as the data reporting and validation requirements.

When fixed laboratory instrumental analyses are performed, under the best of circumstances, the following information will be available to the data validator.

1. A summary level report or data reporting forms giving the contaminants for which analyses were conducted and the concentrations detected. For the contaminants that were not detected, the detection limits or estimated detection limits should be provided. If the laboratory uses "flags" in its data reporting, the definition of each flag must be provided with the data.

2. A summary of all quality control results, including, but not limited to:
   - Instrument tuning,
   - Calibration,
   - Calibration verification,
   - Initial precision and accuracy,
   - Continuing precision and accuracy,
   - Laboratory control sample results,
   - Surrogate recoveries,
   - Matrix spike and matrix spike duplicate results, including recoveries and RPDs,
   - Labeled compound recoveries (isotope dilution methods only),
   - Blank results,
   - QC check standard results, and
   - Quality control charts and limits.

3. Raw data that will allow an independent reviewer to validate each determination and calculation performed by the laboratory, tracing the instrument output (peak height, area, or other signal intensity) to the final result reported. The raw data are method specific and may include:
   - Sample numbers or other identifiers used by both the client and the laboratory
   - Extraction dates
   - Analysis dates and times
   - Sequence of analyses or run logs
   - Sample volume
   - Extract volume prior to each cleanup step
   - Extract volume after each cleanup step
   - Final extract volume prior to injection
   - Digestion volume
   - Titration volume
   - Dilution data, differentiating between dilution of a sample and dilution of an extract or digestate
   - Instrument(s) and operating conditions
   - GC and/or GC/MS operating conditions, including detailed information on:
     - Columns used for determination and confirmation (column length and diameter, stationary phase, solid support, film thickness, etc.),
     - Analysis conditions (temperature programs, flow rates, etc.),
     - Detectors (type, operating conditions, etc.).
   - Chromatograms, ion current profiles, bar graph spectra, library search results
   - Quantitation reports, data system outputs, and other data to link the raw data to the results reported. (Where these data are edited manually,

explanations of why manual intervention was necessary must be included.)

- Direct instrument readouts (i.e., strip charts, printer tapes, etc., and other data to support the final results)
- Laboratory bench sheets and copies of all pertinent logbook pages for all sample preparation and cleanup steps, and for all other parts of the determination.

The raw data described above should be provided not only for the analysis of samples, but also for all calibrations, verifications, blanks, laboratory control samples, duplicate analyses, and other QC analyses.

If all these data are available, then the validation can be very detailed. If these data are not available, then the scope of the validation effort will be significantly reduced. In either case, the scope of the validation effort should be based on the DQOs and the purpose of the analysis and focus on the analytes of concern. Again, it should also be specified in the QAPP.

The third step is to determine the data quality objectives that were intended. Again, this information should be contained in a formal QAPP. If it is not, then one must combine information contained in the methods with professional judgment to formulate a strategy for validation. For instance, in the absence of a formal statement of DQOs, but knowing that benzene is of concern in a solid waste that has been subjected to the TCLP, one can use the regulatory limit of 300 ppb in the leachate as a reference point. Did the laboratory demonstrate that they could analyze the leachate for benzene at 300 ppb? The answer to this question should be able to be derived from the analytical results. Knowledge of the DQOs will allow you to evaluate the QC results.

The review of the holding times is relatively simple. The QAPP may specify holding times, or it may defer to those holding times listed in the individual methods. Holding times remain a somewhat contested issue in that they can appear arbitrary if not capricious in many instances. Nevertheless, they have come to have significant weight in a legal sense, regardless of their possible scientific shortcomings. OSW's specific position is that while results outside of the method-specified holding times may be employed to show that a sample has exceeded a regulatory limit, such results may not be employed to demonstrate compliance with a limit. Again, the focus is on proving the negative, and results past holding times are not considered valid proof.

PE samples and studies can yield important information about a laboratory's application of a specific method. Ideally, the PE samples should be of a matrix similar to those of the real samples. Unfortunately, OSW has never undertaken a formal program of PE studies. As a result, one may be asked to rely on PE results from the Office of Water's Water Pollution (WP) studies or Water Supply (WS) studies, neither of which have any relevance to the analysis of solids or wastes. However, the concept of PE study results can be generalized to include certified reference materials and other check samples prepared outside of the laboratory itself. A number of commercial firms are now providing PE samples based on real matrices along with acceptance limits derived from interlaboratory round-robin studies.

Correlations among results from related test methods can yield important information. For instance, one would expect results for purgeable organic halides (POX) to reflect the presence of volatile organics, particularly halogenated ones. If the results of such analyses differ greatly, one might suspect difficulties with one or the other of the methods. Unfortunately, few samples are subjected to analyses by more than one method that can be readily correlated with another method. Thus, the correlations may not be able to be made, or may be limited to an evaluation of small subsets of the analytes, such as the concentrations of late-eluting dichlorobenzenes in the volatile fraction and the concentrations of these analytes determined during the semivolatile analyses.

C. How Much Validation is Enough?

Another contribution made by the Superfund is the concept of "levels" of data quality and hence, validation effort. The concept carries over fairly well into other EPA programs as well. For instance, the Superfund "Level IV" involves the review of all analyte identifications, including review of mass spectra, library search results, and the like. For a facility that produces or handles a RCRA-regulated compound, it may not be necessary to review mass spectra or other means of compound identification in great detail if the compound is expected to be in the waste being analyzed, but rather, to determine if the concentration determined is sufficiently accurate. Why? Because the purpose of the analysis may simply be to determine if the concentration is lower than a regulatory limit, in which case, the disposal of the waste may proceed under less stringent requirements. The obvious exceptions to this generalization involve analytes that are known to be poorly resolved from one another, or that are known to be subject to interferences from other analytes. Again, knowing the purpose of the analysis is critical to deciding how much validation is enough.

The other obvious limitation is the availability of the data described above. You cannot validate what you do not have, or what the laboratory did not produce. At worst, data validation may be reduced to counting the number of samples taken in the field and the number of samples reported by the laboratory to determine the completeness of the data. Exciting? Hardly. Challenging? No. Important? Yes, as completeness is the most basic aspect of data validation.

D. Basic Data Validation Principles for RCRA Analyses

Beyond this most basic level of cross-referencing field samples and laboratory results lie the more detailed procedures encompassed by the various Superfund "levels." The need to go beyond the basic cross-referencing stage should be stipulated in the QAPP for the project. Lacking such specifics, however, the following basic principles can be applied to the validation of data for RCRA-related analyses.

Chapter Two of SW-846 provides an overview of the quality assurance and quality control procedures determined by EPA to be necessary for RCRA-related decision making. These procedures may be supplemented by the performance specifications for each method, and contain the following elements:

- Purity and traceability of reference standards
- Number of calibration points
- Linearity of calibration
- Calibration verification
- Initial demonstration of capability
- Analysis of blanks
- Recovery of analyte spikes into the sample matrix
- Analysis of QC check samples.

In addition, Chapter Two contains specifications for sample containers, preservation techniques, and holding times for many analyses. Assuming that the relevant data were requested from—and provided by—the laboratory, they can be used to perform the evaluations described below in a fashion analogous to that used for data from EPA's water and drinking water programs.

1. Purity and Traceability of Reference Standards

The accuracy of any non-absolute empirical measurement is dependent on the reference for that measurement. As noted earlier in Chapters 2 and 3, the analytical instrument and analytical process must be calibrated with a known reference standard. The EPA methods require that the standards used for calibration and other purposes be of known purity and traceable to a reliable reference source.

The ultimate reference source for these standards is typically EPA or the National Institute for Standards and Technology (NIST, formerly NBS). Laboratories must be able to prove traceability of the reference standards used in the analysis to EPA or NIST. The ultimate proof of this traceability is a written certification from the supplier of the standard that shows the source and the paper trail to EPA or NIST.

Documentation of the purity and traceability of the standards need not be provided with every sample analysis. Rather, it should be maintained on file at the laboratory and provided on request.

2. Number of Calibration Points

Most SW-846 methods for organic analytes specify a minimum of five calibration points. Some may allow as few as three points. The lowest of these points should be near the MDL. The highest should be near the upper linear range of the analytical system. Beyond that, most SW-846 methods do not require calibration standards at specific concentrations. Thus, each laboratory may determine its own calibration range. Some laboratories establish a relatively narrow calibration range (e.g., a five-fold increase in concentration) because it makes it simpler to meet the linearity specifications of the methods. Other laboratories choose wider calibration ranges to minimize the number of samples that have to be diluted and re-analyzed because the concentration of one or more analytes exceeds the calibration range.

The SW-846 methods for metals may involve only a single-point calibration, performed daily. In these instances, the methods typically require that a linear calibration range be established using three standards prior to the analysis of any samples. This linear calibration range must be updated periodically.

The data reviewer must make certain that all measurements are within the calibration range of the instrument. Samples with analytes above the calibration range should have been diluted and re-analyzed. The diluted sample results need only apply to those analytes that were out of the calibration range in the initial analysis. In other words, analysts are encouraged to report data for different analytes from different levels of dilution within the same sample.

If data from an analysis of the diluted sample are not provided, limited use can be made of the data that are above the calibration range. The response of the analytical instrument will most likely eventually level off (reach saturation) at concentrations above the calibration range. It is not possible to specify at exactly what concentration this will occur from the calibration data. However, it is generally safe to assume that when a reported concentration is above the calibrated range, that the reported value is a lower limit of the actual concentration, i.e., that the method probably underestimates values above the calibration range. Therefore, if a concentration above the calibration range is also above a regulatory limit, it is likely that the actual concentration also would be above that limit.

In addition, if the analyte with a response above the calibration range is not an analyte of concern for the project in question, or is not regulated, then the fact that the response is above the range may not be an important consideration. Yes, the issue may warrant a comment in the data validation report, but if it does not involve an analyte of concern for the specific project, then the validator is wasting his or her time, the time of the laboratory staff, and that of the client in pursuing the matter much further.

3. Linearity of Calibration

The graphic display of the relationship between the response of an analytical instrument to the concentration or amount of an analyte introduced into the system is referred to as the calibration "curve." An analytical instrument can be said to be calibrated in any instance in which an instrumental response can be related to a single concentration of an analyte. While the shape of many calibration "curves" can be modeled by quadratic equations or higher order mathematical functions, most analytical methods focus on calibration range where the response is essentially a linear function of the concentration of the analyte. The response factor (GC/MS methods) or calibration factor (GC, HPLC methods) is the ratio of the response of the instrument to the concentration (or amount) of analyte introduced into the instrument. The advantage of the linear calibration is that the response factor or calibration factor represents the slope of the calibration "curve," and is relatively constant, simplifying the calculations and the interpretation of the data.

All of the SW-846 methods involving multipoint calibrations specify some criterion for determining the linearity of the calibration "curve." The criterion will vary by type of method. For instance, SW-846 metals methods specify a linear regression, and may employ a correlation coefficient as the criterion while most organic methods employ calibration or response factors and utilize the relative standard deviation of those factors as the criterion.

In the 8000 Series methods, the linearity specification varies from method to method, depending on the quantitation technique. The typical limits on the RSD are:

- 20% for the gas chromatography (GC) and high performance liquid chromatography (HPLC) methods, and

- 15% for analytes determined by the internal standard technique in the gas chromatography/mass spectrometry (GC/MS) methods (e.g., 8260 and 8270).

If the calibration is not linear, as determined by the RSD of the response factor or calibration factor, then Method 8000B describes several other techniques that may be used to evaluate the calibration. These include the use of a narrower calibration, a linear regression that is not forced through the origin, and a polynomial regression of third order or less that relates the instrument response to the concentration.

In the case of methods such as 8260 and 8270, EPA has identified two subsets of the target analytes in each method, the calibration check compounds (CCCs) and the system performance check compounds (SPCCs). The CCCs are used to evaluate the linearity of the calibration. If the %RSD of these compounds meet the method specifications, then OSW assumes that the calibration of the other compounds is sufficiently linear to be employed. The SPCCs are evaluated on the basis of minimum response factors. These compounds were chosen as obvious problem compounds in terms of instrument response and sensitivity. If the response factors for the SPCCs meet the minimum criteria, then the instrument conditions are adequate for the other analytes. If the CCCs or the SPCCs are not target analytes for a particular project, then the laboratory need not include these compounds in the calibration standards. However, in that instance, OSW holds the compounds that are in the calibration standards to the stringent linearity criteria listed above.

As noted earlier, the SW-846 inorganic methods for metals may involve a single-point calibration for ICP analyses and a three-point calibration for atomic absorption and graphite furnace analyses. There are no specific QC limits associated with the linearity of the calibration line.

4. Calibration Verification

Calibration verification involves the analysis of a single standard, typically in the middle of the calibration range, at the beginning of each analytical shift. The concentration of each analyte in this standard is determined using the initial calibration data and is compared to specifications in the method. If the results are within the specifications, the laboratory is allowed to proceed with analysis without recalibrating, and use the initial calibration data to quantify sample results.

Calibration verification differs in concept and practice from "continuing calibration" that is described in the CLP methods. In this latter technique, a standard is analyzed, and new response factors or calibration factors are calculated on the basis of that analysis. If the new factors are close to the average from the initial calibration, all subsequent sample analyses are conducted using these "updated" response or calibration factors. The degree of "closeness" is generally measured as the percent difference between the old and new factors. The problem with "continuing calibration" is that it amounts to a daily single-point calibration. Information about the behavior of the instrument at concentrations above and below that of this single standard can only be inferred from the initial multiple-point calibration. OSW does not support the use of a single calibration standard to update response or calibration factors.

Specifications for calibration verification are generally given as a percentage difference from the test concentration, and vary with the specific method, depending on the quantitation technique. For the SW-846 GC and HPLC methods, the difference must be within ± 15%. For GC/MS methods, the difference must be within ± 20%.

If calibration cannot be verified, the laboratory may either recalibrate the instrument, or prepare a fresh calibration standard and make a second attempt to verify calibration. If calibration cannot be verified with a fresh calibration standard, the instrument must be recalibrated. If calibration is not verified, subsequent data are not considered valid until the instrument is recalibrated.

5. Initial Demonstration of Capability

This test is required prior to the use of the method by the laboratory. It is sometimes termed the "start-up test." The laboratory must demonstrate that it can meet the specifications in the method for the recovery of analytes spiked into a reference matrix (reagent water). The test consists of spiking the analytes of interest into a set of four portions of reagent water and analyzing these four samples. The mean concentration and the standard deviation of the mean concentration are calculated for each analyte, and these values are compared to specifications in each method. If the mean and standard deviation are within the limits, the laboratory can use the method to analyze field samples. For some methods, a repeat test is allowed because of the large number of analytes being tested simultaneously.

As with the documentation of the purity of the standards, the start-up test data need not be submitted with each set of sample results, but should be submitted the first time a laboratory is employed for analyses, and updated as changes to the method necessitate (see below).

It is also important to remember that if a change is made to a method, the start-up test must be repeated with the change as an integral part of the method. Such changes may involve alternative extraction, concentration, or cleanup processes, alternative GC columns, GC conditions, or detectors, or other steps designed to address a particular matrix problem. For SW-846 methods, there are a large number of possible combinations of extraction, cleanup, and determinative methods. The initial demonstration test should be completed for each combination of methods used for sample analyses.

6. Analysis of Blanks

Blanks should be analyzed on a routine basis, when any part of the analytical process has been changed, and whenever contamination of the laboratory is suspected. A blank should be prepared and analyzed with each batch of samples. The SW-846 definition of a "batch" leaves something to be desired, but stipulates that a batch is a group of up to 20 samples "processed as a unit." This "processing" is intended to begin with the sample extraction, digestion, or other preparative procedures. In practice this may be interpreted that, on each day that a laboratory prepares samples, they also must prepare a blank, even if fewer than 20 samples are prepared. Another valid interpretation would require a blank every set of 20 samples, even if processed over several days as long as all the reagents and other processing steps remain constant. The batch concept should not be construed as requiring that all samples extracted together must be analyzed together.

The purpose of preparing a blank with each set of samples is to determine the extent of possible contamination of the samples while in the laboratory. If the blank is handled by the same analysts in the same way as the samples, and the blank shows no contamination, then it is likely that the samples will not have been contaminated.

Contamination in the laboratory is a common problem, though there are many opinions on what constitutes contamination. In practice, it is not unusual to find low levels of common laboratory solvents, phthalates, and other ubiquitous compounds in laboratory blanks. The problem is most critical for the analysis of volatile organic contaminants, where the solvents in use in other parts of the laboratory may limit the ultimate sensitivity of the volatile analysis.

Controlling laboratory contamination is an important aspect of each laboratory's quality assurance plan. The laboratory should maintain records—typically in the form of control charts—of blank contaminants. These records should prompt corrective action by the laboratory, including reanalysis of any affected samples. Such control charts or other demonstrations of laboratory contamination monitoring and control, may be requested by the reviewer in evaluating sample results, however, they are not routinely submitted with sample data.

Unfortunately, by the time that the data are submitted, it is usually too late for corrective action insofar as laboratory contamination is concerned. Therefore, the reviewer has several options in making use of the sample data. First, if a contaminant is present in a blank, but not an analyte of concern for the project, then there is little need for concern about the sample results. Secondly, if a contaminant is present in a blank, but not present in a sample, then there is also little need for concern.

The third approach deals with instances where the blank contaminant is also reported in a sample. A useful rule of thumb is that:

- If the sample result is at least ten times that in the blank, then the likely contribution to the sample from the laboratory environment is at most 10%. Because most of the methods are no more accurate than that level, the possible contamination is negligible.

- If the sample result is at least five times but less than ten times the blank result, the compound is probably present in the sample, but the numerical result should be considered an upper limit of the true concentration.

- If the sample result is below five times the level in the blank, there is no adequate means by which to judge whether or not the sample result is attributable to laboratory contamination.

There are two difficulties in evaluating sample results relative to blank contamination. First, the reviewer must be able to associate the samples with the correct blanks. For analysis of volatiles by purge-and-trap techniques, where no sample extraction is required, the blanks and samples are associated by the date and time of analysis, and the results of the blanks are specific to the instrument as well. For methods involving the extraction of organic compounds from the samples, the blanks and samples are primarily associated by the date on which they were extracted.

The second difficulty involves samples that have been diluted. The dilution of the sample with reagent water or the dilution of the extract with solvent represent additional potential sources of contamination that will not be reflected in the results for the blank unless the blank was similarly diluted. Therefore, in applying the ten-times rule, the concentration of the sample is compared to the blank result multiplied by the dilution factor of the sample or sample extract.

Subtracting the concentration of the analyte in the blank from the concentration of the analyte in the sample is not a reliable method of determining the true concentration of the analyte in the sample. The obvious problem occurs when the blank concentration is higher than that in the sample, and subtraction would yield a negative concentration value. Using the ten-times rule above provides a more appropriate means of evaluating the results, and does not require that the reviewer alter the results reported by the laboratory.

7. Matrix Spike Results

SW-846 methods require a spike of the analytes of interest into a second aliquot of the sample after an initial analysis of the sample. The purpose of spiking the sample (often termed a "matrix spike") is to determine if the method is applicable to the sample in question.

If the recovery of the matrix spike is within the limits specified in the method, then the method is judged to be applicable to that sample matrix. If, however, the recovery of the spike is not within the recovery range specified, either the method does not work on the sample, or the analytical process is out of control. If the analytical process is out of control, the laboratory must take immediate corrective action before any more samples are analyzed.

8. QC Check Samples

To separate issues of method performance from issues of laboratory performance, the laboratory should obtain and analyze a quality control check standard from an external source. If such samples are not available, the laboratory should prepare and analyze a spike of the analytes in reagent water. This spiked reagent water aliquot is often called a laboratory control sample (LCS). If the results for the quality control standard are not within the range specified, then the analytical system must be repaired and the sample and spiked sample analyses repeated. If the recovery of this spike is within the range specified, then the analytical process is judged to be in control. However, regardless of the analytical process being in control, the results of the sample analysis are questionable with respect to acceptance for regulatory compliance purposes when the matrix spike results on the specific sample indicate that the method is not applicable to the sample.

In instances where matrix spike recoveries are not within the specifications, it still may be possible to use the sample results for compliance monitoring purposes. In particular, if the recovery of the spiked compound is above the method specifications and the compound is not detected in the sample analysis, it is unlikely that the compound is present in the sample. This is because the factors that caused the analysis to over-estimate the concentration in the spiked sample would not likely have resulted in an under-estimate in the unspiked sample. For samples in which the compound is detected, but the matrix spike is above the method specifications, the concentration reported in the unspiked sample is likely an upper limit of the true concentration.

E. Data Validation Reports

As the saying goes, "No job's over 'till the paperwork's done." Sometimes the hardest part of validating a data package is communicating the validation results to the ultimate data user. The CLP approach typically involves a collection of relatively standardized forms and the application of additional data qualifier "flags." While this approach certainly can work, a data validation report for RCRA analyses may simply take the form of a detailed narrative description of the findings.

A basic format for a validation report includes:

- An introduction that identifies the laboratory, lists each sample that was analyzed by both the client's identifier and any laboratory sample identifier, and indicates what analyses were performed on each sample. This introduction can include a table that cross-references the sample identifiers, lab identifiers, and method numbers.

- A description, in general terms, of the aspects of the data that were evaluated. The list of elements in the section "How Much Data Validation is Enough?" will often suffice.

- References to the sources of all QC criteria employed in the validation, whether from a specific QAPP or described in the individual methods.

- A sample-by-sample list of the validation results. This list may be broken down by analysis type and samples grouped into three or more categories:
  - Sample results that meet all the project expectations
  - Sample results that should be used with some caution
  - Sample results that should not be used, or used only with extreme caution.

The reviewer should avoid finger pointing and accusation at all costs. As noted in Chapter 1, the reviewer's job is not to find fault or cause the laboratory to change its practices, but to determine the quality of the results relative to the end use of the data. The data validation report should focus on the facts, substantiate any concerns with references to specific samples or pages in the data package, and clearly state the conclusions in terms that the end user can understand. Accomplishing all that is often hard enough without playing "Big Brother" to the laboratory.

F. Specific Examples of Methods

1. Volatile Organic Analysis (VOA) by GC/MS Method 8260B

Method 8260B is a determinative method for volatile target analytes using a gas chromatograph-mass spectrometer (GC/MS). The most frequently sample introduction is achieved with a purge and trap (Methods 5030 and 5035) for water and soil samples, although many other methods are listed in SW-846 that are amenable to other matrices. Over 100 compounds are listed that can be determined using this method, although it is impossible to calibrate and analyze for all of them at the same time. The most important asset of the method is the generation of the mass spectrum as an aid to correct identification of calibrated target analytes. Misidentifications of random materials in the sample as target analytes are very rare, thus false positives are minimal with this technique. The downside is that it takes highly trained and very skillful instrument operators and data interpreters to perform the analysis and meet all the method specifications. Many of the quality control requirements and acceptance limits are discussed in Chapter 1, the introduction to Chapter 4, and Methods 3500, 5000, and 8000 of SW-846, in addition to those specifically addressed in Method 8260B.

1.1 Initial Demonstration of Proficiency

This quality control is discussed in Method 8000, Section 8.4. At least four spiked samples of reagent water are analyzed using the appropriate combination of sample preparation and determinative method. The mean and standard deviation of the results are computed and compared to the data presented in the Tables at the end of the method.

1.2 MDL Determinations

The procedure for determination of the method detection limit (MDL) is given in Chapter 1 of SW-846. It should be performed for each target analyte. Verify that a proper MDL study has been performed. Check the equation used for calculation of the standard deviation to insure "n-1" has been used rather than "n" in the denominator. Check the value of the Student's t-test multiplier to verify it has been used correctly.

The value obtained from the MDL study must be less or equal to the reporting limit. There is generally no reliability that can be placed on values or detection limits that are less than demonstrated method detection limits.

1.3 Initial Calibration Requirements

Method 8260B specifically states that any target analyte reported as being determined by this method must be calibrated at five levels of concentration. One of the levels must be at or very near the method detection limit. The other four concentrations define the range of the calibration. The calibration must be performed in the same manner as the sample introduction, *i.e.* using a purge and trap in this example. Calibration is performed using an internal standard procedure with Response factor (Rf) as the quantitation constant. The linearity of the calibration for each compound is acceptable if the %RSD of the individual Rf is less than 15%. If any compound (other than the calibration check compounds, CCC) exhibits %RSD >15%, then one of the alternate calibration options detailed in Method 8000 must be exercised.

The general success of the initial calibration is assessed using the System Performance Check Compounds (SPCC, Table 6-2) and Calibration Check Compounds (CCC, Table 6-3). The acceptance criteria for these checks are included in the Tables. If these criteria are not met the initial calibration must be repeated.

Table 6-2. **System Performance Check Compounds and Acceptance Criteria for Method 8260B**

SPCC	Minimum Rf
Chloromethane	0.10
1,1-Dichloroethane	0.10
Bromoform	0.10
Chlorobenzene	0.30
1,1,2,2-Tetrachloroethane	0.30

Table 6-3. **Calibration Check Compounds (CCC) and Acceptance Criteria for Method 8260B**

CCC	Maximum %RSD	CCC	Maximum %RSD
1,1-Dichloroethene	30	Toluene	30
Chloroform	30	Ethylbenzene	30
1,2-Dichloropropane	30	Vinyl chloride	30

1.4 Continuing Calibration Verification and Tuning Frequency and Acceptance Criteria

On a daily basis 5 to 50 ng of 4-bromofluorobenzene (BFB) is injected into the GC/MS and a mass spectrum acquired. The suggested criteria that the tune should meet are listed in Table 6-4. Other tune criteria can be used. The tune must be checked every 12 hours of operation and prior to initial calibration.

Table 6-4. **Suggested BFB Tune Criteria for Method 8260B**

m/z	Acceptance criteria
50	15-40% of mass 95
75	30-60% of mass 95
95	100%
96	5-9% of mass 95
173	<2% of mass 174
174	>50% of mass 95
175	5-9% of mass 174
176	>95 but <101% of mass 174
177	5-9% of mass 176

Continuing calibration consists of analysis of a mid-range calibration solution at the beginning of each 12-hour work shift. The Rf or amount of each analyte in the solution is calculated. The calibration verification is determined based on the behavior and results obtained for the SPCC and CCC. The SPCC must meet the criteria listed in Table 6-2. The CCC are evaluated based on the percent difference (%D) of the Rf from the initial calibration.

$$\%D = \frac{Rf_I - Rf_D}{Rf_I} \text{x } 110$$

where: Rf_I is the average Rf from the initial calibration for the compound.
           Rf_D is the daily Rf generated from the calibration check.

The %D for each CCC must be less than 20%. If a compound fails to meet the acceptance criteria, the situation must be corrected, and all results generated since the last successful continuing calibration check must be examined closely. Based on the equation used for the calculation of the amount of analyte in the sample:

$$\text{Amount µg/L } = \frac{\text{Area}_{sample} \text{ x Amount}_{int. Std.} \text{ x } 1000}{\text{Area}_{Int. Std.} \text{ x Rf x V}}$$

where: Area_{sample} is the area of the quantitation ion of the target analyte.
         $\text{Amount}_{int. Std.}$ is the amount of the internal standard added to the sample in µg.
         $\text{Area}_{Int. Std.}$ is the area of the quantitation ion of the internal standard.
         Rf is the original Rf generated in the initial calibration.
         V is the volume of the sample in mL.

If the daily Rf generated in the continuing calibration is significantly larger than the RF from the initial calibration (%D > 30%), then falsely high amounts of analyte in the sample will be calculated. Analytes reported as not detected are probably usable. However, analytes reported as greater than the detection limit represent a maximum possible value for the analyte in the sample.

When the daily Rf is significantly (%D >30%) lower than the Rf from the initial calibration, the amount of target analytes reported in the sample is going to be an underestimation. Analytes reported as not-detected may, in fact, be in the sample. Analytes reported as present in the sample are generally underestimated and the value should be viewed as the minimum amount present in the sample.

1.5 Sample Collection, Preservation and Handling Procedures

Sample collection, preservation and handling is matrix dependent. Some directions are given in the Introduction to Chapter 4, while other information may be found in Chapters 2 and 11 of SW-846. In general samples should be collected in glass containers with a Teflon® cap or septum liner, with minimum headspace in the sample. Some samples are acidified to pH >2 with hydrochloric acid and some are dechlorinated if oxidizing agents are present; however, this depends on the specific regulatory program. Samples are cooled to 4°C after sampling, and holding times are most commonly 14 days.

When samples do not meet the specifications for collection, preservation or holding time, the data need to be closely examined. The common evaluation is that target analytes reported as non-detected are not reliable results, while amounts of detected target analytes represent a minimum concentration in the sample. These evaluations are based on the expectations that there will be a loss of target analyte from the sample with improper sampling and handling.

1.6 Sample Batches and Blanks

Sample batches in VOC analysis are generally considered to consist of all the samples that were processed and analyzed over a 12-hour work shift. Blanks should be analyzed with every set of samples or every time there is a change in reagents through each instrument used for generation of results. When a highly contaminated sample has been processed through a multiposition purge and trap instrument, the next use of that port should be closely monitored for the possible presence of carry-over contamination. A blank purged through that position can verify the lack of carry-over. Blanks should be monitored closely for the presence of target analytes and common laboratory contamination such as methylene chloride, acetone, and other solvents. The reagent water prepared in the laboratory through deionization with cartridges can be a significant source of toluene, xylene, and styrene.

Trip and field blanks are a normal part of the sampling and analysis protocol for VOC. When samples are found with target analytes in them, the trip and field blanks must be analyzed and evaluated to rule out the possibility of improper sampling or handling.

1.7 Laboratory Control Samples

Laboratory control samples (LCS) are processed with each batch of samples to monitor laboratory performance on "perfect" samples. In the absence of laboratory generated acceptance limits, control limits of 70-130% are normally used. This range may be unreasonably high for some of the more water-soluble analytes, for example, acetone and some of the ethers and alcohols, which may be target analytes. However, many laboratories will use the matrix spike compound list for the LCS (Table 6-5), and these compounds are, in general, very well behaved. The results obtained from these compounds are not very applicable to more difficult to analyze materials.

The LCS is the primary demonstration on a daily basis of the ability to analyze samples with good qualitative and quantitative accuracy. High recoveries of the LCS relate directly to falsely high reported values of detected analytes in samples. For those analytes not detected in the sample, the data are usable in the sense that the MDL has, in actuality, not been exceeded. However, for analytes reported as greater than the MDL, there is a strong possibility that a false positive has been generated, and the data are not reliable.

Low recoveries in the LCS means that target analytes are reported as lower than they actually are in the sample. Values for analytes reported as larger than the MDL, reflect actual amounts in the sample, which exceed the MDL. However, values reported as not detected may, in fact, be present in greater amounts in the samples and the data are unreliable.

1.8 Matrix spikes

Matrix spikes and matrix spike duplicates are to be run with each batch of samples of a similar matrix to determine any matrix effects on the analysis. In the absence of any specific laboratory generated acceptance limits, control limits of 70-130% can be used as an approximation. The matrix spike compounds suggested in Method 8260B are listed in Table 6-5.

Table 6-5. **Matrix Spike Compounds Used in Method 8260B**

Compound	Nominal Spike Level µg/L
1,1-Dichloroethene	50
Trichloroethene	50
Chlorobenzene	50
Toluene	50
Benzene	50

The most common matrix effect noted in samples is co-eluting background materials, for instance, gasoline. These materials cause interference in two major ways. First they can co-elute with the target analytes and either cause false positive results due to fortuitous presence of the target analyte quantitation ions or they can mask the target analyte and cause false negatives. Second, the background can interfere with the internal standard causing quantitation problems with target analytes. In extreme cases the internal standard can not be found at all. Occasionally, samples high in organic content can present problems in the purge process, and the analytes are not effectively removed from the samples. An examination of the sample itself and the raw data chromatogram and/or mass spectrum will frequently help to sort out the problems. Further, any of these situations may suggest that alternate sample preparation or analysis procedures—and there are many in SW-846—may be needed to successfully determine the target analyte contents of the sample.

1.9 Replicate Analysis

Replicates of either samples or matrix spiked samples are used to evaluate method precision. Precision is normally evaluated through the use of relative percent difference (RPD). Lack of precision may indicate very non-homogeneous samples, a frequent occurrence when solids are analyzed, or it may indicate a problem with the instrument or analyst consistency. If LCS duplicates have been performed and acceptable precision is noted there, in general, instrument or analyst problems can be ruled out as the cause.

1.10 Internal Standard and Surrogate Recoveries

The internal standards and surrogates suggested for use in Method 8260B are presented in Table 6-6. These are added to each sample prior to processing. Normally the surrogates and internal standards are present at 50 µg/L. Surrogates should be fully calibrated at five levels along with the target analytes in the initial calibration.

Table 6-6. **Internal Standards and Surrogates Used in Method 8260B**

Internal Standards	Surrogates
Fluorobenzene	Toluene-D$_8$
Chlorobenzene-D$_5$	4-Bromofluorobenzene
1,4-Dichlorobenzene-D$_4$	1,2-Dichloroethane-D$_4$
	Dibromofluoromethane

Internal standards are used as the quantitation and relative retention time standard for the target analytes. If the retention time of the internal standard changes by more than 30 seconds from the last calibration verification, corrections to the system must be made and the sample re-analyzed. If the area of the internal standard is not within a factor of two (50 - 200%) of the last calibration verification, the quantitation of target analytes may be significantly off. This may be a symptom of instrument malfunction, operator error, or sample matrix effects. Examination of the raw data chromatogram and mass spectrum of the internal standard may help clarify the problem.

Low area counts for the internal standards translates into falsely high reported values for target analytes in the samples. Compounds that are not detected in the sample really do not exceed these limits and the results are reliable. However, target analytes reported from the analysis as above the MDL may, in actuality, be less than the MDL. Any reported value for an analyte is an estimate when aberrations in the internal standards occur.

The laboratory must generate warning and control limits for surrogate recoveries. The surrogate recoveries obtained during analysis of the sample are compared against the laboratory derived acceptance limits. Low surrogate recoveries are an indication of low target analyte recoveries. Target analytes reported as not detected in the sample may, in actuality, be present in larger amounts than reported. Target analytes reported as exceeding the MDL really are present above the MDL. High surrogate recoveries suggest a problem with internal standard areas.

1.11 Target analyte identification

Target analyte identification is performed by matching the retention time of the candidate compound with that of the target analyte in the most recent continuing calibration verification and by matching the mass spectrum of the candidate with a user generated spectrum.

The retention times are evaluated through use of the relative retention time (RRT), the retention time of the target analyte divided by that of the nearest internal standard. The RRT of the target analyte and that of the candidate must agree within ±0.06 RRT.

The spectra are compared by matching the three characteristic (largest or unique) ions of the standard with that of the candidate compound. The characteristic ions must agree within 30% relative abundance and must maximize in abundance within one scan of each other across the peak of the candidate.

Reported target analyte hits that do not meet the identification criteria are false positives.

Non-calibrated compounds present in the chromatogram may be tentatively identified through first performing an automated reference library search, then human evaluation of the tentative identification. The interpretation takes the form of first comparing the reference spectrum against the candidate spectrum. All ions of greater than 10% intensity and all unique ions in the reference spectrum must be present in the candidate spectrum. Second, the candidate spectrum is compared to the reference spectrum. Miscellaneous peaks in the candidate spectrum not present in the reference spectrum should be explainable.

2. Semivolatile Organic Compounds by GC/MS Method 8270C

Method 8270C is a determinative method for semivolatile target analytes using a gas chromatograph-mass spectrometer (GC/MS). There are many sample preparation techniques listed in the 3500-series methods that can be used to generate sample extracts for this procedure. Sample clean-up using one or more of the 3600-series procedures is highly recommended. Over 250 compounds are listed that can be determined using this method, although it is impossible to calibrate and analyze for all of them at the same time. The most important asset of the method is the generation of the mass spectrum as an aid to correct identification of calibrated target analytes. Misidentifications of random materials in the sample as target analytes are very rare, thus false positives are minimal with this technique. The downside is that it takes highly trained and very skillful instrument operators and data interpreters to perform the analysis and meet all the method specifications. Many of the quality control requirements and acceptance limits are discussed in Chapter 1, the introduction to Chapter 4, and Methods 3500 and 8000 of SW-846, in addition to those specifically addressed in Method 8270C.

2.1 Initial Demonstration of Proficiency

This quality control is discussed in Method 8000, Section 8.4. At least four spiked samples of reagent water are analyzed using the appropriate combination of sample preparation and determinative method. The mean and standard deviation of the results are computed and compared to the data presented in the Tables at the end of the method.

2.2 MDL Determinations

The procedure for determination of the method detection limit (MDL) is given in Chapter 1 of SW-846. It should be performed for each target analyte. Verify that a proper MDL study has been performed. Check the equation used for calculation of the standard deviation to insure "n-1" has been used rather than "n" in the denominator. Check the value of the Student's t-test multiplier to verify it has been used correctly.

The value obtained from the MDL study must be less or equal to the reporting limit. There is generally no reliability that can be placed on values or detection limits that are less than demonstrated method detection limits.

2.3 Initial Calibration Requirements

Method 8270C specifically states that any target analyte reported as being determined by this method must be calibrated at five levels of concentration. One of the levels must be at or very near the method detection limit. The other four concentrations define the range of the calibration. Calibration is performed using an internal standard procedure with Response factor (Rf) as the quantitation constant. The linearity of the calibration for each compound is acceptable if the %RSD of the individual Rf is less than 15%. If any compound (other than the calibration check compounds, CCC) exhibits %RSD >15%, then one of the alternate calibration options detailed in Method 8000 must be exercised.

The general success of the initial calibration is assessed using the System Performance Check Compounds (SPCC, Table 6-7) and Calibration Check Compounds (CCC, Table 6-8). The acceptance criteria for these checks are included in the Tables. If these criteria are not met, the initial calibration must be repeated.

Table 6-7. **System Performance Check Compounds and Acceptance Criteria for Method 8270C**

SPCC	Minimum Rf
N-Nitroso-di-n-propylamine	0.05
Hexachlorocyclopentadiene	0.05
2,4-Dinitrophenol	0.05
4-Nitrophenol	0.05

Table 6-8. **Calibration Check Compounds (CCC) and Acceptance Criteria for Method 8270C**

CCC	Maximum %RSD	CCC	Maximum %RSD
Acenaphthene	30	4-Chloro-3-methylphenol	30
1,4-Dichlorobenzene	30	2,4-Dichlorophenol	30
Hexachlorobutadiene	30	2-Nitrophenol	30
N-Nitrosodiphenylamine	30	Phenol	30
Di-n-octylphthalate	30	Pentachlorophenol	30
Fluoranthene	30	2,4,6-Trichlorophenol	30
Benzo(a)pyrene	30		

2.4 Continuing Calibration Verification and Tuning Frequency and Acceptance Criteria

On a daily basis 50 ng of decafluorotriphenylphosphine (DFTPP) is injected into the GC/MS and a mass spectrum acquired. The suggested criteria that the tune should meet are listed in Table 6-9. Other tune criteria can be used. The tune must be checked every 12 hours of operation and prior to initial calibration.

Table 6-9. **Suggested DFTPP Tune Criteria for Method 8270C**

m/z	Acceptance criteria
51	30-60% of mass 198
68	<2% of mass 69
70	<2% of mass 69
127	40-60% of mass 198
197	<1% of mass 198
198	Base peak
199	5-9% of mass 198
275	10-30% of mass 198
365	>1% of mass 198
441	Present but less than mass 443
442	>40% of mass 198
443	17-23% of mass 442

Continuing calibration consists of analysis of a mid-range calibration solution at the beginning of each 12-hour work shift. The Rf or amount of each analyte in the solution is calculated. The calibration verification is determined based on the behavior and results obtained for the SPCC and CCC. The SPCC must meet the criteria listed in Table 6-8. The CCC are evaluated based on the percent difference (%D) of the Rf from the initial calibration.

$$\%D = \frac{Rf_I - Rf_D}{Rf_I} \times 110$$

where: Rf_I is the average Rf from the initial calibration for the compound.
Rf_D is the daily Rf generated from the calibration check.

The %D for each CCC must be less than 20%. If a compound fails to meet the acceptance criteria, the situation must be corrected, and all results generated since the last successful continuing calibration check must be examined closely. Based on the equation used for the calculation of the amount of analyte in the sample:

$$\text{Amount } \mu g/L = \frac{\text{Area}_{\text{sample}} \times \text{Amount}_{\text{int. Std.}} \times 1000}{\text{Area}_{\text{Int. Std.}} \times Rf \times V}$$

where: $\text{Area}_{\text{sample}}$ is the area of the quantitation ion of the target analyte.
 $\text{Amount}_{\text{int. Std.}}$ is the amount of the internal standard added to the sample in μg.
 $\text{Area}_{\text{Int. Std.}}$ is the area of the quantitation ion of the internal standard.
 Rf is the original Rf generated in the initial calibration.
 V is the volume of the sample in mL.

if the daily Rf generated in the continuing calibration is significantly larger than the RF from the initial calibration (%D > 30%), then falsely high amounts of analyte in the sample will be calculated. Analytes reported as not detected are probably usable as data. However, analytes reported as greater than the detection limit represent a maximum possible value for the analyte in the sample.

When the daily Rf is significantly (%D >30%) lower than the Rf from the initial calibration, the amount of target analytes reported in the sample is going to be an underestimation. Analytes reported as not-detected may, in fact, be in the sample. Analytes reported as present in the sample are generally underestimated, and the value should be viewed as the minimum amount present in the sample.

2.5 Sample Collection, Preservation and Handling Procedures

Sample collection, preservation, and handling are matrix dependent. Some directions are given in the Introduction to Chapter 4, while other information may be found in Chapters 2 and 11 of SW-846. In general, samples should be collected in glass containers with a Teflon® cap liner. Some samples are dechlorinated if oxidizing agents are present; however, this depends on the specific regulatory program. Samples are cooled to 4°C after sampling, and holding times are most commonly seven days until extraction. Sample extracts should be stored in screw-capped vials with unpierced Teflon® faced septa at -10°C in the dark until analysis. In most cases sample extracts may be held up to 40 days until analysis.

When samples do not meet the specifications for collection, preservation, or holding time, the data need to be closely examined. The common evaluation is that target analytes reported as non-detected are not reliable results, while amounts of detected target analytes represent a minimum concentration in the sample. These evaluations are based on the expectations that there will be a loss of target analyte from the sample with improper sampling and handling.

2.6 Sample Preparation Batches and Blanks

Sample batches in semivolatile analysis are keyed to the sample extraction/preparation process. Blanks should be processed and analyzed with every set of samples of up to 20 samples or every time there is a change in reagents. Blanks should be monitored closely for the presence of target analytes and common laboratory contamination such as the phthalates.

Field blanks and equipment rinses are a normal part of the sampling and analysis protocol for semivolatile target analytes. When samples are found with target analytes in them, the field and equipment blanks must be analyzed and evaluated to rule out the possibility of improper sampling or handling.

When blank contamination is found, normally the ten-times rule is applied, although for some applications, such as contaminant plume mapping or risk assessment a twenty-times multiplier is thought to be more appropriate. The ten-times rule suggests that target analytes present in samples at more than ten-times the level of the same analyte found in the blank, should be viewed as really present in the sample. If the analyte is found in the sample at less than ten-times the amount found in the blank, then the conclusion is that sample contamination by the laboratory or sampling process has occurred.

2.7 Laboratory Control Samples

Laboratory control samples (LCS) are processed with each batch of samples to monitor laboratory performance on "perfect" samples. The spike solution used for the LCS is normally the same as that used for the matrix spike solution (Table 6-10). In the absence of laboratory generated acceptance limits, control limits of 70-130% for recovery are suggested. This range may be unreasonably narrow for many semivolatile target analytes, and the QA acceptance tables given at the end of the method may have more realistic ranges. When LCS duplicates have been performed, the average recovery of the two analyses is a better guide to recovery determination for the batch. An estimate of precision (RPD) is also possible.

The LCS is the primary demonstration on a daily basis of the ability to analyze samples with good qualitative and quantitative accuracy. Surrogate compound recoveries in the LCS must be within acceptance limits. High recoveries of the LCS relate directly to falsely high reported values of detected analytes in samples. For those analytes that are not detected in the sample, the data are usable in the sense that the MDL has, in actuality, not been exceeded. However, for analytes reported as greater than the MDL, there is a strong possibility that a false positive has been generated, and the data are not reliable.

Low recoveries in the LCS means that target analytes are reported as lower than they actually are in the sample. Values for analytes reported as larger than the MDL, reflect actual amounts in the sample that exceed the MDL. However, values reported as not detected may, in fact, be present in greater amounts in the samples, and the data are unreliable.

2.8 Matrix Spikes

Matrix spikes and matrix spike duplicates are to be run with each batch of samples of a similar matrix to determine any matrix effects on the analysis. In the absence of any specific laboratory generated acceptance limits, control limits of 70-130% can be used as an approximation. This range may be unreasonably narrow for many semivolatile target analytes and the QA acceptance tables given at the end of the method may have more realistic ranges. The matrix spike compounds suggested in Method 3500B/8270C are listed in Table 6-10.

Table 6-10.   Matrix Spike Compounds Used in Method 3500B/8270C

Compound	Nominal Spike Level µg/L
1,2,4-Trichlorobenzene	100
Acenaphthene	100
2,4-Dinitrotoluene	100
Pyrene	100
N-Nitroso-di-n-propylamine	100
1,4-Dichlorobenzene	100
Pentachlorophenol	200
Phenol	200
2-Chlorophenol	200
4-Chloro-3methylphenol	200
4-Nitrophenol	200

The most common matrix effect noted in samples is co-eluting background materials, for instance petroleum based fuels. These materials cause interference in two major ways. First they can co-elute with the target analytes and either cause false positive results due to fortuitous presence of the target analyte quantitation ions or they can mask the target analyte and cause false negatives. Second, the background can interfere with the internal standard causing quantitation problems with target analytes. In extreme cases the internal standard can not be found at all. Occasionally, samples high in organic content can present problems in the purge process, and the analytes are not effectively removed from the samples. An examination of the sample itself and the raw data chromatogram and/or mass spectrum will frequently help to sort out the problems. Further, any of these situations may suggest that alternate sample preparation, clean-up or analysis procedures—and there are many in SW-846—may be needed to successfully determine the target analyte contents of the sample.

2.9 Replicate Analysis

Replicates of either samples or matrix-spiked samples are used to evaluate method precision. Precision is normally evaluated through the use of relative percent difference (RPD). Lack of precision may indicate very non-homogeneous samples, a frequent occurrence when solids are analyzed, or it may indicate a problem with the instrument or analyst consistency. If LCS duplicates have been performed, and acceptable precision is noted there, in general, instrument or analyst problems can be ruled out as the cause.

2.10 Internal Standard and Surrogate Recoveries

The internal standards and surrogates suggested for use in Method 3500B/8270C are presented in Table 6-11. These are added to each sample prior to processing. Normally the acid (phenolic) surrogates are used at 200 µg/L; the other surrogates at 100 µg/L, and internal standards are added at 40 µg/L. Surrogates should be fully calibrated at five levels along with the target analytes in the initial calibration.

Table 6-11.   Internal Standards and Surrogates Used in Method 3500B/8270C

Internal Standards	Surrogates
1,4-Dichlorobenzene-D_4	Phenol-D_5
Naphthalene-D_8	2-Fluorophenol
Acenaphthene-D_{10}	2,4,6-Tribromophenol
Phenanthrene-D_{10}	Nitrobenzene-D_5
Chrysene-D_{12}	2-Fluorobiphenyl
Perylene-D_{12}	Terphenyl-D_{14}

Internal standards are used as the quantitation and relative retention time standard for the target analytes. If the retention time of the internal standard changes by more than 30 seconds from the last calibration verification, corrections to the system must be made and the sample re-analyzed. If the area of the internal standard is not within a factor of two (50 - 200%) of the last calibration verification the quantitation of target analytes may be significantly off. This may be a symptom of instrument malfunction, operator error, or sample matrix effects. Examination of the raw data chromatogram and mass spectrum of the internal standard may help clarify the problem.

Low area counts for the internal standards translates into falsely high reported values for target analytes in the samples. Compounds that are not-detected in the sample really do not exceed these limits, and the results are reliable. However, target analytes reported from the analysis as above the MDL may, in actuality, be less than the MDL. When aberrations in the internal standards occur, any reported value for an analyte is an estimate.

The laboratory must generate warning and control limits for surrogate recoveries. The surrogate recoveries obtained during analysis of the sample are compared against the laboratory derived acceptance limits. Low surrogate recoveries are an indication of low target analyte recoveries. Target analytes reported as not detected in the sample may, in actuality, be present in larger amounts than reported. Target analytes reported as exceeding the MDL really are present above the MDL. High surrogate recoveries suggest a problem with internal standard areas.

2.11 Target Analyte Identification

Target analyte identification is performed by matching the retention time of the candidate compound with that of the target analyte in the most recent continuing calibration verification and by matching the mass spectrum of the candidate with a user-generated spectrum.

The retention times are evaluated through use of the relative retention time (RRT), the retention time of the target analyte divided by that of the nearest internal standard. The RRT of the target analyte and that of the candidate must agree within ±0.06 RRT.

The spectra are compared by matching the three characteristic (largest or unique) ions of the standard with that of the candidate compound. The characteristic ions must agree within 30% relative abundance and must maximize in abundance within one scan of each other across the peak of the candidate.

Reported target analyte hits that do not meet the identification criteria are false positives.

Non-calibrated compounds present in the chromatogram may be tentatively identified through first performing an automated reference library search, then human evaluation of the tentative identification. The interpretation takes the form of first comparing the reference spectrum against the candidate spectrum. All ions of greater than 10% intensity and all unique ions in the reference spectrum must be present in the candidate spectrum. Second, the candidate spectrum is compared to the reference spectrum. Miscellaneous peaks in the candidate spectrum not present in the reference spectrum should be explainable.

3. Metals by ICP-AES Method 6010B

Method 6010B is an inductively coupled plasma-atomic emission spectrometry (ICP-AES) procedure for determination of up to 28 or more elements per analysis. Sample preparation involves digestion of an aliquot of the sample in strong mineral acid with heating to obtain a solution suitable for introduction into the instrument. The ICP-AES provides both qualitative and quantitative analysis of the elements in the sample. However, the many spectral interferences that can be generated from non-target elements in samples can give erroneous results, both negative and positive. It takes trained personnel to perform successful digestions of the samples without loss of analytes and introduction of laboratory contamination and highly skilled instrument operators/data interpreters to provide reliable results.

3.1 Initial Demonstration of Performance and MDL Determinations

Initial demonstration of performance consists of evaluation of the linear dynamic range of the instrument for each target analyte, selection of background correction points for each analyte, method and instrument detection limit studies, and verification of the interelement correction factors. These procedures must be documented and the data available for inspection.

The linear range evaluation is performed by analysis of successively higher concentrations (minimum of three—and preferably five—different concentrations) of analytes until deviation (<10%) from the linear calibration curve is obtained. The procedure should be repeated at least every six months.

The method detection limit (MDL) is performed and calculated in compliance with Chapter 1, SW-846. Spike concentrations of two to three times the estimated instrument detection limit are normally sufficient to generate suitable data. The replicates within the MDL study should be performed over several days rather than all in one day. An alternative to perform seven replicates on each of two or more non-consecutive days, then average the calculated MDL results. An MDL should be performed on each instrument by each operator at least once a year. If there are changes in the instrumentation, a new MDL needs to be performed.

It is important to verify that a proper MDL study has been performed. Check the equation for standard deviation used for the MDL calculation to insure "n-1" has been used rather than "n" in the denominator. Also check that the correct Student's t-value has been used. The calculated MDL should be checked against the reporting limit for each analyte. If the MDL is at or higher than the reporting limit, then no data concerning that analyte, which indicate that it is present in the samples at less than the reporting limit, are acceptable.

3.2 Initial Calibration Requirements

The ICP-AES must be calibrated at least daily and more frequent calibration may be required. Minimum requirements for Method 6010B calibration consist of analysis of a blank and a calibration standard. More calibration points are recommended including at least a calibrated point at the MDL or at the reporting limit. Some state programs specifically require the addition of a calibration point at the reporting limit. All calibrations are linear, and the calibration range must reside within the determined linear dynamic range. The calibration must be checked by immediate analysis of at least two exposures of the calibration verification standard. The results must lie within ±10% of the true value and the %RSD of the exposures <3%. As a practical note it has been discovered by many laboratories that the number of calibration levels used in an initial calibration relates directly to the stability of the calibration. A four-level calibration is normally observed to last two to three times as long as the blank and single standard calibration. In the long run the laboratory saves time and effort by performing a calibration that exceeds the minimum requirements of the method.

Results reported from instruments that are not calibrated daily are not reliable. The sample introduction system of the ICP is very sensitive to environmental conditions of temperature, barometric pressure, and humidity. Even climate-controlled facilities exhibit minor day-to-day and hour-to-hour fluctuations that are sufficient to disturb an ICP calibration. The calibration must be frequently (see Section 3.3) checked, and as soon as the check fails, the instrument must be re-calibrated.

3.3 Continuing Calibration Frequency and Acceptance Criteria

Continuing calibration verification consists of analysis of a calibration blank followed immediately by the continuing calibration verification (CCV) solution. The CCV is prepared from preferably different standards than those used in the initial calibration solutions. The calibration blank and CCV must be performed every ten samples, and as the last analyses of the day.

The calibration blank should always read less than the reporting limit for each target analyte. The CCV results for each target analyte must lie within ±10% of the true value of the solution.

Sample results must be bracketed by successful calibration blank and CCV analyses. If a CCV fails to meet the acceptance criteria, all sample results for the failed elements since the last successful CCV are invalidated, the instrument must be recalibrated, and the samples must be re-run.

3.4 Sample Collection, Preservation and Handling Procedures

Instructions for sample collection, preservation and handling are contained in Chapter 2, Chapter 3, and Chapter 11 of SW-846 and the 3000-series sample digestion methods. Samples must be collected in contaminant-free sampling containers. The best containers are made of high density polyethylene (HDPE). Samples may be preserved at the moment of collection by the addition of nitric acid to achieve a pH of <2. The various holding time, container, and preservation tables should be consulted for specific requirements.

3.5 Sample Preparation Procedures

On rare occasion samples will be collected for RCRA analysis that are particulate-free and exhibit turbidities less than 1.0 NTU. More frequently samples will be filtered on-site to obtain dissolved metals. These samples can be prepared by addition of nitric acid to achieve a 1% nitric acid concentration and are suitable to analyze without further sample preparation.

The majority of samples for RCRA analysis must be prepared by one of the 3000-series digestion procedures. In general a portion of the sample is mixed with nitric and/or hydrochloric acids and concentrated with heating. Oxidizing agents such as hydrogen peroxide may be added to assist in the dissolution of the sample. After cooling the sample is filtered and diluted to 50 or 100 mL; then it is ready for analysis.

3.6 Blanks

There are a number of blanks associated with Method 6010B. These include field blanks, sample preparation blanks and calibration blanks. All blanks should be checked closely as an indication of sample contamination.

Sample preparation blanks must be prepared at a rate of one for every 20 samples processed within a 12-hour work shift. If contamination is detected in the sample preparation blank at levels exceeding the MDL, or if analytes are found in samples at less than ten times the blank level, the samples and blanks should be reprepared for analysis. Sample results are never corrected for contamination found in any blank.

Calibration blanks are for the purpose of monitoring sample carryover in the sample introduction part of the ICP. When high levels of analytes are detected in samples, calibration blanks are performed to verify that the instrument has been rinsed clean. If the instrument is determined to still have contamination, rinsing is continued until a calibration blank is obtained that is clean. Every set of ten sample results must be bracketed by clean calibration blanks.

If analytes are detected in samples, the field blank is examined to determine possible contamination introduced during the sampling process. The same guidelines used for interpretation of sample preparation blanks apply to field blanks. If the field blank is discovered to be contaminated, it may be due to the sample containers, the preservative acid, or the sampling technique. All need to be examined closely, the problem discovered and corrected; and the sampling event repeated.

3.7 Laboratory Control Samples

Laboratory control samples (LCS) are performed at a rate of one per 20 samples processed within a batch. Recovery limits for analytes in the LCS are 75-125%. The laboratory may establish its own control limits for the LCS recoveries based on mean ±3 standard deviations.

The LCS is the primary demonstration on a daily basis of the ability to analyze samples with good qualitative and quantitative accuracy. High recoveries of the LCS relate directly to falsely high reported values of detected analytes in samples. For those analytes that are not detected in the sample the data are usable in the sense that the MDL has, in actuality, not been exceeded. However, for analytes reported as greater than the MDL, there is a strong possibility that a false positive has been generated, and the data are not reliable.

Low recoveries in the LCS means that target analytes are reported as lower than they actually are in the sample. Values for analytes reported as larger than the MDL reflect actual amounts in the sample that exceed the MDL. However, values reported as not detected may, in fact, be present in greater amounts in the samples, and the data are unreliable.

3.8 Matrix Spikes

Matrix spikes are present in Method 6010B in two different types. The first is the spike that is added to the samples prior to any sample preparation. This must be performed in duplicate at a rate of at least one for every 20 samples processed. The other matrix spike performed is added after the digestion procedure—a post-digestion spike (PDS). The recovery limits for each element in the matrix spike, in the absence of laboratory generated performance expectations, are 75-125%. The expectations for precision on the matrix spike and duplicate results is <20% RPD. The PDS recovery expectations are also 75-125%.

If matrix spike recoveries are not within expectations; however, the laboratory control samples are acceptable, then matrix effects inherent to the sample may be present. If an element is present in the sample at background levels greater than five times the matrix spike level, the poor recovery of the element should be discounted. Possible interpretations for poor recoveries other than high background are presented in the previous Section (3.7). However, it should be recognized that there is also the distinct problem of uncorrected spectral interference being present in the sample, as discussed in Chapter 2 of this book.

3.9 Replicate Analysis

Replicates of samples and matrix spiked samples are used to evaluate method precision. Precision is normally evaluated through the use of relative percent difference (RPD). Lack of precision may indicate very non-homogeneous samples, a frequent occurrence when solids are analyzed, or it may indicate a problem with the instrument or analyst consistency. If LCS duplicates have been performed and acceptable precision is noted there, in general, instrument or analyst problems can be ruled out as the cause.

References

1. *RCRA Groundwater Monitoring Technical Enforcement Guidance Document, (TEGD)*. EPA OSWER-9950.1. September, 1986.

2. *Test Methods for Evaluating Solid Waste - Physical/Chemical Methods, EPA/SW-846*, 3rd Edition, 1986, Revision 2, September, 1994 and Revision 3 (Proposed), January, 1995.

CHAPTER 7

CERCLA Contract Laboratory Program

The Comprehensive Environmental Response, Compensation and Liability Act (CERCLA) or, as it is more commonly known as, Superfund, is a program administered by EPA to evaluate hazardous waste contaminated areas and then find the persons responsible for creating the mess. The ultimate goal is to have the responsible parties pay for the remediation of the site. The Contract Laboratory Program (CLP) was established to provide sufficient laboratory capacity, over that available from the existing EPA regional and state laboratories, to evaluate the sites.

The meat of the CLP is the Statement of Work (SOW). It is a bid proposal and details exactly how the laboratory will perform the analysis in fulfillment of the contract, assuming one is awarded. There are SOWs for analysis of inorganics (metals and cyanide) and organics (volatiles, semivolatiles and pesticide/PCBs). There are separate SOWS for low level concentration and multimedia multiconcentration samples. There are a number of versions of these SOWs that have been released over time, reflecting the changes in the program as it evolved. There are also SOWs for analysis of dioxins, air contaminants, and Quick-Turn-Around analysis. Copies of most of the SOWs are available from the National Technical Information Service (NTIS) as listed in Table 7-1.

Table 7-1.   CLP Documents Available from NTIS

NTIS Number	Title
PB94-963501	USEPA CLP National Functional Guidelines for Organic Data Review 2/94
PB94-963502	USEPA CLP National Functional Guidelines for Inorganic Data Review 2/94
PB95-963519	USEPA CLP National Functional Guidelines for Organic Data Review, Multimedia, multiconcentration (OLM01.0) and Low concentration water (OLC01.0) 6/91
PB95-963525	Laboratory Data Validation Functional Guidelines for Evaluating Inorganics Analyses 7/88
PB95-963526	Laboratory Data Validation Functional Guidelines for Evaluating Organics Analyses 2/88
PB95-963503	USEPA CLP SOW for Organic Analysis OLM03.1 8/94
PB95-963508	USEPA CLP SOW for Organics Analysis, Multimedia, multiconcentration OLM01.1 and revisions 8/91
PB95-963505	Superfund Analytical Methods for Low Concentration Water for Organics Analysis 6/91
NTIS Number	Title
PB95-963512	USEPA CLP SOW for Organics Analysis, multimedia, multiconcentration 2/88
PB95-963523	USEPA CLP draft SOW for Quick Turnaround Analysis 8/94
PB95-963524	USEPA Volatile Organics of Ambient Air in Canisters VCAAO 1.0 12/91
PB95-963506	USEPA CLP SOW for Inorganics Analysis, multimedia, multiconcentration ILM03.0 12/94

Table 7-1.   CLP Documents Available from NTIS, *continued*

NTIS Number	Title
PB95-963514	USEPA CLP SOW for Inorganics Analysis, multimedia, multiconcentration ILM02.1 9/91
PB95-963515	USEPA CLP SOW for Inorganics Analysis, multimedia, multiconcentration ILM01.0
PB95-963517	Superfund Analytical Methods for Low Concentration Water for Inorganics Analysis 10/91
PB95-963516	USEPA CLP SOW for Inorganics Analysis, multimedia, multiconcentration 7/88

The SOWs follow the general format presented in Table 7-2. Aside from the variety of the specific analytical methods, the single most distinguishing feature of the SOWs is the set of Forms, included in Exhibit B of each SOW, used for reporting the results of the analysis.

Table 7-2.   Exhibits of the SOW (OLM03.1 and ILM03.0)

Exhibits	Title
A	Summary of Requirements
B	Reporting and Deliverables Requirements
C	Target Compound (Analyte) List and Contract Required Quantitation Limits
D	Analytical Methods
E	Quality Assurance/Quality Control Requirements
F	Chain-of-custody, Document Control, and Standard Operating Procedures
G	Glossary of Terms
H	Data Dictionary and Format for Data Deliverables in Computer-Readable Format

Although all the supporting raw data generated from the analysis of each sample are included in the package of Deliverables, the Forms present in a concise fashion the salient parts of the analysis for review and evaluation. EPA has established protocols for contractual evaluation of the Deliverables package and the data. These protocols are focused upon the Forms, with some use of the raw data to verify the information on the Forms. The available documents concerning data evaluation are listed in Table 7-1. For each SOW there is a related guidance document for evaluation. As the SOWs have evolved, so have the evaluation guidelines; however, in some specific instances the guidelines have evolved at a slightly faster pace. Thus it is necessary not only to match-up the appropriate evaluation guideline with the specific SOW used, but also to have a detailed knowledge of the SOW so that the reviewer is aware of the divergences.

The analytical methods in the SOWs are designed to meet the needs of the program (CERCLA) under which they are developed. To a large degree the needs of the program are to perform an initial evaluation of a site containing suspected hazardous and toxic waste and then to be prepared to take legal action to force the responsible generators of the waste to clean it up. In these initial site assessments, the identity of the contaminants present is the prime concern to facilitate the tracking of the waste to the generator. Thus the SOWs are written to stress qualitative analysis. Recognizing that any limited list of target analytes cannot possibly contain all the contaminants that could be potentially encountered upon a site, there is a specific protocol within the SOW to perform identifi-cations of non-calibrated analytes. These are called tentatively identified compounds

(TICs). Once analytes, both target and non-target, are identified as being present in the samples, the methods proceed to provide an estimation of the amount present. However, quantitative accuracy is a secondary consideration when compared to the emphasis placed upon correct identification.

The emphasis on qualitative analysis and contract compliance, rather than quantitative accuracy, changes the mode of approach as to how the data generated from an SOW is evaluated. The data reviewer needs to be versed in mass spectra data interpretation and compound identification, in addition to the normal checking of quality control results. There is also the industry-wide problem of laboratories being required to use CLP SOWs on samples when the analytical need at the site is for quantitative accuracy. This situation commonly arises when groundwater monitoring wells are placed around an identified hazardous waste site to allow tracking of the hazardous components as they migrate through the substrata. The need is for quantitative accuracy to enable development of reliable models. However, since the site was initially evaluated using SOW methods, there is a tendency on the part of contractors to continue to require use of the same methods for the monitoring phase even when a different method would be more appropriate and provide consistent quantitative data. The bottom line is that the contractors pay a premium price for the analysis and the generated data are of lesser quantitative accuracy than a less expensive method might provide.

In this discussion the focus is upon SOW ILM03.0 and OLM03.1, the Multimedia Multiconcentration methods, SOW ILC01.0 and OLC01.0, the Low Concentration for water methods, and the appropriate data evaluation guidelines, PB94-963501 and PB94-963502. It must be recognized by the reader that the specifics of data evaluation related to other SOWs may be different.

A. Data Qualifier Flags

CLP data reports are characterized by flags. These are letters attached to reported results as data qualifier codes. There are flags used by the laboratory to qualify data, and there are flags used by the data reviewers. The definitions and uses of the flags are presented in Tables 7-3 through 7-6.

Table 7-3.   **Laboratory Flags for Organic Data**

Flag	Use
U	Compound was a target analyte but was not detected
J	Reported value is estimated. This could arise because the compound is a TIC and was not calibrated or the compound was detected at a level less than the CRQL.
N	Applied to all TICs when a definitive compound is reported. Not used for generic descriptions of TICs such as "chlorinated hydrocarbon."
NJ	Applied to TICs when an estimated amount has been determined for a definitive compound.
P	Used for Pesticide/PCB target analytes when more than 25% difference in quantitation exists between the two columns. The lower of the two values is reported and flagged.
C	Used for Pesticide/PCB target analytes when the presence is confirmed by GC-MS.
B	Used when the reported target analyte or TIC is also found in the blank
E	Used for target analytes when the reported value exceeds the upper limit of the calibration curve.
D	Used to indicate that the value for the analyte was obtained from a diluted re-analysis. Separate Form I used for original analysis and diluted re-analysis. All results on the diluted Form I will be flagged with a D.

Table 7-3.   Laboratory Flags for Organic Data, *continued*

Flag	Use
A	Used to indicate that the reported TIC is a suspected aldol condensation product.
X, Y, Z	Laboratory-defined flags.

Table 7-4.   Data Reviewer Flags for Organic Data

Flag	Use
U	Compound was a target analyte but was not detected.
J	Reported value is estimated. This could arise because the compound is a TIC and was not calibrated, or the compound was detected at a level less than the CRQL.
N	Applied to all TICs when a definitive compound is reported. Not used for generic descriptions of TICs such as "chlorinated hydrocarbon."
NJ	Applied to TICs when an estimated amount has been determined for a definitive compound.
R	Sample results are rejected due to a serious deficiency in the ability to analyze the sample and meet quality control criteria. The presence or absence of the target analyte cannot be verified.
UJ	The analyte was not detected at the stated quantitation limit. However, the value is an estimate and may be inaccurate or imprecise.

Table 7-5.   Laboratory Flags for Inorganic Data. (The fields are Concentration (C), Qualifier (Q), and Method (M).)

Field	Flag	Use
C	B	The reported value was obtained from a reading that was less than the CRDL but greater than or equal to the IDL.
	U	Target analyte was not detected.
Q	E	Estimated value.
	M	Duplicate injection precision not met.
	N	Spiked sample recovery not within control limits.
	S	Reported value determined by method of standard additions (MSA).
	W	Post digestion spike for graphite furnace AA analysis is out of control limits, and sample absorbance is less than 50% of spike absorbance.
	*	Duplicate analysis not within control limits.
	+	Correlation coefficient for MSA is less than 0.995.
M	P	ICP-AES
	A	Flame AA
	F	Furnace AA
	M	Microwave digestion used
	CV	Manual cold vapor AA
	AV	Automated cold vapor AA
	CA	Midi-distillation spectrophotometric
	AS	Semi-automated spectrophotometric
	C	Manual spectrophotometric
	T	Titrimetric
	NR	Analyte not required to be analyzed

Table 7-6. Data Reviewer Flags for Inorganic Data

Flag	Use
U	Compound was a target analyte but was not detected.
J	Reported value is estimated. This could arise because the compound was detected at a level less than the CRQL.
R	Sample results are rejected due to a serious deficiency in the ability to analyze the sample and meet quality control criteria. The presence or absence of the target analyte cannot be verified.
ω	The analyte was not detected at the stated quantitation limit. However, the value is an estimate and may be inaccurate or imprecise.

B. Volatile Organic Analysis (VOA)

The target analytes for volatiles analysis are listed in Table 7-7, and the Forms required in the deliverables are presented in Table 7-8. The deliverables also include copies of the chain-of-custody record, total ion chromatograms and quantitation reports for each sample, initial and continuing calibration standard, blank, BFB tune, laboratory control sample and laboratory control sample duplicate, and matrix spike and matrix spike duplicate. The raw and background-corrected mass spectra for each target analyte and TIC found, along with results of library searches and a sample case narrative, complete the data deliverables.

Table 7-7. CLP VOA Target Compound List (TCL)

Analyte	CAS	Low Conc.CRQL Water µg/L	Multi-Conc. CRQL Water µg/L	Multi-mediaCRQL Soil µg/kg
Chloromethane	74-87-3	1	10	10
Bromomethane	74-83-9	1	10	10
Vinyl chloride	75-01-4	1	10	10
Chloroethane	75-00-3	1	10	10
Methylene chloride	75-09-2	2	10	10
Acetone	67-64-1	5	10	10
Carbon disulfide	75-15-0	1	10	10
1,1-Dichloroethene	75-35-4	1	10	10
1,1-Dichloroethane	75-34-3	1	10	10
1,2-Dichloroethene	540-59-0	-	10	10
cis-1,2-Dichloroethene	156-59-4	1	-	-
trans-1,2-Dichloroethene	156-60-5	1	-	-
Chloroform	67-66-3	1	10	10
1,2-Dichloroethane	107-06-2	1	10	10
2-Butanone	78-93-3	5	10	10
Bromochloromethane	74-97-5	1	-	-
1,1,1-Trichloroethane	71-55-6	1	10	10
Carbon tetrachloride	56-23-5	1	10	10
Bromodichloromethane	75-27-4	1	10	10
1,2-Dichloropropane	78-87-5	1	10	10
cis-1,3-Dichloropropane	10061-01-5	1	10	10
Trichloroethene	79-01-6	1	10	10

Table 7-7.   CLP VOA Target Compound List (TCL), continued

Analyte	CAS	Low Conc.CRQL Water µg/L	Multi-Conc. CRQL Water µg/L	Multi-mediaCRQL Soil µg/kg
Dibromochloromethane	124-48-1	1	10	10
1,1,2-Trichloroethane	79-00-5	1	10	10
Benzene	71-43-2	1	10	10
trans-1,3-Dichloropropene	10061-02-6	1	10	10
Bromoform	75-25-2	1	10	10
4-Methyl-2-pentanone	108-10-1	5	10	10
2-Hexanone	591-78-6	5	10	10
Tetrachloroethene	127-18-4	1	10	10
1,1,2,2-Tetrachloroethane	79-34-5	1	10	10
1,2-Dibromoethane	106-93-4	1	-	-
Toluene	108-88-3	1	10	10
Chlorobenzene	108-90-7	1	10	10
Ethylbenzene	100-41-4	1	10	10
Styrene	100-42-5	1	10	10
Xylenes (total)	1330-20-7	1	10	10
1,3-Dichlorobenzene	541-73-1	1	-	-
1,4-Dichlorobenzene	106-46-7	1	-	-
1,2-Dichlorobenzene	95-50-1	1	-	-
1,2-Dibromo-3-chloropropane	96-12-8	1	-	-

Table 7-8.   CLP Forms Included as Deliverables with Each Sample for VOA

Form	Title
I VOA	Volatile Organics Analysis Data Sheet
I VOA-TIC	Volatile Organics Analysis Data Sheet Tentatively Identified Compounds
II VOA-1	Water Volatile System Monitoring Compound Recovery
II VOA-2	Soil Volatile System Monitoring Compound Recovery
III VOA-1	Water Volatile Matrix Spike/Matrix Spike Duplicate Recovery
III VOA-2	Soil Volatile Matrix Spike/Matrix Spike Duplicate Recovery
IV VOA	Volatile Method Blank Summary
V VOA	Volatile Organic Instrument Performance Check Bromofluorobenzene (BFB)
VI VOA	Volatile Organics Initial Calibration Data
7 VOA	Volatile Continuing Calibration Check
7I VOA	Volatile Internal Standard Area and RT Summary

There are 15 areas listed in the *National Functional Guidelines* as necessary to check during the data evaluation process. The areas are listed in Table 7-9 and discussed in the following paragraphs.

Table 7-9.   Points of CLP SOW Volatiles Data Evaluation

1.	Holding Times
2.	GC/MS Instrument Performance Check
3.	Initial Calibration
4.	Continuing Calibration
5.	Blanks
6.	System Monitoring Compounds
7.	Matrix Spike and Matrix Spike Duplicate
8.	Laboratory Control Samples
9.	Regional Quality Assurance and Quality Control
10.	Internal Standards
11.	Target Compound Identification
12.	Compound Quantitation and Reported Contract Required Quantitation Limits
13.	Tentatively Identified Compounds
14.	System Performance
15.	Overall Assessment of Data

1. Holding Time

The SOW distinguishes between **Technical Holding Time** and **Method Holding Time**. The technical holding time is the amount of time that elapsed between the moment of sampling in the field and the beginning of analysis at the laboratory. The method holding time is an absolute contractual requirement to analyze the sample within ten days of the **Verified Time of Sample Receipt** (VTSR) at the laboratory.

The evaluation of the technical holding time depends upon what the sample is and how the sample was collected, preserved, and shipped. All water samples for volatiles analysis should have zero headspace; *i.e.* no bubbles in the sample container. Samples other than water should have minimum headspace. For non-aromatic volatile analytes in water, when the samples have been maintained at $4 \pm 2°C$, the technical holding time is 14 days. For aromatic volatile analytes (benzene, toluene, ethylbenzene, dichloro-benzenes, *etc.*) in water, the samples are to be acidified to pH<2 with hydrochloric acid and maintained at $4 \pm 2°C$ until analysis, giving a technical holding time of 14 days. For unpreserved water samples which are not cooled to $4 \pm 2°C$, the technical holding time is 7 days. There are no specific criteria for non-aqueous samples, such as soil or sludge samples; however, a technical holding time of 14 days for samples maintained at $4 \pm 2°C$ is recommended.

The technical holding time is determined through examination of the sampling date listed on the chain-of-custody record and the time of analysis listed on Form I and the raw instrument data report. The dates on Form I and the instrument report must be identical. The preservation of the samples should be indicated upon the chain-of-custody record and the pH verified on the run-log or sample preparation record. If no record of the preservation is found, then it should be assumed that the sample was not preserved. The lack of headspace in the samples should be mentioned in the case narrative for the sample and the run log, and possibly on the chain-of-custody record as notes by the sample receipt technician. The lack of any specific mention of headspace found in the sample is generally interpreted as that there was no headspace in the sample.

If it is found that the 7-day technical holding time on unpreserved water samples has been exceeded, aromatic analytes reported as present should be flagged with a "J" and undetected aromatic analytes flagged with a "UJ." If the 14-day technical holding time has been exceeded for either unpreserved or preserved water samples, all reported analytes are flagged with a "J," and all non-detected analytes flagged with a "UJ." For samples other than water the reviewer must use their professional judgment. The reviewer is referred to the discussion on holding times in Chapter 2 for guidance.

It is possible for the technical holding time for a sample to be exceeded yet the laboratory accomplished the analysis within the method holding time. The data should still be flagged; however, the laboratory is generally not held at fault. Note of this occurrence should be made in the reviewer's evaluation report.

2. GC/MS Instrument Performance Check

The Instrument Performance check is an evaluation of the tune conditions of the mass spectrometer. It is performed every 12 hours and consists of an analysis of 50 ng of a 4-bromofluorobenzene standard. The tune chromatogram, tabularized mass spectrum, tune report and Form V are checked to insure that the tune meets the criteria in Table 7-10.

Table 7-10. 4-Bromofluorobenzene CLP-SOW Tune Criteria

m/z	Ion Abundance Criteria
50	8.0 - 40.0% of m/z 95
75	30.0 - 66.0% of m/z 95
95	Base peak, 100% relative abundance
96	5.0 - 9.0% of m/z 95
173	Less than 2.0% of m/z 174
174	50.0 - 120.0% of m/z 95
175	4.0 - 9.0% of m/z 174
176	93.0 - 101.0% of m/z 174
177	5.0 - 9.0% of m/z 176

Masses not assigned correctly in the mass spectrum are cause for rejection (R) of all data associated with the tune. The reviewer should check to insure the correct ion abundance criteria were used for generation of the tune report. Inability to meet all the abundance criteria is a contract compliance failure as is not performing the tune every 12 hours of operation. The effect upon the data generated from the instrument when the tune criteria have not been met is to be evaluated by the reviewer, however, as discussed in Chapter 2, the effect is not clear-cut nor the evaluation straightforward.

The specified procedure for obtaining the tune is to average the three mass spectral scans across the apex of the BFB peak (the apex scan and the scans immediately prior to—and immediately following—the apex scan), then correct the averaged spectrum for background noise. The background noise correction is accomplished by subtracting from the average a spectrum obtained within 20 scans prior to the beginning of the BFB peak. The subtraction of a scan obtained from part of the BFB peak as background is specifically prohibited. This practice is termed "peak shaving" and has been used in the past to obtain tune results that are passable.

3. Initial Calibration

Form VI and the quantitation reports and chromatograms from the initial calibration runs are required for evaluation of the initial calibration. There must be separate calibrations for water samples and for solid samples. The heating of the sparge tube during the purging of solid samples means that there will be a different transfer efficiency of target analytes from the solid samples as compared to those obtained from the unheated purge used for liquid samples.

Volatiles GC-MS calibration is performed by the internal standard technique. The initial calibration is a five-point calibration and consists of standards of 10, 20, 50, 100 and 200 µg/L concentration. Each compound on the target analyte list must be calibrated. The success of the calibration is evaluated through checking the magnitude of the Relative Response Factors (RRF) and the Percent Relative Standard Deviation (%RSD) of the RRF of the individual calibration standards. The reviewer should verify the number and concentration of the calibration standards and that all target analytes are calibrated.

The individual RRF is calculated as follows:

$$RRF = \frac{A_{TA} \times C_{IS}}{A_{IS} \times C_{TA}}$$

where: A_{TA} is the area of the target analyte primary quantitation ion
A_{IS} is the area of the internal standard quantitation ion
C_{IS} is the concentration of the internal standard, and
C_{TA} is the concentation of the target analyte.

The average RRF is calculated as the arithmetic mean of the individual RRF.
The %RSD is calculated as follows:

$$\%RSD = \frac{\text{Standard deviation}}{\text{average RRF}} \times 100$$

Specific target analytes and system monitoring compounds are assigned to specific internal standards. The assignments are presented in Table 7-11.

Table 7-11.   Assignment of Target Analytes and System Monitoring Compounds to Internal Standards

Bromochloromethane	1,4-Difluorobenzene	Chlorobenzene-d$_5$
Chloromethane	1,1,1-Trichloroethane	2-Hexanone
Bromomethane	Carbon tetrachloride	4-Methyl-2-pentanone
Vinyl chloride	Bromodichloromethane	Tetrachloroethene
Chloroethane	1,2-Dichloropropane	1,1,2,2-Tetrachloroethane
Methylene chloride	trans-1,3-Dichloropropene	Toluene
Acetone	Trichloroethene	Chlorobenzene
Carbon disulfide	Dibromochloromethane	Ethylbenzene
1,1-Dichloroethene	1,1,2-Trichloroethane	Styrene
1,1-Dichloroethane	Benzene	o, m and p-Xylene
1,2-Dichloroethenes	cis-1,3-Dichloropropene	4-Bromofluorobenzene
Chloroform	Bromoform	Toluene-d$_8$
1,2-Dichloroethane		
2-Butanone		
1,2-Dichloroethane-d$_4$		

There is a recognized list of target analytes that are considered as poor performers. They are presented in Table 7-12.

Table 7-12. Volatile Target Analytes Exhibiting Poor Performance in GC-MS Analysis

Acetone	1,2-Dichloroethene	Methylene chloride
2-Butanone	cis-1,2-Dichloroethene	4-Methyl-2-pentanone
Carbon disulfide	trans-1,2-Dichloroethene	Toluene-d8
Chloroethane	1,2-Dichloropropane	1,2-Dichloroethane-d4
Chloromethane	2-Hexanone	1,2-Dibromo-3-chloropropane

For volatile target analytes the average RRF is used for calculating sample results and should be larger than 0.05. Although the SOW allows for up to two analytes to have average RRF as low as 0.01, all data generated for target analytes that do not meet the 0.05 minimum should be flagged. If the analyte is reported as present, the reported value should be flagged as estimated (J). If the analyte is undetected in a sample, the result is flagged as unusable (R).

The %RSD is used as a measure of the linearity of the calibration. %RSD values around 5% or less are indicative of a very linear calibration response. Larger %RSD values indicate increasing deviation from linearity. The SOW allows for up to two target analytes to have up to 40 %RSD. Regardless, for target analytes that have %RSD greater than 30% and achieve the minimum RRF, flag all sample results as estimated (J) if a positive result is reported. Undetected target analytes should be flagged based on the reviewer's judgment.

4. Continuing Calibration

A continuing calibration standard containing all target analytes and system monitoring compounds is required to be performed at the beginning of each 12-hour period of sample analysis. The success of the continuing calibration is evaluated through use of the relative response factor (RRF) and the percent difference (%D) of the RRF as compared to the average RRF obtained in the initial calibration. The %D is calculated as follows:

$$\%D = \frac{RRF - average\ RRF}{average\ RRF} \times 100$$

where: RRF is the relative response factor obtained from the continuing calibration average RRF is the value from the initial calibration.

The data available for evaluation of the continuing calibration include Form VII, and the quantitation report and chromatogram. The minimum RRF for all compounds is 0.05, regardless of the results on the initial calibration. The %D for all calibrated compounds is less than 25%. The reviewer should verify which initial calibration is being used as a basis for the continuing calibration and that this is the same initial calibration that relates to the samples.

If the %D for any compound is outside of the 25% criteria, flag all positive and non-detected results for that compound as estimated (J). If any compound has a RRF less than 0.05, positive results are flagged as estimated (J) while non-detected results are unusable (R).

5. Blanks

Four types of blanks are required to be analyzed and evaluated. The first is the field blank prepared at the point of sampling in the field. The second is a storage blank prepared in the laboratory and stored with the samples in the refrigerator until they are analyzed. The third is called the method blank and is analyzed on each GC-MS every 12 hours of operation. Separate method blanks are analyzed for heated purged (soils) and non-heated purged (water) samples. The instrument blank is analyzed immediately on the instrument after samples that exhibit saturated ions (high concentration analytes).

The review actions depend on the results of the blanks and the samples. If the blank exhibits target analytes but the samples are clean, then no action is taken with regard to the samples. Note should be made of the blank contamination. If the blank and samples exhibit the common laboratory contaminants methylene chloride, acetone and/or 2-butanone (methyl ethyl ketone), the relative amounts in the blank and samples are evaluated. If the samples have levels higher than ten times the amounts present in the blank, then the assumption is made that the analyte is in the sample. If the samples have levels of the contaminants less than ten times the amount in the blank then laboratory contamination is the presumed source. In these cases the CRQL is raised to the level found in the sample and the sample result flagged with a "U." When there is gross contamination of the blanks and the samples, then all results are flagged as unusable (R). For target analytes and TICs other than the common laboratory contaminants, a five-times rule is used for guidance.

If storage blanks or field blanks are found to be contaminated at levels greater than the CRQL, detected analytes in both the storage blanks and the samples should be flagged as estimated values (J). If gross contamination is found then all results are unusable (R).

6. System Monitoring Compounds

These compounds are referred to as surrogates in most other methods and are listed in Table 7-13. The appropriate compounds are added to every sample and blank to achieve a final concentration of 50 µg/L in the sample. The recoveries of the compounds are used to assess the matrix effects of the sample upon the analysis and to assess the performance of the analytical system for each sample analysis. Poor recoveries may indicate either matrix effects, poor purging efficiency, or non-quantitative transfer of the analytes from the purging system to the GC-MS. The data used to review the recoveries are found on Form II, and verified through checking the raw data chromatograms and quantitation reports.

There is no acceptable reason for system monitoring compound recoveries on blanks to be out of the acceptance ranges (Table 7-14). If samples also exhibit unacceptable recoveries then all the data generated in the sample set are probably unusable. When blank recoveries are unacceptable but all the samples have acceptable recoveries, it may be the judgment of the reviewer that the blank results are a single aberration in the analytical system. However, if this is the case then the re-analysis of the blank should have given acceptable recoveries. Failure to re-analyze the blank is not good laboratory procedure.

When analysis of a sample results in an unacceptable system monitoring compound recovery, the sample should be re-analyzed to verify that the unacceptable recovery is a matrix-derived problem rather than a laboratory artifact. If the re-analysis generates acceptable recoveries, then sample results are reported from the run with the acceptable system monitoring compound recoveries and the reviewer may never see the unacceptable sample results. When the re-analysis exhibits recoveries that are still outside the acceptance limits, the laboratory reports both sets of results and sample results are accepted based upon the judgment of the reviewer. Factors to be taken into consideration to make the decision include technical holding times, which analysis exhibits the better recoveries, comparison of the target analyte and TIC values from the initial and re-analysis, and other quality control results, such as internal standard area counts.

Table 7-13.   **System Monitoring Compounds**

Medium and High Concentration Methods	Low Concentration Method
1,2-Dichloroethane-d$_4$	Bromofluorobenzene
Bromofluorobenzene	
Toluene-d$_8$	

Table 7-14.   **System Monitoring Compound Recovery Acceptance Limits**

Compound	Water Samples	Soil Samples
Medium and High Concentration Methods		
1,2-Dichloroethane-d$_4$	76-114	70-121
Bromofluorobenzene	86-115	59-113
Toluene-d$_8$	88-110	84-138
Low Concentration Method		
Bromofluorobenzene	80-120	

When system monitoring compound recoveries are low, it is an indication that target analyte recoveries are also low. For system monitoring compound recoveries in the range from 10% to the lower acceptance limit, detected target analyte values are probably low, and the results are flagged as estimates (J). Target analytes reported as undetected at the CRQL may, in fact, be present in the sample, and, therefore, the non-detects are estimates (UJ). If the system monitoring compounds exhibit recoveries less than 10%, the non-detected results are unusable (R).

When system monitoring compound recoveries are high, the target analyte recoveries are also high. Detected target analytes values are probably high and flagged as estimates (J). Target analytes which are not detected above the CRQL are also assumed to exhibit high recoveries and are therefore probably not in the sample, thus the data are reliable as reported.

Although it may be possible to relate recoveries of a system monitoring compound to a limited group of the target analytes, such as the internal standard groups presented in Table 7-11, in general this is not done.

7. Matrix Spikes and Duplicates

Matrix spike and matrix spike duplicate (MS and MSD) are required to be performed and the recoveries calculated on at least one sample out of each sample set of 20 samples of a similar matrix. However, the results on the MS and MSD are not by and of themselves used to qualify data. The compounds used in the matrix spike solution are listed in Table 7-15 along with the associated accuracy (%R) and precision (RPD) quality objectives. The MS and MSD compounds are spiked into the water and low concentration soil samples to achieve a 50 µg/L or 50 µg/kg level in the sample. The medium level soil directions result in a 6200 µg/kg concentration of each MS component in the sample. MS and MSD are not required to be performed in the Low Concentration SOW.

Table 7-15. **VOA Matrix Spike Compounds and Recovery Acceptance Limits**

Compound	Water		Soil	
	%R	RPD	%R	RPD
1,1-Dichloroethene	61-145	14	59-172	22
Trichloroethene	71-120	14	62-137	24
Benzene	76-127	11	66-142	21
Toluene	76-125	13	59-139	21
Chlorobenzene	75-130	13	60-133	21

Recoveries (%R) for matrix spike compounds are calculated as:

$$\%R = \frac{SSR - SR}{SA} \times 100$$

where: SSR is the spiked sample result,
SR is the unspiked sample result, and
SA is the spike amount.

Precision (RPD) is calculated as:

$$RPD = \frac{2|MSR - MSRD|}{MSR + MSRD} \times 100$$

where: MSR is the matrix spike percent recovery (%R), and
MSRD is the matrix spike duplicate percent recovery (%R).

The data used for the evaluation of the matrix spikes are found on Form III VOA-1, Form III VOA-2, and the raw data chromatograms and quantitation reports. The reviewer should recalculate several of the recoveries and RPD numbers listed on Form III to verify that the calculations were performed correctly. In a strict sense, the MS and MSD recoveries are applicable to only the sample that was spiked. High or low MS compound recoveries can be related to the behavior of compounds of similar chemical structure or similar volatility (Table 7-11), or the recoveries may be indicative of problems with the results obtained for all target analytes in the sample.

On the other hand, repeated inability to generate acceptable matrix spike results over a period of time is indicative of system-specific analytical problems in the laboratory. This situation should be investigated as it may suggest that no results being generated by the lab are usable.

8. Laboratory Control Samples

Laboratory Control Samples (LCS) are required in the Low Concentration SOW but not in the Multimedium Multiconcentration SOW. The data to be reviewed are found on

Form III LCV-1, and the raw chromatograms and quantitation reports. The compounds used in the LCS and the acceptance limits are presented in Table 7-16. They are added to a portion of reagent water as a solution to yield a final concentration of 5 µg/L in the sample.

Table 7-16. VOA Laboratory Control Sample Compounds and Acceptance Limits

LCS Compound	%R Acceptance Limit
Vinyl chloride	60-140
1,2-Dichloroethane	60-140
Carbon tetrachloride	60-140
1,2-Dichloropropane	60-140
Trichlorethene	60-140
1,1,2-Trichloroethane	60-140
Benzene	60-140
cis-1,2-Dichloroethene	60-140
Bromoform	60-140
Tetrachloroethene	60-140
1,2-Dibromoethane	60-140
1,4-Dichlorobenzene	60-140

Recoveries (%R) for laboratory control sample compounds are calculated as:

$$\%R = \frac{SSR}{SA} \times 100$$

where: SSR is the spiked sample result,
SA is the spike amount.

There is no acceptable reason for the LCS recovery objectives not to be met for each component. Failure to meet the acceptance criteria on this "perfect" matrix generates substantial doubts about the laboratory's ability to generate reliable results on any sample. However, assuming that all the sample results in the sample set are not unilaterally flagged as estimates (J) or unusable (R), the relationship of the recovery for specific members of the LCS solution to recovery of target analytes in samples needs to take into account the chemical nature, the recovery efficiency, volatility and analytical difficulty presented by the compounds. If LCS recoveries are high, then associated results for target analytes are estimates (J) for those analytes reported above the CRDL and acceptable for those compounds reported as less than the CRDL.

When individual LCS compounds recoveries are low, then related target analyte results reported greater than the CRDL are estimates (J) while the non-detects are unusable (R). If more than 50% of the LCS components are reported with less than acceptable recoveries, then all target analyte compounds reported above the CRDL are estimates (J) while none of the non-detected analytes are usable (R).

Surrogate recoveries and internal standard performance criteria must be met for acceptable LCS recoveries to be valid.

9. Regional Quality Assurance and Quality Control

These are suggested in the National Functional Guidelines to consist of checking Performance Evaluation sample results, field duplicates, blind spikes and/or blind blanks. Region III[1] reviews the results of Performance Evaluation samples and requires that all analytes present in the PE sample be correctly identified and quantitated. Region III also evaluates the results of field duplicates in terms of RPD. The RPDs obtained from the field duplicates are cross-checked against those listed as Data Quality Objectives in the Quality Assurance Project Plan.

10. Internal Standards

The internal standards used in volatiles analysis are presented in Table 7-11. They are added to every sample (water) to achieve a final concentration of 50 µg/L. A 5-g soil sample has a final concentration of internal standards of 50 µg/kg. Form VIII VOA and the raw chromatograms and quantitation reports are used for evaluation. The two items to check are the area counts of the internal standard peak (quantitation ion) and the retention time. The criteria are to have the area counts of the internal standards in the sample within a factor of 2 (50% to 200%) of the area counts exhibited on the last continuing calibration. In the low concentration procedure the criteria are tightened to ±40%. For retention times the internal standards must elute within ±30 seconds of the retention time exhibited in the last continuing calibration. The low concentration procedure tightens the requirements to ±20 seconds.

For reported target analytes where the associated internal standards do not meet the factor of two criteria, the results are flagged as estimated (J). Non-detected analytes where the internal standard has an area count greater than a factor of two (200%) are considered to be reliable. Non-detected analytes that have internal standards with low area counts are estimates and should be flagged (UJ). If extremely low area counts are reported then the non-detected analytes results are unusable (R).

Large retention time shifts of the internal standards can generate false positive or negative results, and it may be appropriate to flag all results for that sample as unusable (R). The reviewer should check the chromatograms for detected and non-detected compounds and then examine the associated mass spectra for correct identification. This may avoid flagging the detected analytes as unusable (R).

11. Target Compound Identification

Identifications are first based upon relative retention time (RRT) matches of the analyte in the sample with that in the standard. The relative retention time is the retention time of the analyte divided by the retention time of the same compound in the continuing calibration standard run within the same 12-hour work shift. If the compound elutes at exactly the same time as that of the standard, a RRT of 1.00 is obtained. There can be no more than ±0.06 variation in the relative retention times to support a positive identification, which gives an acceptance range of 0.94 to 1.06 for the RRT.

The second criterion for identification is a mass spectrum match of the reported hit with that of the laboratory generated mass spectrum of the standard. Most data systems used to operate mass spectrometers will generate a quantitation report (Figure 7-1). The identifications of target analytes listed upon this report are based on the correct quantita-

---

[1] Region III Modifications to National Functional Guidelines for Organic Data Review Multi-Media, Multi-Concentration (OLM)1.1-OLMO1.9), September 1994

tion ion (quant ion, Table 7-17) and other characteristic ions being found at the correct retention time.

The software performs spectral matching according to the entries in the ID (Identification) file in the process of preparing the quantitation report. How completely the ID file is populated with characteristic ions and up-to-date abundances for those ions, relates directly to the number of false positives in the quantitation report. The matching of the spectra from the sample with those obtained during the daily continuing calibration is done either manually or within the context of an automated library search routine. The spectral comparison is conducted in two directions: the standard spectrum is compared against that of the sample analyte, and then the sample analyte spectrum is compared against that of the standard. All ions in the standard spectrum of greater than 10% intensity must be present in the sample spectrum, and the relative intensities of the ions must agree within ±20%. This builds confidence that the target analyte is actually represented by the spectrum from the sample. However, there is a distinct probability that the spectrum of the analyte in the sample includes other ions (greater than 10%) not present in the standard and this is the reason for checking the sample against the standard. The additional ions should be accountable as either a co-eluting compound with that of the target analyte or some recognizable and reasonable artifact such as column bleed (ions at m/z 73, 207, 283, 355). If the ions can't be accounted for there is the distinct possibility that a misidentification has been made.

```
                          QUANT REPORT                        Page   1

Operator ID: MANAGER         Quant Rev: 7     Quant Time:  960311 04:32
Output File: ^LD490::QN                      Injected at:  960311 03:59
Data File:   >LD490::D1                    Dilution Factor:       1.00000
Name: 70280RA                              Instrument ID:  VOA1
Misc:


ID File: ID_VL::SC
Title: New VOA Standards for Daily Update
Last Calibration: 960115 13:58                Last Qcal Time: 960308 05:58



            Compound                 R.T. Q ion    Area    Conc    Units   q
     ------------------------------  ---- -----  -------- ------- ------- --
  1) *Pentafluorobenzene (IS)        9.66 168.0    56486   50.00  ug/L    10
  7)  Trichlorofluoromethane         4.86 101.0      366    .486  ug/L    10
 10)  Freon 113 (NON TARGET)         4.86 101.0      366    .592  ug/L    10
 11)  Acetone                        5.69  58.0      640   51.62  ug/L     9
 16)  Carbon disulfide               6.79  76.0    49810   37.51  ug/L    10
 17)  Methylene chloride             6.77  84.0      405    .821  ug/L    10
 28)  Methyl acrylate (NON TARGET)   9.69  55.0     2040    7.90  ug/L    10
 35) *Fluorobenzene (IS)            11.32  96.0    90484   50.00  ug/L    10
 37)  1,2-Dichloroethane-d4 (SURR)  10.72  65.0    38020   64.03  ug/L     9
 38)  1,2-Dichloroethane            11.34  62.0     1446    1.87  ug/L    10
 39)  Benzene                       10.93  78.0      473    .261  ug/L    10
 49)  1,1-Dichloro-2-propanone (NT) 13.44  43.0      557    2.75  ug/L    10
 51) *Chlorobenzene-d5 (IS)         17.11 117.0    52492   50.00  ug/L     9
 52)  Toluene-d8 (SURR)             14.24  98.0    70937   57.36  ug/L    10
 53)  Toluene                       14.38  92.0     6185    7.54  ug/L    10
 62)  Ethylbenzene-d10 (SURR)       17.11  98.0    85693   47.80  ug/L    10
 63)  Chlorobenzene                 17.11 112.0      428    .424  ug/L    10
 65)  Ethylbenzene                  17.30  91.0      641    .388  ug/L     8
 66)  m- & p-Xylene                 17.46 106.0      470    .860  ug/L    10
 72)  Bromofluorobenzene (SURR)     19.48  95.0    31219   40.60  ug/L    10
 73) *1,4-Dichlorobenzene-d4 (IS)   21.94 152.0    16393   50.00  ug/L     9
 77)  n-Propylbenzene               19.51  91.0      315    .210  ug/L    10
 85)  p-Isopropyltoluene            21.60 119.0     2559    2.48  ug/L    10

    * Compound is ISTD
```

Figure 7-1.   Quantitation report from a gas chromatograph - mass spectrometer.

Table 7-17. **Quantitation Ions Required for Volatile Target Analytes, System Monitoring Compounds and Internal Standards.** (List includes the target analytes from both the Low Concentration and the Multiconcentration Multimedia SOW.)

Analyte	CAS	Quantitation ion
Chloromethane	74-87-3	50
Bromomethane	74-83-9	94
Vinyl chloride	75-01-4	62
Chloroethane	75-00-3	64
Methylene chloride	75-09-2	84
Acetone	67-64-1	43
Carbon disulfide	75-15-0	76
1,1-Dichloroethene	75-35-4	96
1,1-Dichloroethane	75-34-3	63
1,2-Dichloroethene	540-59-0	96
cis-1,2-Dichloroethene	156-59-4	96
trans-1,2-Dichloroethene	156-60-5	96
Chloroform	67-66-3	83
1,2-Dichloroethane	107-06-2	62
2-Butanone	78-93-3	43
Bromochloromethane	74-97-5	128
1,1,1-Trichloroethane	71-55-6	97
Carbon tetrachloride	56-23-5	117
Bromodichloromethane	75-27-4	83
1,2-Dichloropropane	78-87-5	63
cis-1,3-Dichloropropene	10061-01-5	75
Trichloroethene	79-01-6	130
Dibromochloromethane	124-48-1	129
1,1,2-Trichloroethane	79-00-5	97
Benzene	71-43-2	78
trans-1,3-Dichloropropene	10061-02-6	75
Bromoform	75-25-2	173
4-Methyl-2-pentanone	108-10-1	43
2-Hexanone	591-78-6	43
Tetrachloroethene	127-18-4	164
1,1,2,2-Tetrachloroethane	79-34-5	83
1,2-Dibromoethane	106-93-4	107
Toluene	108-88-3	91
Chlorobenzene	108-90-7	112
Ethylbenzene	100-41-4	106
Styrene	100-42-5	104
Xylenes (total)	1330-20-7	106
1,3-Dichlorobenzene	541-73-1	146
1,4-Dichlorobenzene	106-46-7	146
1,2-Dichlorobenzene	95-50-1	146
1,2-Dibromo-3-chloropropane	96-12-8	75

Table 7-17. **Quantitation Ions Required for Volatile Target Analytes, System Monitoring Compounds and Internal Standards.** (List includes the target analytes from both the Low Concentration and the Multiconcentration Multimedia SOW.), *continued*

Analyte	CAS	Quantitation ion
1,4-Difluorobenzene	540-36-3	114
Chlorobenzene-d_5	3114-55-4	117
4-Bromofluorobenzene	460-00-4	95
1,2-Dichloroethane-d_4	17060-07-0	65
Toluene-d_8	2037-26-5	98

Identifications of target analytes need to be reviewed in two respects. First, reported hits for target analytes in the samples must be verified as accurate. This is done through checking the Form I VOA and the raw chromatogram, quantitation report, and the mass spectra for the hit. Reported hits that are not correct are termed "false positives." The second aspect of target compound identification is to verify that analytes which are reported as not present (U) are, in fact, absent from the sample. Not reporting target compounds that are actually present is termed a "false negative." Examination of the raw chromatogram and quantitation report and Form I VOA will help build confidence in the lack of false negatives. Incorrect identifications are flagged as either undetected (U) or unusable (R).

False negatives are harder to ascertain. The reviewer must examine the raw chromatogram very closely and verify that every peak has been correctly identified as either a system monitoring compound, internal standard, or target analyte, or is listed as a TIC. The TICs should be very closely examined to verify that they are not, in fact, target analytes. Peaks not accounted for are subject to further investigation.

12. Compound Quantitation and Reported CRQLs

Information related to the review of reported amounts of identified target analytes is found on Forms 1 VOA and 7 VOA, and the sample preparation sheets, raw chromatograms and quantitation reports. Quantitation is based upon the area of the quant ion present for the target analyte (Table 7-17) compared with the area of quant ion found for the appropriate internal standard (Table 7-11) corrected with the response factor generated during the daily calibration check, using the equation:

$$\text{Amount} = \frac{(\text{Area target analyte quant ion}) \times (\text{Amount internal standard})}{(\text{Area internal standard quant ion}) \times (R_f)}.$$

If a secondary quantitation ion was used for the target analyte due to spectral interference with the primary ion, the reviewer needs to verify that the target analyte was calibrated for the secondary ion instead of the primary quant ion.

If reduced sample sizes have been analyzed due to high levels of target analytes or other interferences in the samples, the raw result is corrected for the dilution factor. The dilution factor is listed in the heading of Form 1 VOA. The raw result obtained from the quantitation report is multiplied by the dilution factor to obtain the final result. For water samples the reviewer can check the calculation by dividing the result on Form 1 by the dilution factor, and this should agree with the number on the quant report for that analyte.

Solid samples are reported in terms of dry weight. The dry weight is calculated from the wet result by dividing by the fraction solids in the sample. Form I lists the percent moisture. The fraction solids can be generated from the percent moisture by:

$$\text{fraction solids} = \frac{100 - \text{percent moisture}}{100}.$$

$$\text{dry weight result} = \frac{\text{Wet result}}{\text{fraction solids}}.$$

For low concentration samples normally 5.0 g of the solid is placed in the sparge tube similar to the 5.0 mL used for a water sample, and thus the result on the raw quantitation report is directly the wet result. However, for high concentration solid samples, a different procedure is used. A weighed portion of the sample (approximately 4 g) is extracted with a known volume of methanol (10.0 mL), then a portion of the methanol is added to 5.0 mL water and transferred to the sparge tube for analysis. The raw result on the quant report must be corrected for all of these factors using the following equation:

$$\text{Wet result} = \frac{(\text{Raw result}) \times (10.0 \text{ mL methanol extract})}{(\text{volume methanol added to sparge tube}) \times (\text{sample weight})}.$$

For the complete calculation of the dry weight solid result, the equation is as follows:

$$\text{Final result} = \frac{(A_{TA}) \times (I_S) \times (V_T) \times (D_f)}{(A_{IS}) \times (R_f) \times (V_A) \times (W_S) \times (D)}.$$

where: A_{TA} is the area of the quantitation ion for the target analyte.

I_S is the amount of the internal standard added to the analysis.

V_T is the total volume of the methanol extract in mL.

D_f is the dilution factor of the methanol extract added to the sparge tube if it must be reduced below 0.100 mL.

A_{IS} is the area of the quant ion from the internal standard.

R_f is the response factor generated during the daily continuing calibration.

V_A is the volume of methanol extract or methanol extract further diluted added to the sparge tube (0.100 mL min.) in mL.

W_S is the wet weight of sample extracted in g.

D is the fraction solids in the sample.

The Contract Required Quantitation Level (CRQL) is also adjusted based on the above considerations. The factors of dry weight and sample dilution are performed upon the CRQL just like they are on a sample result to generate the adjusted CRQL.

13. Tentatively Identified Compounds

These are compounds found in the sample that elute from the GC-MS as defined peaks, yet are not calibrated analytes. The information in the packet that can be used to review the identification of the Tentatively Identified Compounds (TICs) includes the Form 1 VOA-TIC report, the sample chromatograms, and library search printouts, and mass spectra for the closest matches.

Up to 30 peaks that are greater than 10% in area or height of the nearest internal standard are candidate TICs. This requirement is changed to 40% of the height or area of the nearest internal standard for the Low Concentration SOW. A forward library search is conducted against a standard commercially available mass spectral database, such as the NIST/EPA/NIH collection or the Wiley collection. The following cautions are appropriate when considering spectral matches from these libraries. First, most of the spectra in the collections were not obtained from mass spectrometers tuned to meet 4-bromofluorobenzene acceptance criteria. Second, the supervisors of the collections accepted spectra from anyone who submitted spectra, and some of the compound/spectra identifications are simply wrong. Third, some of the spectra have been background corrected to remove artifact signals, and others have not. Last, in the interests of conservation of storage space the spectra have been reduced to eliminate many of the small signals, leaving just the major signals.

Once the search program has identified possible matches, the spectra are manually compared to that of the candidate TIC from the sample. Some of the comparisons include:

1. Verifying that all peaks of greater than 10% relative abundance in the library spectrum are present in the TIC spectrum.

2. The abundance of the matching ions should agree within ±20% relative intensity in the library and TIC spectra.

3. Molecular ions present in the library spectrum should also be present in the TIC spectrum. The molecular ion has the same mass as the molecular mass of the compound and is generally the highest mass in the spectrum.

4. Major peaks present in the TIC spectrum but not in the library spectrum should be reviewed as to indicating the presence of co-eluting compounds or indicating a misidentification.

The TIC spectrum should be reviewed as to whether it makes analytical sense in terms of recognized mass spectral fragmentation patterns based on the proposed molecular structure of the compound. This skill is very rare among GC-MS operators, but is an absolute necessity for reliable mass spectral interpretation. The vast majority of TICs which are reported from environmental laboratories are simply the top choice generated from the forward search algorithm with no further examination by the operator.

Peaks that have not generated creditable candidates from the library, can be labeled as "unknown." They can be further classified as unknown chlorinated hydrocarbon, unknown aromatic, etc. based on the judgment of the mass spectral interpreter. If a molecular weight can be determined from the mass spectrum, it is also included.

For multipeak materials, for example gasoline and mineral spirits, which are not calibrated, but are easily recognized as such, all the peaks related to the material should be reported as a single TIC (gasoline). It is incorrect to report this type TIC as individual peaks, such as methylpentane, hexane, dimethyl-heptane, *etc.*

Approximate quantities of the TICs and the peaks listed as unknown are generated. The procedure is to calculate a quantity based on the total ion current area of the TIC and the total ion current area of the nearest internal standard. A response factor of 1.00 is used.

$$\text{Amount of TIC} \quad = \quad \frac{(\text{Area of TIC}) \times (\text{Amount of Internal Standard})}{(\text{Area of Internal Standard})}$$

TIC results are flagged as presumed present and estimated quantity (NJ). Quantities reported for compounds listed as unknown are flagged as estimated (J).

The following peaks are not to be reported as TICs:

1. Peaks of less than 10% of the height or area of the nearest internal standard

2. Peaks eluting more than 30 seconds before the retention time of the first VOA target analyte

3. Peaks eluting more than 3 minutes after the retention time of the last VOA target analyte

4. Carbon dioxide

5. Peaks that are target analytes in other analytical fractions such as SVO or pesticides

6. Peaks that are also found in the blank

7. Surrogates and internal standards

8. Common laboratory contaminants such as carbon dioxide, siloxanes (m/z 73, 207, 281), diethyl ether, hexanes, Freon 113, t-butyl-methyl ether, phthalates and other materials used in the laboratory at levels less than 100 µg/L or 4000 µg/Kg

9. Solvent preservatives such as cyclohexene, cyclohexanone, cyclohexanol, chlorocyclohexene, chlorocyclohexanone, chlorocyclohexanol, and chlorocyclohexane.

10. Aldol condensation products such as 4-methyl-4-hydroxy-2-pentanone and 4-methyl-3-penten-2-one, and 5,5-dimethyl-2(5H)-furanone (condensation products of acetone commonly found in laboratories).

The reviewer has a number of choices as to how to deal with TICs that are believed to be incorrectly reported. They may choose to flag the individual TICs as unusable (R) in the case of suspected laboratory artifacts, physical impossibility of presence in the GC-MS result (such as an identified amino acid or glycol), or gross misinterpretation of the mass spectrum. Individual TICs may be grouped into an aggregate TIC, such as gasoline, if that is more appropriate. The identification of the TIC may be changed from a specific identification to a more general identification, if in the judgment of the reviewer, the specificity is unwarranted. For example, a reported TIC of 2,3,7,8-tetramethylnaphalene might be changed to the less specific tetramethylnaphalene isomer or substituted aromatic hydrocarbon.

14. System Performance

The reviewer should evaluate the performance of the GC-MS system as evidenced through the appearance of the chromatogram and the recoveries of the system performance monitoring compounds for each sample. The items to review are Form VIII VOA (Internal Standard summary), Form III VOA-1, Form III VOA-2 (Matrix Spike summaries), Form II VOA (Surrogate summary), and the raw chromatograms.
  Specific areas to look for include:

1. Baseline rise particularly in the later part of the chromatogram
2. Degradation of peak definition and shape
3. Loss of sensitivity of the mass analyzer

  The baseline rise is generally due to previously injected grossly contaminated samples. The loss of internal standard area counts during the day are evidence of degrading performance and potential build-up of contamination within the mass analyzer. Loss of peak resolution or even possible peak splitting are clues of active site development within the gas chromatograph. Peaks losing an even Gaussian or symmetrical appearance and development of lopsided peaks, called peak tailing, are another clue to system degradation.
  Any of these symptoms may be an indication that the system is in need of preventative maintenance. They also suggest that the results obtained from such a system may not be entirely reliable.

15. Overall Assessment of Data

The Overall Assessment of Data is a written narrative prepared by the reviewer. It is used as a place to express qualifications and concerns about the sample results not expressly covered in the other areas of review. Besides the data package, the reviewer may wish to refer to the Quality Assurance Project Plan and the Sampling and Analysis Plan. Reviewers may wish to consider to what purpose the data will be applied as a guide to their summary of the data usability. Thus data known to be proceeding directly into the legal arena will be viewed in a different light than data being used to prepare an initial evaluation of a site and to be followed by further sampling and analysis efforts.

C. Semivolatile Organics (SVO)

The target analytes for semivolatile analysis by GC-MS are listed in Table 7-18, and the Forms required in the deliverables are presented in Table 7-19. The deliverables also include copies of the chain-of-custody record, total ion chromatograms and quantitation reports for each sample, initial and continuing calibration standard, blank, DFTPP tune, laboratory control sample and laboratory control sample duplicate, and matrix spike and matrix spike duplicate. The raw and background-corrected mass spectra for each target analyte and TIC found, along with results of library searches and a sample case narrative complete the data deliverables.

Table 7-18.   CLP Target Analyte List (TCL) for Semivolatile Organic Compounds with the Contract Required Quantitation Limits (CRQL)

Analyte	CAS	Low Conc. CRQL Water µg/L	Multimedia Multiconc CRQL Water µg/L	Multimedia Multiconc CRQL Soil µg/kg
Phenol	108-95-2	5	10	330
Bis(2-Chloroethyl)ether	111-44-4	5	10	330
2-Chlorophenol	95-57-8	5	10	330
1,3-Dichlorobenzene	541-73-1	-	10	330
1,4-Dichlorobenzene	106-46-7	-	10	330
1,2-Dichlorobenzene	95-50-1	-	10	330
2-Methylphenol	95-48-7	5	10	330
2,2'-oxybis(1-Chloropropane)	108-60-1	5	10	330
4-Methylphenol	106-44-5	5	10	330
N-Nitroso-di-n-propylamine	621-64-7	5	10	330
Hexachloroethane	67-72-1	5	10	330
Nitrobenzene	98-95-3	5	10	330
Isophorone	78-59-1	5	10	330
2-Nitrophenol	88-75-5	5	10	330
2,4-Dimethylphenol	105-67-9	5	10	330
Bis(2-Chloroethoxy)methane	111-91-1	5	10	330
2,4-Dichlorophenol	120-83-2	5	10	330
1,2,4-Trichlorobenzene	120-82-1	5	10	330
Naphthalene	91-20-3	5	10	330
4-Chloroaniline	106-47-8	5	10	330
Hexachlorobutadiene	87-68-3	5	10	330
4-Chloro-3-methylphenol	59-50-7	5	10	330
2-Methylnaphthalene	91-57-6	5	10	330
Hexachlorocyclopentadiene	77-47-4	5	10	330
2,4,6-Trichlorophenol	88-06-2	5	10	330
2,4,5-Trichlorophenol	95-95-4	20	25	830
2-Chloronaphthalene	91-58-7	5	10	330
2-Nitroaniline	88-74-4	20	25	830
Dimethylphthalate	131-11-3	5	10	330
Acenaphthylene	208-96-8	5	10	330
2,6-Dinitrotoluene	606-20-2	5	10	330
3-Nitroaniline	99-09-2	20	25	830
Acenaphthene	83-32-9	5	10	330
2,4-Dinitrophenol	51-28-5	20	25	830
4-Nitrophenol	100-02-7	20	25	830
Dibenzofuran	132-64-9	5	10	330
2,4-Dinitrotoluene	121-14-2	5	10	330
Diethylphthalate	84-66-2	5	10	330
4-Chlorophenylphenylether	7005-72-3	5	10	330
Fluorene	86-73-7	5	10	330

Table 7-18. **CLP Target Analyte List (TCL) for Semivolatile Organic Compounds with the Contract Required Quantitation Limits (CRQL),** *continued*

| Analyte | CAS | Low Conc. CRQL Water µg/L | Multimedia Multiconc | |
			CRQL Water µg/L	CRQL Soil µg/kg
4-Nitroaniline	100-01-6	20	25	830
4,6-Dinitro-2-methylphenol	534-52-1	20	25	830
N-Nitroso-diphenylamine	86-30-6	5	10	330
4-Bromophenylphenylether	101-55-3	5	10	330
Hexachlorobenzene	118-74-1	5	10	330
Pentachlorophenol	87-86-5	20	25	830
Phenanthrene	85-01-8	5	10	330
Anthracene	120-12-7	5	10	330
Carbazole	86-74-8	-	10	330
Di-n-butylphthalate	84-74-2	5	10	330
Fluoranthene	206-44-0	5	10	330
Pyrene	129-00-0	5	10	330
Butylbenzylphthalate	85-68-7	5	10	330
3,3'-Dichlorobenzidine	91-94-1	5	10	330
Benzo(a)anthracene	56-55-3	5	10	330
Chrysene	218-01-9	5	10	330
Bis(2-Ethylhexyl)phthalate	117-81-7	5	10	330
Di-n-octylphthalate	117-84-0	5	10	330
Benzo(b)fluoranthene	205-99-2	5	10	330
Benzo(k)fluoranthene	207-08-9	5	10	330
Benzo(a)pyrene	50-32-8	5	10	330
Indeno(1,2,3-cd)pyrene	193-39-5	5	10	330
Dibenzo(a,h)anthracene	53-70-3	5	10	330
Benzo(g,h,i)perylene	191-24-2	5	10	330

Table 7-19. **CLP Forms Included as Deliverables with Each Sample for Semivolatile Organic Compounds**

Form	Title
I SV-1	Semivolatiles Organics Analysis Data Sheet
I SV-2	Semivolatiles Organics Analysis Data Sheet (page 2)
I SV-TIC	Semivolatile Organics Analysis Data Sheet Tentatively Identified Compounds
II SV-1	Water Semivolatile Surrogate Recovery
II SV-2	Soil Semivolatile Surrogate Recovery
III SV-1	Water Semivolatile Matrix Spike/Matrix Spike Duplicate Recovery
III SV-2	Soil Semivolatile Matrix Spike/Matrix Spike Duplicate Recovery
IV SV	Semivolatile Method Blank Summary
V SV	Semivolatile Organic Instrument Performance Check Decafluorotriphenylphosphine (DFTPP)
VI SV-1 & 2	Semivolatile Organics Initial Calibration Data
7 SV-1 & 2	Semivolatile Continuing Calibration Check
7I SV-1 & 2	Semivolatile Internal Standard Area and RT Summary

There are 15 areas listed in the *National Functional Guidelines* as necessary to check during the data evaluation process. The areas are listed in Table 7-20 and discussed in the following paragraphs.

Table 7-20.   Points of CLP SOW Semivolatiles Data Evaluation

1.	Holding Times
2.	GC/MS Instrument Performance Check
3.	Initial Calibration
4.	Continuing Calibration
5.	Blanks
6.	Surrogate Spikes
7.	Matrix Spike and Matrix Spike Duplicate
8.	Laboratory Control Samples
9.	Regional Quality Assurance and Quality Control
10.	Internal Standards
11.	Target Compound Identification
12.	Compound Quantitation and Reported Contract Required Quantitation Limits
13.	Tentatively Identified Compounds
14.	System Performance
15.	Overall Assessment of Data

1. Holding Time

The SOW distinguishes between **Technical Holding Time** and **Method Holding Time**. The method holding time is an absolute contractual requirement to extract water samples within 5 days and soil samples within 10 days of the **Verified Time of Sample Receipt** (VTSR) at the laboratory and to analyze the sample within 40 days following the extraction. The technical holding time is the amount of time which elapsed between the moment of sampling in the field and the beginning of analysis at the laboratory.

The data to be checked are the Forms I SV-1 and SV-2, the chain-of-custody record, the quantitation report, and the sample extraction sheets. The evaluation of the technical holding time depends upon what the sample is and how the sample was collected, preserved, and shipped. For water samples, the preservation is cooling to 4°C. This gives a technical holding time of 7 days to extraction. Soil samples are also preserved by cooling to 4°C but have a technical holding time of 14 days until extraction.

When technical holding times are exceeded, all results are flagged as estimates (J or UJ). If technical holding times are grossly exceeded, the positive results are flagged as estimates (J), however the reviewer needs to make a judgment as to whether the results that are less than the CRQL are either estimates (UJ) or unusable (R).

It is possible for the technical holding time for a sample to be exceeded yet the laboratory accomplished the analysis within the method holding time. The data should still be flagged; however, the laboratory is generally not held at fault. Note of this occurrence should be made in the reviewer's evaluation report.

2. GC-MS Instrument Performance Check

The instrument performance check is an evaluation of the tune conditions of the mass analyzer. It is performed every 12 hours and consists of an analysis of 50 ng of decafluorotriphenylphosphine (DFTPP) standard. The tune chromatogram, tabularized mass spectrum, tune report and Form V are checked to insure that the tune meets the criteria in Table 7-21.

Table 7-21. Decafluorotriphenylphosphine (DFTPP) CLP-SOW Tune Criteria

M/z	Ion Abundance Criteria
51	30.0 - 80.0% of m/z 198
68	Less than 2.0% of m/z 69
69	Present
70	Less than 2.0% of m/z 69
127	25.0 - 75.0% of m/z 198
197	Less than 1.0% of m/z 198
198	Base peak, 100% relative intensity
199	5.0 - 9.0% of m/z 198
275	10.0 - 30.0% of m/z 198
365	Greater than 0.75% of m/z 198
441	Present, but less than m/z 443
442	40.0 - 110.0% of m/z 198
443	15.0 - 24.0% of m/z 442

Masses not assigned correctly in the mass spectrum are cause for rejection (R) of all data associated with the tune. The reviewer should check to insure the correct ion abundance criteria were used for generation of the tune report. Inability to meet all the abundance criteria is a contract compliance failure, as is not performing the tune every 12 hours of operation.

The effect upon the data generated from the instrument when the tune criteria have not been met is to be evaluated by the reviewer, however, as discussed in Chapter 2, the effect is not clear-cut nor the evaluation straightforward. The m/z ratios for the ion pairs 198/199 and 442/443 are based on carbon isotope ratios and therefore reflect physical reality. The abundances for m/z 68, 70, 197 and 441 are reflections of the m/z resolution for the instrument.

The specified procedure for obtaining the tune is to average the three mass spectral scans across the apex of the DFTPP peak (the apex scan and the scans immediately prior to and immediately following the apex scan), then correct the averaged spectrum for background noise. The background noise correction is accomplished by subtracting from the average a spectrum obtained within 20 scans prior to the beginning of the DFTPP peak. The subtraction of a scan obtained from part of the DFTPP peak as background is specifically prohibited. This practice is termed "peak shaving" and has been used in the past to obtain tune results that are passable.

3. Initial Calibration

The data to be reviewed for the evaluation of the initial calibration are found in the quantiation reports and chromatograms of the calibration standards and are summarized on Form 4 SV-1 and SV-2.

The calibration is performed by the internal standard technique. The required internal standards and their assigned target analytes and surrogates are presented in Table 7-22. The SOW for semivolatiles analysis requires that 2 μL injections be made into the instrument. The initial calibration is performed with five standards consisting of 20, 50, 80, 120 and 160 ng of each component injected on column. All internal standards are at

40 ng on column. Surrogate compounds are calibrated just like target analytes. For the eight compounds with raised CRQL (Table 7-18) only the four higher levels of calibration are used.

The component amounts in the low concentration method are modified to 5, 10, 20, 50 and 80 ng injected on column. The eight compounds that have elevated CRQL (Table 7-18) and the surrogate 2,4,6-tribromophenol are required to be calibrated at 20, 50, 80, 100 and 120 ng on column.

Table 7-22.   Internal Standards and Their Assigned Target Analytes and Surrogates

1,4-Dichlorobenzene-d4	Naphthalene-d8	Acenaphthene-d10
Phenol	Nitrobenzene	Hexachlorocyclopentadiene
bis(2-chloroethyl) ether	Isophorone	2,4,6-Trichlorophenol
2-Chlorophenol	2,4-Dimethylphenol	2,4,5-Trichlorophenol
1,2-Dichlorobenzene	2-Nitrophenol	2-Chloronaphthalene
1,3-Dichlorobenzene	bis(2-chloroethoxy)methane	2-Nitroaniline
1,4-Dichlorobenzene	2,4-Dichlorophenol	Dimethylphthalate
2-Methylphenol	1,2,4-Trichlorobenzene	Acenaphthylene
2,2'-Oxybis(1-chloropropane)	Naphthalene	3-Nitroaniline
4-Methylphenol	4-Chloroaniline	Acenaphthene
N-nitroso-di-n-propylamine	Hexachlorobutadiene	2,4-Dinitrophenol
Hexachloroethane	4-Chloro-3-methylphenol	4-Nitrophenol
2-Fluorophenol (surr)	2-Methylnaphthalene	Dibenzofuran
Phenol-d5 (surr)	Nitrobenzene-d5 (surr)	2,4-Dinitrotoluene
2-Chlorophenol-d4 (surr)		2,6-Dinitrotoluene
1,2-Dichlorobenzene-d4 (surr)		Diethylphthalate
		4-Chlorophenylphenylether
		Fluorene
		4-Nitroaniline
		2-Fluorobiphenyl (surr)

Phenanthrene-d10	Chrysene-d12	Perylene-d12
4,6-dinitro-2-methylphenol	Pyrene	Di-n-octylphthalate
N-nitroso-di-phenylamine	Butylbenzylphthalate	Benzo(b)fluoranthene
4-Bromophenylphenylether	3,3'-Dichlorobenzidine	Benzo(k)fluoranthene
Hexachlorobenzene	Benzo(a)anthracene	Benzo(a)pyrene
Pentachlorophenol	bis(2-Ethylhexyl)phthalate	Indeno(123-cd)pyrene
Carbazole	Chrysene	Benzo(ghi)perylene
Phenanthrene	Terphenyl-d14 (surr)	Dibenzo(ah)anthracene
Anthracene		
Di-n-butylphthalate		
Fluoranthene		
2,4,6-Tribromophenol (surr)		

The success of the initial calibration is based upon meeting minimum relative response factor (RRF) criteria as compared to the appropriate internal standard, and maximum percent relative standard deviation (%RSD) for the set of calibration points.

These criteria are presented in Table 7-23. It should be noted that these criteria do not match those listed in the *National Functional Guidelines for Organic Data Review*, which state that for review purposes a minimum RRF of 0.05 and maximum %RSD of 30% are used. The calculations of the RRF and %RSD are:

$$RRF = \frac{A_{TA} \times C_{IS}}{A_{IS} \times C_{TA}}$$

where: A_{TA} is the area of the target analyte primary quantitation ion
A_{IS} is the area of the internal standard quantitation ion
C_{IS} is the concentration of the internal standard, and
C_{TA} is the concentration of the target analyte.

The average RRF is calculated as the arithmetic mean of the individual RRF. The %RSD is calculated by:

$$\%RSD = \frac{Standard\ deviation}{average\ RRF} \times 100$$

Table 7-23. Initial Calibration Criteria for Minimum RF and Maximum %RSD. (Values in parentheses are differing values from the low concentration SOW.)

Analyte	Minimum RF	Maximum %RSD
Phenol	0.800	20.5
Bis(2-Chloroethyl)ether	0.700	20.5
2-Chlorophenol	0.800 (0.700)	20.5
1,3-Dichlorobenzene	0.600	20.5
1,4-Dichlorobenzene	0.500	20.5
1,2-Dichlorobenzene	0.400	20.5
2-Methylphenol	0.700	20.5
2,2'-oxybis(1-Chloropropane)	0.010	-
4-Methylphenol	0.600	20.5
N-Nitroso-di-n-propylamine	0.500	20.5
Hexachloroethane	0.300	20.5
Nitrobenzene	0.200	20.5
Isophorone	0.400	20.5
2-Nitrophenol	0.100	20.5
2,4-Dimethylphenol	0.200	20.5
Bis(2-Chloroethoxy)methane	0.300	20.5
2,4-Dichlorophenol	0.200	20.5
1,2,4-Trichlorobenzene	0.200	20.5
Naphthalene	0.700	20.5
4-Chloroaniline	0.010	-
Hexachlorobutadiene	0.010	-
4-Chloro-3-methylphenol	0.200	20.5
2-Methylnaphthalene	0.400	20.5
Hexachlorocyclopentadiene	0.010	-
2,4,6-Trichlorophenol	0.200	20.5

Table 7-23. **Initial Calibration Criteria for Minimum RF and Maximum %RSD.** (Values in parentheses are differing values from the low conc. SOW.), *continued*

Analyte	Minimum RF	Maximum %RSD
2,4,5-Trichlorophenol	0.200	20.5
2-Chloronaphthalene	0.800	20.5
2-Nitroaniline	0.010	-
Dimethylphthalate	0.010	-
Acenaphthylene	0.900 (1.300)	20.5
2,6-Dinitrotoluene	0.200	20.5
3-Nitroaniline	0.010	-
Acenaphthene	0.900 (0.800)	20.5
2,4-Dinitrophenol	0.010	-
4-Nitrophenol	0.010	-
Dibenzofuran	0.800	20.5
2,4-Dinitrotoluene	0.200	20.5
Diethylphthalate	0.010	-
4-Chlorophenylphenylether	0.400	20.5
Fluorene	0.900	20.5
4-Nitroaniline	0.010	-
4,6-Dinitro-2-methylphenol	0.010	-
N-Nitroso-diphenylamine	0.010	-
4-Bromophenylphenylether	0.100	20.5
Hexachlorobenzene	0.100	20.5
Pentachlorophenol	0.050	20.5
Phenanthrene	0.700	20.5
Anthracene	0.700	20.5
Carbazole	0.010	-
Di-n-butylphthalate	0.010	-
Fluoranthene	0.600	20.5
Pyrene	0.600	20.5
Butylbenzylphthalate	0.010	-
3,3'-Dichlorobenzidine	0.010	-
Benzo(a)anthracene	0.800	20.5
Chrysene	0.700	20.5
Bis(2-Ethylhexyl)phthalate	0.010	-
Di-n-octylphthalate	0.010	-
Benzo(b)fluoranthene	0.700	20.5
Benzo(k)fluoranthene	0.700	20.5
Benzo(a)pyrene	0.700	20.5
Indeno(1,2,3-cd)pyrene	0.500	20.5
Dibenzo(a,h)anthracene	0.400	20.5
Benzo(g,h,i)perylene	0.500	20.5
Surrogates		
Nitrobenzene-d$_5$	0.200 (0.010)	20.5
2-Fluorobiphenyl	0.700	20.5

Table 7-23. **Initial Calibration Criteria for Minimum RF and Maximum %RSD.** (Values in parentheses are differing values from the low conc. SOW.), *continued*

Analyte	Minimum RF	Maximum %RSD
Surrogates, *continued*		
Terphenyl-d$_{14}$	0.500	20.5
Phenol-d$_5$	0.800	20.5
2-Fluorophenol	0.600	20.5
2,4,6-Tribromophenol	0.010	-
2-Chlorophenol-d$_4$	0.800	20.5
1,2-Dichlorobenzene-d$_4$	0.400	20.5

RRF is a measure of the sensitivity of the instrument for a particular analyte. %RSD is a measure of either the linearity of the calibration curve or the presence of a botched calibration standard. Botched standards can be recognized by the presence of an individual RRF that is way out of line with the other four for that analyte.

If the RRF for an individual compound is greater than 0.05, and the initial calibration %RSD is greater than 30.0%, then all reported results for that compound greater than the CRQL are flagged as estimated values (J). Results below the CRQL are flagged at the reviewer's discretion. If the RRF is less than 0.05, then, based on the reviewer's judgment, all reported results for that compound greater than the CRQL may be flagged as estimated values (J) and the non-detects may be flagged as unusable (R).

The initial calibration data can be further examined when the %RSD criteria have been exceeded to determine if the linearity of the curve can be improved by dropping either the lowest or highest calibration point. If the %RSD is substantially improved, the reviewer may re-evaluate the sample results so that only those values obtained from the non-linear part of the calibration curve are flagged as estimates (J) or unusable (R).

4. Continuing Calibration

A continuing calibration standard containing all target analytes and system monitoring compounds is required to be performed at the beginning of each 12-hour period of sample analysis. The success of the continuing calibration is evaluated through use of the relative response factor (RRF) and the percent difference (%D) of the RRF as compared to the average RRF obtained in the initial calibration. The %D is calculated as follows:

$$\%D = \frac{RRF - average\ RRF}{average\ RRF} \times 100$$

where: RRF is the relative response factor obtained from the continuing calibration
average RRF is the value from the initial calibration.

The data available for evaluation of the continuing calibration includes Form VII, and the quantitation report and chromatogram. The minimum RRF for all compounds is 0.05, regardless of the results on the initial calibration. The %D for all calibrated compounds is less than 25%. The reviewer should verify which initial calibration is being used as a basis for the continuing calibration and that this is the same initial calibration that relates to the samples.

If the %D for any compound is outside of the ±25% criteria, flag all positive and non-detected results for that compound as estimated (J). If any compound has a RRF less than 0.05, positive results are flagged as estimated (J) while non-detected results are unusable (R).

5. Blanks

Blanks are used to evaluate sample contamination that arises from either the field or the laboratory. Two types of blanks are normally evaluated for semivolatile analysis, equipment rinses from field decontaminated equipment and sample preparation blanks performed with each batch of samples. Separate sample preparation blanks are used with soil and water samples because of the differences in the sample extraction. A blank should also be generated from the gel permeation clean-up (GPC) required for each sample. Blanks are prepared by spiking analyte-free portions of either water or a soil substitute (sodium sulfate) with surrogates, then taking the blank through the entire analytical procedure simultaneously with all the associated samples. The idea is that no compounds other than the surrogates and internal standards are found in the blank.

The data to be reviewed are found on Form I SV-1 and SV-2, Form IV SV, and raw quantitation reports, chromatograms, and sample extraction sheets.

The review actions depend on the results of the blanks and the samples. If the blank exhibits target analytes but the samples are clean, then no action is taken with regard to the samples. Note should be made of the blank contamination. If the blank and samples exhibit the common laboratory contaminants 1,4-dichlorobenzene, naphthalene or the ubiquitous phthalates, the relative amounts in the blank and samples are evaluated. If the samples have levels higher than ten times the amounts present in the blank, then the assumption is made that the analyte is in the sample. If the samples have levels of the contaminants less than ten times the amount in the blank, then laboratory contamination is presumed source. In these cases the CRQL is raised to the level found in the sample and the sample result flagged with a "U." When there is gross contamination of the blanks and the samples, then all results are flagged as unusable (R). For target analytes and TICs other than the common laboratory contaminants a five-times rule is used for guidance.

6. Surrogate Spikes

Surrogate compounds are added to each sample prior to the beginning of analysis and are used to monitor the success of the sample preparation. The surrogate compounds are calibrated just like the target analytes of the methods. The concentrations of the surrogates in the samples, based on a normal sample size, are listed in Table 7-24. The last two surrogates in the Table, 2-chlorophenol-d_4 and 1,2-dichlorobenzene-d_4 are in the Multiconcentration, Multimedia SOW and are not mentioned in the Low-concentration SOW.

Table 7-24.   Concentration of Surrogates in Samples Based on Normal Sample Size
(1 L Water and 30 g Soil)

Surrogates	Low-Conc. µg/L	Multiconc. Water µg/L	Soil µg/Kg
Nitrobenzene-d_5	40	50	1650
2-Fluorobiphenyl	40	50	1650
Terphenyl-d_{14}	40	50	1650

Table 7-24. **Concentration of Surrogates in Samples Based on Normal Sample Size (1 L Water and 30 g Soil),** *continued*

Surrogates	Low-Conc. µg/L	Multiconc. Water µg/L	Multiconc. Soil µg/Kg
Phenol-d$_5$	40	75	2475
2-Fluorophenol	40	75	2475
2,4,6-Tribromophenol	120	75	2475
2-Chlorophenol-d$_4$	-	75	2475
1,2-Dichlorobenzene-d$_4$	-	50	1650

The recoveries of the surrogate compounds are calculated using the following equation:

$$\%R = \frac{\text{Concentration found}}{\text{Concentration spiked}} \times 100 .$$

Recoveries of surrogate compounds are calculated for all samples, blanks, and quality control samples. The data are summarized on Form II SV-1 and SV-2 and the raw data are found in the individual quantitation reports and chromatograms. The acceptance limits for the surrogates are listed in Table 7-25.

Table 7-25. **Surrogate Compound Recovery Acceptance Limits**

Surrogates	Low Conc. %R	Multiconc. Water %R	Multiconc. Soil %R
Nitrobenzene-d$_5$	40-112	35-114	23-120
2-Fluorobiphenyl	42-110	43-116	30-115
Terphenyl-d$_{14}$	24-140	33-141	18-137
Phenol-d$_5$	17-113	10-110	24-113
2-Fluorophenol	16-110	21-110	25-121
2,4,6-Tribromophenol	18-126	10-123	19-122
2-Chlorophenol-d$_4$	-	33-110	20-130
1,2-Dichlorobenzene-d$_4$	-	16-110	20-130

The surrogates are divided into two groups for data evaluation purposes, the acids and the base/neutrals. The acid group consists of phenol-d$_5$, 2-fluorophenol, 2,4,6-tribromophenol and 2-chlorophenol-d$_4$. The base/neutral group consists of nitrobenzene-d$_5$, terphenyl-d$_{14}$, 2-fluorobiphenyl and 1,2-dichlorobenzene-d$_4$. Although the SOW's do not provide for sequential adjustment of sample pH to strongly basic and strongly acidic to assist extraction of the surrogates and analytes, there are a number of reasons such as specific matrix interference for one surrogate from one of the groups to not be within the acceptance limits. However, if two surrogates from the same group fail to meet acceptance limits, the reviewer is advised to qualify data for the sample. The SOW directs the analyst to re-analyze the extract at least once if two or more surrogates from the same group fail, or if any single surrogate has a recovery less than 10%. The analyst is directed to re-extract and analyze the sample if the initial re-analysis also fails. If the re-analysis or re-extraction passes surrogate criteria, the laboratory is required to report only the successful results.

The guidelines for data qualification depend on the recoveries of the out-of-compliance surrogates. The behavior of the surrogate is interpreted as reflecting the behavior of the associated target analytes. If surrogate recoveries are high, then the target analyte recoveries are also assumed to be biased high. Therefore, reported detected analytes should be flagged as estimates (J) on the high side. Non-detected analytes are interpreted to be acceptable although the quantitation level may be an estimate (UJ). If surrogate recoveries are low, especially when less than 10% recovery, then the target analyte recoveries are also assumed to be biased low. Therefore reported detected analytes should be flagged as estimates (J) on the low side. Non-detected target analytes may, in fact, be present in the sample, and thus the data are flagged as unusable (R).

Certain patterns of surrogate recoveries can lead to other interpretations of data usability. Although they are not specifically addressed within the published CLP SOW data review guidelines, Chapter 2 presents other possibly valuable suggestions.

7. Matrix Spikes/Matrix Spike Duplicates

Matrix spike and matrix spike duplicate (MS and MSD) are required to be performed and the recoveries calculated on at least one sample out of each sample set of 20 samples of a similar matrix. However, the results on the MS and MSD are not by and of themselves used to qualify data. The compounds used in the matrix spike solution are listed in Table 7-26 along with the associated accuracy (%R) and precision (RPD) quality objectives. The MS and MSD compounds are spiked into the water to achieve a 50 µg/L for the base/neutral compounds and 75 µg/L for the acidic compounds. Low concentration soil samples are spiked to achieve a 1,670 µg/kg level in the sample for the base/neutral compounds and 2,500 µg/kg for the acidic compounds. The medium level soil directions result in a 50,000 µg/kg concentration of each base/neutral MS component in the sample and 75,000 µg/kg for the acidic compounds. MS and MSD are not required to be performed in the Low Concentration SOW.

Table 7-26. SVO Matrix Spike Compounds and Recovery Acceptance Limits. (A) denotes acidic compound, (BN) denotes base/neutral compound.

Compound	Water		Soil	
	%R	RPD	%R	RPD
Phenol (A)	12-110	42	26-90	35
2-Chlorophenol (A)	27-123	40	25-102	50
1,4-Dichlorobenzene (BN)	36-97	28	28-104	27
N-nitroso-di-n-propylamine (BN)	41-116	38	41-126	38
1,2,4-Trichlorobenzene (BN)	39-98	28	38-107	23
4-Chloro-3-methylphenol (A)	23-97	42	26-103	33
Acenaphthene (BN)	46-118	31	31-137	19
4-Nitrophenol (A)	10-80	50	11-114	50
2,4-Dinitrotoluene (BN)	24-96	38	28-89	47
Pentachlorophenol (A)	9-103	50	17-109	47
Pyrene (BN)	26-127	31	35-142	36

Recoveries (%R) for matrix spike compounds are calculated as:

$$\%R = \frac{SSR - SR}{SA} \times 100$$

where: SSR is the spiked sample result.
SR is the unspiked sample result.
SA is the spike amount.

Precision (RPD) is calculated as:

$$RPD = \frac{2|MSR - MSRD|}{MSR + MSRD} \times 100$$

where: MSR is the matrix spike percent recovery (%R).
MSRD is the matrix spike duplicate percent recovery (%R).

If the sample chosen for the MS/MSD needed to be diluted, then the MS and MSD should be performed on the diluted sample (reduced sample size) rather than dilute the MS or MSD extract after spiking.

The data used for the evaluation of the matrix spikes are found on Form III SVO-1, Form III SVO-2 and the raw data chromatograms and quantitation reports. The reviewer should recalculate several of the recoveries and RPD numbers listed on Form III to verify that the calculations were performed correctly. In a strict sense the MS and MSD recoveries are applicable to only the sample that was spiked. High or low MS compound recoveries can be related to the behavior of compounds of similar chemical structure or similar volatility (Table 7-22), or the recoveries may be indicative of problems with the results obtained for all target analytes in the sample.

On the other hand repeated inability to generate acceptable matrix spike results over a period of time is indicative of system-specific analytical problems in the laboratory. This situation should be investigated as it may suggest that no results being generated by the lab are usable.

8. Laboratory Control Samples

Laboratory control samples (LCS) are actually specified only under the Low Concentration water SOW where they are used to replace the requirement of a matrix spike and duplicate in every batch of 20 analytical samples. The data reviewed are found on Form III LCSV, and the raw chromatograms and quantitation reports. The compounds used in the LCS, and the acceptance limits are presented in Table 7-27. They are added to a portion of reagent water as a solution to form a final concentration of 20 µg/L in the sample, with the exceptions of the first four compounds in Table 7-27, which are added at 40 µg/L. These four compounds are the three acidic compounds and the only true base in the LCS solution.

Table 7-27. **SVO Laboratory Control Sample Compounds and Acceptance Limits.**
(A) denotes acidic compounds, (BN) denotes base/neutral compounds.

LCS Compound	%R Acceptance Limit
Phenol (A)	44-120
2-Chlorophenol (A)	58-110
4-Chloroaniline (BN)	35-98
2,4,6-Trichlorophenol (A)	65-110
bis (2-Chloroethyl)ether (BN)	64-110
N-nitroso-di-n-propylamine (BN)	34-102
Hexachloroethane (BN)	32-77
Isophorone (BN)	49-110
1,2,4-Trichlorobenzene (BN)	44-96
Naphthalene (BN)	56-160
2,4-Dinitrotoluene (BN)	61-140
Diethylphthalate (BN)	76-104
N-nitroso-diphenylamine (BN)	35-120
Hexachlorobenzene (BN)	30-95
Benzo(a)pyrene	55-92

Recoveries (%R) for laboratory control sample compounds are calculated as:

$$\%R = \frac{SSR}{SA} \times 100$$

where: SSR is the spiked sample result.
SA is the spike amount.

The LCS is prepared by adding the LCS spike solution and surrogates to one liter of reagent grade water, then processing the LCS along with the rest of the samples in the batch. There is no acceptable reason for the LCS recovery objectives not to be met for each component. Failure to meet the acceptance criteria on this "perfect" matrix generates substantial doubts about the laboratory's ability to generate reliable results on any sample. However, assuming that all the sample results in the sample set are not unilaterally flagged as estimates (J) or unusable (R), the relationship of the recovery for specific members of the LCS solution to recovery of target analytes in samples needs to take into account the chemical nature, the recovery efficiency, volatility and analytical difficulty presented by the compounds. If LCS recoveries are high, then associated results for target analytes are estimates (J) for those analytes reported above the CRDL and acceptable for those compounds reported as less than the CRDL.

When individual LCS compound recoveries are low, then related target analyte results greater than the CRDL are estimates (J) while the non-detects are unusable (R). If more than 50% of the LCS components are reported with less than acceptable recoveries, then all target analyte compounds reported above the CRDL are estimates (J) while none of the non-detected analytes are usable (R).

Surrogate recoveries and internal standard performance criteria must be met for acceptable LCS recoveries to be valid.

9. Regional Quality Assurance and Quality Control

These are suggested in the National Functional Guidelines to consist of checking Performance Evaluation sample results, field duplicates, blind spikes and/or blind blanks. Region III[2] reviews the results of Performance Evaluation samples and requires that all analytes present in the PE sample be correctly identified and quantitated. Region III also evaluates the results of field duplicates in terms of RPD. The RPDs obtained from the field duplicates are cross-checked against those listed as Data Quality Objectives in the Quality Assurance Project Plan.

10. Internal Standards

The internal standards used in semivolatiles analysis are presented in Table 7-22. They are added to every sample extract to achieve a final concentration of 40 ng/2 μL, the 2 μL being the volume of sample extract injected into the GC-MS. Form VIII SVO and the raw chromatograms and quantitation reports are used for evaluation. The two items to check are the area counts of the internal standard peak (quantitation ion) and the retention time. The criteria are to have the area counts of the internal standards in the sample within a factor of two (50% to 200%) of the area counts exhibited on the last continuing calibration. In the low concentration procedure the criteria are tightened to ±40%. For retention times the internal standards must elute within ±30 seconds of the retention time exhibited in the last continuing calibration. The low concentration procedure tightens the requirements to ±20 seconds.

For reported target analytes where the associated internal standards do not meet the factor of two criteria, the results are flagged as estimated (J). Non-detected analytes where the internal standard has an area count greater than a factor of two (200%) are considered to be reliable. Non-detected analytes that have internal standards with low area counts are estimates and should be flagged (UJ). If extremely low area counts are reported then the non-detected analytes results are unusable (R).

Large retention time shifts of the internal standards can generate false positive or negative results, and it may be appropriate to flag all results for that sample as unusable (R). The reviewer should check the chromatograms for detected and non-detected compounds and then examine the associated mass spectra for correct identification. This may avoid flagging the detected analytes as unusable (R).

11. Target Compound Identification

Identifications of target analytes need to be checked in two respects. First, reported hits for target analytes in the samples must be verified as accurate. This is done through checking the Form I SVO and the raw chromatogram, quantitation report, and the mass spectra for the hit. Reported hits not correct are termed "false positives." The second aspect of target compound identification is to verify that analytes reported as not present (U) are in fact absent from the sample. Not reporting target compounds actually present is termed a "false negative." Examination of the raw chromatogram and quantitation report and Form I SVO will help build confidence in the lack of false negatives.

Identifications are based upon first, relative retention time (RRT) matches of the analyte in the sample with that in the standard. The relative retention time is the retention time of the analyte divided by the retention time of the same compound in the continuing

---

2 Region III Modifications to National Functional Guidelines for Organic Data Review Multi-Media, Multi-Concentration (OLM)1.1-OLMO1.9), September 1994

calibration standard run within the same 12-hour work shift. If the compound elutes at exactly the same time as that of the standard, a RRT of 1.00 is obtained. There can be no more than ±0.06 variation in the relative retention times to support a positive identification, which gives an acceptance range of 0.94 to 1.06 for the RRT.

The second criteria for identification is a mass spectrum match of the reported hit with that of the laboratory generated mass spectrum of the standard. Most data systems that used to operate mass spectrometers will generate a quantitation report (Figure 7-1). The identifications of target analytes listed upon this report are based on the correct quantitation ion (quant ion, Table 7-28) and other characteristic ions being found at the correct retention time.

Table 7-28. **Quantitation Ions Required for Semivolatile Target Analytes, Surrogate Compounds and Internal Standards.** (List includes the target analytes from both the Low Concentration and the multiconcentration multimedia SOW.)

Analyte	CAS	Quant. Ion
Phenol	108-95-2	94
Bis(2-Chloroethyl)ether	111-44-4	93
2-Chlorophenol	95-57-8	128
1,3-Dichlorobenzene	541-73-1	146
1,4-Dichlorobenzene	106-46-7	146
1,2-Dichlorobenzene	95-50-1	146
2-Methylphenol	95-48-7	108
2,2'-oxybis(1-Chloropropane)	108-60-1	45
4-Methylphenol	106-44-5	108
N-Nitroso-di-n-propylamine	621-64-7	70
Hexachloroethane	67-72-1	117
Nitrobenzene	98-95-3	77
Isophorone	78-59-1	82
2-Nitrophenol	88-75-5	139
2,4-Dimethylphenol	105-67-9	107
Bis(2-Chloroethoxy)methane	111-91-1	93
2,4-Dichlorophenol	120-83-2	162
1,2,4-Trichlorobenzene	120-82-1	180
Naphthalene	91-20-3	128
4-Chloroaniline	106-47-8	127
Hexachlorobutadiene	87-68-3	225
4-Chloro-3-methylphenol	59-50-7	107
2-Methylnaphthalene	91-57-6	142
Hexachlorocyclopentadiene	77-47-4	237
2,4,6-Trichlorophenol	88-06-2	196
2,4,5-Trichlorophenol	95-95-4	196
2-Chloronaphthalene	91-58-7	162
2-Nitroaniline	88-74-4	65
Dimethylphthalate	131-11-3	163
Acenaphthylene	208-96-8	152
2,6-Dinitrotoluene	606-20-2	165

Table 7-28.   **Quantitation Ions Required for Semivolatile Target Analytes, Surrogate Compounds and Internal Standards.** (List includes the target analytes from both the Low Concentration and the multiconcentration multimedia SOW.), *continued*

Analyte	CAS	Quant. Ion
3-Nitroaniline	99-09-2	138
Acenaphthene	83-32-9	153
2,4-Dinitrophenol	51-28-5	184
4-Nitrophenol	100-02-7	109
Dibenzofuran	132-64-9	168
2,4-Dinitrotoluene	121-14-2	165
Diethylphthalate	84-66-2	149
4-Chlorophenylphenylether	7005-72-3	204
Fluorene	86-73-7	166
4-Nitroaniline	100-01-6	138
4,6-Dinitro-2-methylphenol	534-52-1	198
N-Nitroso-diphenylamine	86-30-6	169
4-Bromophenylphenylether	101-55-3	248
Hexachlorobenzene	118-74-1	284
Pentachlorophenol	87-86-5	266
Phenanthrene	85-01-8	178
Anthracene	120-12-7	178
Carbazole	86-74-8	167
Di-n-butylphthalate	84-74-2	149
Fluoranthene	206-44-0	202
Pyrene	129-00-0	202
Butylbenzylphthalate	85-68-7	149
3,3'-Dichlorobenzidine	91-94-1	252
Benzo(a)anthracene	56-55-3	228
Chrysene	218-01-9	228
Bis(2-Ethylhexyl)phthalate	117-81-7	149
Di-n-octylphthalate	117-84-0	149
Benzo(b)fluoranthene	205-99-2	252
Benzo(k)fluoranthene	207-08-9	252
Benzo(a)pyrene	50-32-8	252
Indeno(1,2,3-cd)pyrene	193-39-5	276
Dibenzo(a,h)anthracene	53-70-3	278
Benzo(g,h,i)perylene	191-24-2	276
Surrogates		
Phenol-d$_5$		99
2-Fluorophenol		112
Nitrobenzene-d$_5$		82
2,4,6-Tribromophenol		330
2-Fluorobiphenyl		172

Table 7-28. **Quantitation Ions Required for Semivolatile Target Analytes, Surrogate Compounds and Internal Standards.** (List includes the target analytes from both the Low Concentration and the multiconcentration multimedia SOW.), *continued*

Analyte	CAS	Quant. Ion
Surrogates, *continued*		
Terphenyl-d$_{14}$		244
2-Chlorophenol-d$_4$		132
1,2-Dichlorobenzene-d$_4$		152
Internal Standards		
1,4-Dichlorobenzene-d$_4$		152
Naphthalene-d$_8$		136
Acenaphthene-d$_{10}$		164
Phenanthrene-d$_{10}$		188
Chrysene-d$_{12}$		240
Perylene-d$_{12}$		264

The software performs spectral matching according to the entries in the ID (Identification) file in the process of preparing the quantitation report. How completely the ID file is populated with characteristic ions and up-to-date abundances for those ions relates directly to the number of false positives in the quantitation report. The matching of the spectra from the sample with those obtained during the daily continuing calibration is done either manually or within the context of an automated library search routine. The spectral comparison is conducted in two directions: the standard spectrum is compared against that of the sample analyte, and then the sample analyte spectrum is compared against that of the standard. All ions in the standard spectrum of greater than 10% intensity must be present in the sample spectrum, and the relative intensities of the ions must agree within ±20%. This builds confidence that the target analyte is actually represented by the spectrum from the sample. However, there is a distinct probability that the spectrum of the analyte in the sample includes other ions (greater than 10%) not present in the standard, and this is the reason for checking the sample against the standard. The additional ions should be accountable for as either a co-eluting compound with that of the target analyte or some recognizable and reasonable artifact such as column bleed (ions at m/z 73, 207, 283, 355). If the ions can't be accounted for there is the distinct possibility that a misidentification has been made. Incorrect identifications are flagged as either undetected (U) or unusable (R).

False negatives are harder to ascertain. The reviewer must examine the raw chromatogram very closely and verify that every peak has been correctly identified as either a surrogate compound, internal standard, or target analyte, or is listed as a TIC. The TICs should be very closely examined to verify that they are not, in fact, target analytes. Peaks not accounted for are subject to further investigation.

12. Compound Quantitation and Contract Required Quantitation Limits (CRQLs)

Information related to the review of reported amounts of identified target analytes is found on Forms 1 SVO and 7 SVO, and the sample preparation sheets, raw chromatograms and quantitation reports. Quantitation is based upon the area of the quant ion present for the target analyte (Table 7-28) compared with the area of quant ion found for the appropriate internal standard (Table 7-22) corrected with the response factor generated during the daily calibration check, using the equation:

$$\text{Raw Amount} = \frac{\text{(Area target analyte quant ion) x (Amount internal standard)}}{\text{(Area internal standard quant ion) x } (R_f)}.$$

This equation is further modified if GPC cleanup was used in the sample preparation. The modified calculation is:

$$\text{Result } \mu g/L = \frac{(\text{Area}_{TA}) \times (C_{IS}) \times (V_t) \times (Df) \times (GPC)}{(\text{Area}_{IS}) \times (Rf) \times (V_o) \times (V_I)}$$

where: Area_{TA} is the area of the quant ion for the target analyte.

Area_{IS} is the area of the quant ion for the internal standard.

C_{IS} is the amount of internal standard in ng injected into the GC-MS.

Rf is the response factor from the daily calibration check.

V_t is the final concentrated volume of the extract in μL - 1000 μL if the sample was not processed through GPC, 500 μL if the sample was subjected to GPC.

V_o is the mL of sample extracted initially, normally 1000 mL.

V_I is the volume of sample injected into the GC-MS in μL.

Df is the dilution factor.

GPC is the GPC factor: - 1 if GPC was not used, 2 if GPC was used. The product $(V_t) \times (GPC)$ should always equal 1000.

If a secondary quantitation ion was used for the target analyte due to spectral interference with the primary ion, the reviewer needs to verify that the target analyte was calibrated for the secondary ion instead of the primary quant ion.

If reduced sample sizes have been analyzed due to high levels of target analytes or other interferences in the samples, the raw result is corrected for the dilution factor. The dilution factor is listed in the heading of Form 1 SVO.

The dilution factor is calculated as follows:

$$Df = \frac{\text{(μL of extract used to make dilution)} + \text{(μL clean solvent added for dilution)}}{\text{(μL of extract used to make dilution)}}.$$

The raw result obtained from the quantitation report is multiplied by the dilution factor to obtain the final result. For water samples the reviewer can check the calculation by dividing the result on Form 1 by the dilution factor and 2 (for the 2 μL injected into the GC-MS), and this should agree with the number on the quant report for that analyte.

Solid samples are reported in terms of dry weight. The dry weight is calculated from the wet result by dividing by the fraction solids in the sample. Form I lists the percent moisture. The fraction solids can be generated from the percent moisture by:

$$D = \text{fraction solids} = \frac{100 - \text{percent moisture}}{100}$$

$$\text{dry weight result} = \frac{\text{Wet result}}{\text{fraction solids}}.$$

The complete calculation for the solids results is:

$$\text{Final result } \mu g/Kg = \frac{(ATA) \times (IS) \times (VT) \times (Df) \times (GPC)}{(A_{IS}) \times (R_f) \times (V_I) \times (W_S) \times (D)}$$

where: A_{TA} is the area of the quantitation ion for the target analyte.

I_S is the amount of the internal standard in ng injected into the GC-MS.

V_T is the total volume in μL of the extract. It should be 500 μL.

Df is the dilution factor.

A_{IS} is the area of the quant ion from the internal standard.

R_f is the response factor generated during the daily continuing calibration.

V_I is the volume of extract in μL injected into the GC-MS.

W_S is the wet weight of sample extracted in g.

D is the fraction solids in the sample.

GPC is equal to 2 if GPC has been used.

The Contract Required Quantitation Level (CRQL) is also adjusted based on the above considerations. The factors of dry weight and sample dilution are performed upon the CRQL, just like they are on a sample result, to generate the adjusted CRQL.

The reviewer should verify that results and adjustments to the CRQL have been calculated correctly.

13. Tentatively Identified Compounds

These are compounds found in the sample that elute from the GC-MS as defined peaks, yet are not calibrated analytes. The information in the packet that can be used to review the identification of the Tentatively Identified Compounds (TICs) includes the Form 1 SVO-TIC report, the sample chromatograms, and library search printouts, and mass spectra for the closest matches.

Up to 30 peaks greater than 10% in area or height of the nearest internal standard are candidate TICs. This requirement is changed to 50% of the height or area of the nearest internal standard for the Low Concentration SOW. A forward library search is conducted against a standard mass spectral database, either the NIST/EPA/NIH or the Wiley collections. The following cautions are appropriate when considering spectral matches from these libraries. First, most of the spectra in the collections were not obtained from mass spectrometers tuned to meet decafluorotriphenyl phosphine acceptance criteria. Second, the supervisors of the collections accepted spectra from anyone who submitted spectra, and some of the compound/spectra identifications are simply wrong. Third, some of the spectra have been background corrected to remove artifact signals, and others have not. Last, in the interests of conservation of storage space, the spectra have been reduced to eliminate many of the small signals, leaving just the major signals.

Once the search program has identified possible matches, the spectra are manually compared to that of the candidate TIC from the sample. Some of the comparisons include:

1. Verifying that all peaks of greater than 10% relative abundance in the library spectrum are present in the TIC spectrum.

2. The abundance of the matching ions should agree within ±20% relative intensity in the library and TIC spectra.

3. Molecular ions present in the library spectrum should also be present in the TIC spectrum. The molecular ion has the same mass as the molecular mass of the compound and is generally the highest mass in the spectrum.

4. Major peaks present in the TIC spectrum, but not in the library spectrum, should be reviewed as to indicating the presence of co-eluting compounds or indicating a misidentification.

The TIC spectrum should be reviewed as to whether it makes analytical sense in terms of recognized mass spectral fragmentation patterns based on the proposed molecular structure of the compound. This skill is very rare among GC-MS operators but is an absolute necessity for reliable mass spectral interpretation. The vast majority of TICs are reported from environmental laboratories are simply the top choice generated from the forward search algorithm with no further examination from the operator.

Peaks that have not generated creditable candidates from the library, can be labeled as "unknown". They can be further classified as unknown chlorinated hydrocarbon, unknown aromatic, *etc.* based on the judgment of the mass spectral interpreter. If a molecular weight can be determined from the mass spectrum, it is also included.

For multipeak materials, for example toxaphene, PCBs, kerosene, and diesel fuel, which are not calibrated, but are easily recognized as such, all the peaks related to the material should be reported as a single TIC (alkanes C_9-C_{25}). It is incorrect to report these type TICs as individual peaks such as methylpentane, hexane, dimethyl-heptane, *etc.*

Approximate quantities of the TICs and the peaks listed as unknown are generated. The procedure is to calculate a quantity based on the total ion current area of the TIC and the total ion current area of the nearest internal standard. A response factor of 1.00 is used. Dilution factors, sample weight/volume and GPC cleanup activities are factored into the calculation as discussed in the above section.

$$\text{Amount of TIC} = \frac{(\text{Area of TIC}) \times (\text{Amount of Internal Standard})}{(\text{Area of Internal Standard})} .$$

TIC results are flagged as presumed present and estimated quantity (NJ). Quantities reported for compounds listed as unknown are flagged as estimated (J).

The following peaks are not to be reported as TICs:

1. Peaks of less than 10% of the height or area of the nearest internal standard

2. Peaks eluting more than 30 seconds before the retention time of the first SVO target analyte

3. Peaks eluting more than 3 minutes after the retention time of the last SVO target analyte

4. Peaks that are target analytes in the VOA fraction. Pesticides are reported as TICs.

5. Peaks also found in the blank at approximately the same concentration (within a factor of 5 or 10)

6. Surrogates and internal standards

7. Common laboratory contaminants such as, siloxanes (m/z 73, 207, 281, 355, *etc*), hexanes and other alkane solvents, phthalates and other materials used in the laboratory at levels less than 100 μg/L or 4000 μg/Kg

8. Aldol condensation products such as 4-methyl-4-hydroxy-2-pentanone and 4-methyl-3-penten-2-one, and 5,5-dimethyl-2(5H)-furanone are condensation products of acetone and are commonly found in laboratories.

9. Individual alkanes in a series are not reported as individual TICs, but are lumped together as C_9-C_{15} with an estimated total amount given.

The reviewer has a number of choices as to how to deal with TICs believed to be incorrectly reported. They may choose to flag the individual TICs as unusable (R) in the case of suspected laboratory artifacts, physical impossibility of presence in the GC-MS result (such as an identified amino acid or glycol), or gross misinterpretation of the mass spectrum. Individual TICs may be grouped into an aggregate TIC, such as kerosene, if that is more appropriate. The identification of the TIC may be changed from a specific identification to a more general identification if in the judgment of the reviewer the specificity is unwarranted. For example, a reported TIC of 2,3,7,8-tetramethylnaphalene might be changed to the less specific tetramethylnaphalene isomer or substituted aromatic hydrocarbon.

14. System Performance

The reviewer should evaluate the performance of the GC-MS system as evidenced through the appearance of the chromatogram and the recoveries of the surrogate compounds and internal standards for each sample. The items to review are Form VIII SVO (Internal Standard summary), Form III SVO-1, Form III SVO-2 (Matrix Spike summaries), Form II SVO (Surrogate summary), and the raw chromatograms.

Specific areas to look for include:

1. Baseline rise, particularly in the later part of the chromatogram

2. Degradation of peak definition and shape

3. Loss of sensitivity of the mass analyzer.

The baseline rise is generally due to previously injected grossly contaminated samples. The loss of internal standard area counts during the day are evidence of degrading performance and potential build-up of contamination within the mass analyzer. Loss of peak resolution or even possible peak splitting are clues of active site development within the gas chromatograph. Peaks losing an even Gaussian or symmetrical appearance and development of lopsided peaks, called peak tailing, is another clue to system degradation.

Any of these symptoms may be an indication that the system is in need of preventative maintenance. They also suggest that the results obtained from such a system may not be entirely reliable.

15. Overall Assessment of Data

The Overall Assessment of Data is a written narrative prepared by the reviewer. It is used to express qualifications and concerns about the sample results not expressly covered in the other areas of review. Besides the data package, the reviewer may wish to refer to the Quality Assurance Project Plan and the Sampling and Analysis Plan. The reviewer may wish to consider to what purpose the data will be applied as a guide to their summary of the data usability. Thus data known to be proceeding directly into the legal arena will be viewed in a different light than data being used to prepare an initial evaluation of a site and to be followed by further sampling and analysis efforts.

16. Gel Permeation Chromatography

An area not covered within the *National Functional Guidelines* is Gel permeation chromatography (GPC) Cleanup. GPC columns are packed with a styrene-divinyl-benzene polymer has a well-defined range of pore sizes in it. The clean-up serves as a molecular size/shape sifting mechanism to remove very large molecules from the sample extract. These materials degrade thermally in the heated injection port of the GC-MS and create active sites in the system. They also contribute to raised baselines and "hump-o-grams" in the chromatograms. GPC is required for water extracts which appear to contain higher molecular weight material and for all soil extracts.

GPC is performed by diluting the sample extract to 10.0 mL with methylene chloride, then injecting it upon the GPC. The injection is through a 5.00 mL calibrated injection loop. The first 3-5 mL of the sample are used to rinse out the loop and are then passed to waste. The second 5.00 mL of sample actually make it on to the column. Methylene chloride is used to elute the components of interest from the column. The higher weight undesired materials pass rapidly through the column, the desired target analytes and surrogates move through the column at a slower pace.

The calibration mix consists of corn oil, which represents the heavy undesired materials, bis(2-ethylhexyl)phthalate, methoxychlor and perylene which define the range of molecular weights and shapes exhibited by the target analytes and surrogates, and sulfur, which is used to represent undesired small molecules. The idea is to calibrate the instrument so that the undesired materials are passed to waste, while all the important compounds are collected for concentration and then subsequent analysis by GC-MS. A UV detector is used to monitor the calibration separation and a trace of the UV absorbance generates a chromatogram. The following criteria apply:

1. Peaks must be observed and should be symmetrical for all compounds in the calibration mixture.

2. Corn oil and the phthalate peaks must exhibit >85.0% resolution. The corn oil peak should actually appear as two overlapping peaks.

3. The phthalate and methoxychlor and methoxychlor and perylene peaks must exhibit >85.0% resolution.

4. The perylene and sulfur peaks must exhibit >90.0% resolution.

The switching times between the waste and collection cycles are set between the corn oil and phthalate peaks and the perylene and sulfur peaks. The instrument is calibrated upon the award of the contract and again each time the column is repacked or replaced. The calibration is checked at least once every seven days. Operational flow for the instrument may not vary outside the 4.5 - 5.5 mL/min range as set and monitored by the column backpressure. As the column becomes fouled, the column backpressure will increase, and the flow will decrease. After GPC the final sample extract is adjusted to 0.5 mL.

If samples in a batch are subjected to GPC, all the blanks and matix spikes/matrix spike duplicates will also be run through the GPC. Copies of the GPC calibration chromatogram must accompany the sample result deliverables. An example of a GPC chromatogram is presented in Figure 7-2.

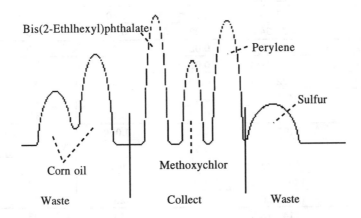

Figure 7-2. **Example of an idealized GPC calibration chromatogram**

D. Pesticides/PCB

The target analytes for pesticide/PCB analysis are listed in Table 7-29. The Forms required in the deliverables are listed in Table 7-30. The rest of the deliverables package includes the chromatograms from the primary and second column and GC integration reports for the samples, blanks, calibration standards, matrix spike and matrix spike duplicate, calibration plots, manual work sheets detailing calculations and sample preparation/analysis, chain-of-custody record, chromatograms and mass spectra of samples and standards from the GC-MS confirmation, and a case narrative.

Table 7-29. **CLP Pesticide/Aroclor Target Compound List (TCL)[3]**

Analyte	CAS	Low Conc. Water µg/L	Multiconc. Water µg/L	Multimedia Soil µg/kg
α-BHC	319-84-6	0.01	0.050	1.7
β-BHC	319-85-7	0.01	0.050	1.7
δ-BHC	319-86-8	0.01	0.050	1.7

---

[3] CLP-SOW OLM02.1, 1993

Table 7-29.   CLP Pesticide/Aroclor Target Compound List (TCL)[4] *continued*

Analyte	CAS	Low Conc. Water µg/L	Multiconc. Multimedia Water µg/L	Soil µg/kg
γ-BHC (Lindane)	58-89-9	0.01	0.050	1.7
Heptachlor	76-44-8	0.01	0.050	1.7
Aldrin	309-00-2	0.01	0.050	1.7
Heptachlor epoxide	111024-57-3	0.01	0.050	1.7
Endosulfan I	959-98-8	0.01	0.050	1.7
Dieldrin	60-57-1	0.02	0.10	3.3
4,4'-DDE	72-55-9	0.02	0.10	3.3
Endrin	72-20-8	0.02	0.10	3.3
Endosulfan II	33213-65-9	0.02	0.10	3.3
4,4'-DDD	72-54-8	0.02	0.10	3.3
Endosulfan sulfate	1031-07-8	0.02	0.10	3.3
4,4'-DDT	50-29-3	0.02	0.10	3.3
Methoxychlor	72-43-5	0.10	0.50	17
Endrin ketone	53494-70-5	0.02	0.10	3.3
Endrin aldehyde	7421-93-4	0.02	0.10	3.3
α-Chlordane	5103-71-9	0.01	0.050	1.7
γ-Chlordane	5103-74-2	0.01	0.050	1.7
Toxaphene	8001-35-2	1.0	5.0	170
Aroclor-1016	12674-11-2	0.20	1.0	33
Aroclor-1221	11104-28-2	0.40	2.0	67
Aroclor-1232	11141-16-5	0.02	1.0	33
Aroclor-1242	53469-21-9	0.02	1.0	33
Aroclor-1248	12672-29-6	0.02	1.0	33
Aroclor-1254	11097-69-1	0.02	1.0	33
Aroclor-1260	11096-82-5	0.02	1.0	33

Table 7-30.   CLP Forms Included as Deliverables with Each Sample for Pesticide/Aroclor

Form	Title
I PEST	Pesticide Organics Analysis Data Sheet
II PEST-1	Water Pesticide Surrogate Recovery
II PEST-2	Soil Pesticide Surrogate Recovery
III PEST-1	Water Pesticide Matrix Spike/Matrix Spike Duplicate Recovery
III PEST-2	Soil Pesticide Matrix Spike/Matrix Spike Duplicate Recovery
IV PEST	Pesticide Method Blank Summary
VI PEST-1	Pesticide Initial Calibration of Single Component Analytes (RT Data)
VI PEST-2	Pesticide Initial Calibration of Single Component Analytes (Calibration Factor Data)
VI PEST-3	Pesticide Initial Calibration of Multicomponent Analytes
VI PEST-4	Pesticide Analyte Resolution Summary

---

[4] CLP-SOW OLM02.1, 1993

Table 7-30. **CLP Forms Included as Deliverables with Each Sample for Pesticide/Aroclor,** *continued*

Form	Title
VI PEST-5	Performance Evaluation Mixture
VI PEST-6	Individual Standard Mixture A
VI PEST-7	Individual Standard Mixture B
VII PEST-1	Pesticide Calibration Verification Summary (Breakdown Summary)
VII PEST-2	Pesticide Calibration Verification Summary (Mixtures A & B Summary)
VIII PEST	Pesticide Analytical Sequence
IX PEST-1	Pesticide Florisil Cartridge Check
IX PEST-2	Pesticide GPC Calibration
X PEST-1	Pesticide Identification Summary for Single Component Analytes
X PEST-2	Pesticide Identification Summary for Multicomponent Analytes

There are 13 areas listed in the *National Functional Guidelines* as necessary to check during the data evaluation process. These are listed in Table 7-31 and are discussed in detail in the following paragraphs.

Table 7-31. **Points of CLP SOW Pesticide/PCB Data Evaluation**

1.	Holding Times
2.	GC/ECD Instrument Performance Check
3.	Initial Calibration
4.	Calibration Verification
5.	Blanks
6.	Surrogate Spikes
7.	Matrix Spikes/Matrix Spike Duplicates
8.	Laboratory Control Samples
9.	Regional Quality Assurance and Quality Control
10.	Pesticide Cleanup Checks
11.	Target Compound Identification
12.	Compound Quantitation and Reported Contract Required Quantitation Limits (CRQL)
13.	Overall Assessment of Data

1. Holding Time

The SOW distinguishes between **Technical Holding Time** and **Method Holding Time**. The method holding time is an absolute contractual requirement to extract the sample within 5 days for water samples and 10 days for soil/sediment samples of the **Verified Time of Sample Receipt** (VTSR) at the laboratory. The analysis must be accomplished within 40 days of sample extraction. The Low Concentration SOW is slightly different in that the samples must be analyzed within 40 days of VTSR. The technical holding time is the amount of time elapsed between the moment of sampling in the field and the beginning of extraction and analysis at the laboratory.

The evaluation of the technical holding time depends upon what the sample is and how the sample was collected, preserved, and shipped. All water and soil/sediment samples for pesticide/PCB analysis are to be cooled to $4 \pm 2°C$ in the dark from sampling until the extraction. Extracts are to be stored at $4 \pm 2°C$ in the dark until analysis. Water samples have a technical holding time of 7 days from sampling to extraction and 40 days after extraction to the analysis. The recommended time for soils is 14 days to extraction. The pH of water samples is to be in the 5-9 range.

The technical holding time is determined through examination of the sampling date listed on the chain-of-custody record and the time of analysis listed on Form I, the extraction worksheet, and the raw instrument data report. The dates on Form I, the extraction worksheet, and the instrument report must be identical.

If technical holding times are exceeded, all detected analytes are flagged as estimated (J) and the sample quantitation limits are flagged as undetected and estimated (UJ). If the technical holding times are grossly exceeded, then the reviewer may flag the undetected analytes as unusable (R). Application of these guidelines to soil/sediment data is at the discretion of the reviewer. Finally, note of the failure to meet technical holding times is to be included in the reviewer's written report.

2. GC/ECD Instrument Performance Check

The data to be reviewed to assure that the instrument is capable of adequate resolution and sensitivity is contained on Form VI PEST -4, -5, Form VII PEST, Form VIII Pest, and the chromatograms and data printouts. Resolution and sensitivity are considered to be inherent characteristics of the instrument and independent of the sample. Therefore the criteria to be met are mandatory.

Resolution is evaluated through injection of the Resolution Check Mixture, Table 7-32, at the beginning of each initial calibration sequence. The same solution is used for the Low concentration and the Multiconcentration methods.

Table 7-32.   Pest/PCB Resolution Check Mixture

Compound	Conc. ng/mL	Compound	Conc. ng/mL
γ-Chlordane	10.0	Endrin ketone	20.0
Endosulfan I	10.0	Methoxychlor	100.0
4,4'-DDE	20.0	Tetrachloro-m-xylene	20.0
Dieldrin	20.0	Decachlorobiphenyl	20.0
Endosulfan sulfate	20.0		

The resolution is evaluated by calculating the depth of the valley between adjacent peaks. The valley depth is expressed as a percentage of the shorter of the two peaks. The calculation is:

$$\% \text{ Resolution} = \frac{\text{Valley depth}}{\text{Smaller peak height}} \times 100 \, .$$

The criteria is that resolution must be greater than 60% between adjacent peaks. Depending on the particular capillary columns chosen, this may be difficult to meet for the following pairs of peaks and should be checked carefully: DDE:dieldrin, methoxychlor:endrin ketone, endosulfan I:gamma-chlordane, methoxychlor:endosulfan sulfate.

Sensitivity is evaluated through analysis of the Performance Evaluation Mixture (PEM), Table 7-33, at the beginning and end of the initial calibration sequence and every 12 hours of operation of the instrument. The results of analysis of the PEM are used to evaluate resolution, retention time shifts, quantitation, and breakdown of analytes.

Table 7-33.   Performance Evaluation Mixture

Compound	Conc. mg/mL	Compound	Conc. ng/mL
γ-BHC	10.0	Endrin	50.0
α-BHC	10.0	Methoxychlor	250.0
4,4'-DDT	100.0	Tetrachloro-m-xylene	20.0
β-BHC	10.0	Decachlorobiphenyl	20.0

The criteria for resolution is that adjacent components of the PEM must exhibit a minimum percent resolution of 90%. The retention time criteria is that each of the components must elute within the appropriate time window established during the initial calibration. The quantitation criteria are based upon the calculation of percent difference (%D) by:

$$C_{found} = \frac{Peak\ Response}{CF_{mp}}$$

$$\%D = \frac{C_{found} - C_{true}}{C_{true}} \times 100$$

where: Peak response is the area of the peak or the peak height.

CF_{mp} is the calibration factor of the mid-point calibration standard in the initial calibration.

C_{found} is the amount of the component calculated from analysis of the PEM.

C_{true} is the amount of analyte in the PEM (Table 7-33).

The criteria for the quantitation check is that the %D must be within ±25%. Breakdown is calculated for 4,4'-DDT and endrin. The calculations are:

$$\%\ Breakdown\ DDT\ =\ \frac{DDD + DDE}{DDT} \times 100$$

$$\%\ Breakdown\ Endrin\ =\ \frac{Endrin\ aldehyde + Endrin\ ketone}{Endrin} \times 100$$

where: DDD, DDE, endrin aldehyde and endrin ketone are the amounts of these compounds quantitated from the PEM.

DDT and endrin are the amounts in the PEM (Table 7-33).

The criteria for the breakdown checks are that the percent breakdown must be less than 20% for each of the two check compounds and that the total breakdown of the two compounds must be less than 30%. These criteria apply to both the primary and the secondary analytical columns, in addition to any GC-MS system used for identification confirmation.

If the required frequency of analysis of the Resolution Check Mixture and the Performance Evaluation Mixture has not been achieved, this is a contract violation. If resolution criteria are not met in either or both mixtures and on both analytical columns, this is an indication that peaks are inadequately separated from each other in the analysis. Compounds reported as present in the sample and known to be subject to resolution problems should be flagged as estimated (J). Reported non-detects of compounds subject to resolution problems may be unreliable and flagged as unusable (R). These evaluations should be applied on a compound-by-compound basis with careful consideration of all the analytical data available. It is a frequent occurrence that compounds that are not resolved well on one column exhibit baseline resolution on the secondary column, and reliable information is present that can allow unqualified results to be reported. Also, if no target analyte peaks are observed in the appropriate retention time windows on both the primary and secondary analytical columns, the non-detects are very confident. For further considerations see the following discussion under item XI. Target Compound Identification.

The retention time criteria are critical to the identification of target analytes in the samples. If the criteria are not met, then all detected target analytes should be flagged as presumed present and estimated (NJ). Target analytes which are reported as not present may, in fact, be falling just outside the retention time windows. Inspection of the chromatograms may warrant the non-detects being flagged as estimates (UJ). Gross failure to reaffirm retention time windows should result in flagging all data as unusable (R).

If the quantitation differences exceed the criteria of within ±25%, all results are flagged as estimates (J or UJ). Gross failure to meet quantitation criteria should result in flagging all data as unusable (R).

Failure to meet breakdown criteria should result in qualification of the reported sample data for DDT and endrin and the breakdown products. All positive results for DDT and/or endrin are flagged as estimated (J). If endrin and/or DDT are reported as not present but the appropriate breakdown products are present, then the parent compound results should be flagged as unusable (R). Reported results for the breakdown products should be flagged as estimated and presumed present (NJ). Reported non-detects for both DDT and/or endrin and non-detects for the related breakdown products is an indication that none of the compounds were in the samples and the data should not be qualified.

3. Initial Calibration

Pesticide/PCB analysis is performed on a electron capture detector (ECD) equipped gas chromatograph. Since the ECD is a two dimensional detector, analysis of the sample on two different columns is required and both columns must be fully calibrated. The calibration is further complicated by having both single component target analytes and muticomponent target analytes such as toxaphene and the PCBs. Although chlordane is a multicomponent material, its presence in the sample is determined through reporting the single peaks alpha- and gamma-chlordane. Single component analytes are calibrated at three different concentrations, whereas the multicomponent analytes are calibrated using a single point. The data which are reviewed for the calibration includes Forms VI-PEST 1, 2, 3 and 4, VII PEST and VIII Pest, the raw chromatograms and quantitation reports and other data system printouts.

Heptachlor epoxide exists in two forms, the difference being either an exo- or an endo- orientation of the epoxide. The target analyte specified in the SOW is the exo-isomer, also commonly referred to as the B isomer

The instrument is calibrated upon the award of the contract, following major instrument maintenance and whenever continuing calibration fails. Many laboratories perform an initial calibration at the beginning of each instrument run, which may extend to 72 hours in length. Due to the complexity of the suite of target analytes, a number of calibration solutions are used. The single component analytes are contained in Individual Standard Mixtures A and B, see Table 7-34. The three concentration levels are also given. The multicomponent target analytes are calibrated as individual solutions at a concentration of 100 ng/mL, with the exception of Arochlor 1221, which is calibrated with a 200 ng/mL solution and toxaphene, which is calibrated with a 500 ng/mL solution. The run order for Pesticide/PCB initial calibration sequences is presented in Table 7-35.

Table 7-34.   Pesticide/PCB Calibration Mixtures. Units are ng/mL.

Individual Standard Mixture A			
Analyte	CRQL	Mid-level	High-Level[5]
α-BHC	5	20	80
Heptachlor	5	20	80
γ-BHC (Lindane)	5	20	80
Endosulfan I	5	20	80
Dieldrin	10	40	160
Endrin	10	40	160
4,4'-DDD	10	40	160
4,4'-DDT	10	40	160
Methoxychlor	50	200	800
TCMX (surrogate)	5	20	80
DCB (surrogate)	10	40	160

Individual Standard Mixture B			
Analyte	CRQL	Mid-level	High-Level[5]
β-BHC	5	20	80
δ-BHC	5	20	80
Aldrin	5	20	80
Heptachlor epoxide	5	20	80
α-Chlordane	5	20	80
γ-Chlordane	5	20	80
4,4'-DDE	10	40	160
Endosulfan sulfate	10	40	160
Endrin aldehyde	10	40	160
Endrin ketone	10	40	160
Endosulfan II	10	40	160
TCMX (surrogate)	5	20	80
DCB (surrogate)	10	40	160

Multicomponent Calibration Solutions	
Analyte	Concentration
Toxaphene	500
TCMX (surrogate)	20
DCB (surrogate)	20

---

[5] At the discretion of the contractor, the concentration of the highest standard may be at a greater level than that listed.

Table 7-34.   Pesticide/PCB Calibration Mixtures. Units are ng/mL. *Continued*

Multicomponent Calibration Solutions, *continued*	
Analyte	**Concentration**
Aroclor-1016	100
Aroclor-1260	100
TCMX (surrogate)	20
DCB (surrogate)	20
Aroclor-1221	200
TCMX (surrogate)	20
DCB (surrogate)	20
Aroclor-1232	100
TCMX (surrogate)	20
DCB (surrogate)	20
Aroclor-1242	100
TCMX (surrogate)	20
DCB (surrogate)	20
Aroclor-1248	100
TCMX (surrogate)	20
DCB (surrogate)	20
Aroclor-1254	100
TCMX (surrogate)	20
DCB (surrogate)	20

Table 7-35.   Run Order for Pesticide/PCB Initial Calibration

1.	Resolution Check	10.	CRQL Standard A
2.	Performance Evaluation Mixture	11.	CRQL Standard B
3.	Aroclor 1016/1260	12.	Mid-level Standard A
4.	Aroclor 1221	13.	Mid-level Standard B
5.	Aroclor 1232	14.	High-level Standard A
6.	Aroclor 1242	15.	High-level Standard B
7.	Aroclor 1248	16.	Instrument Blank
8.	Aroclor 1254	17.	Perfomance Evaluation Mixture
9.	Toxaphene		

Retention time windows are established for both columns for each single component analyte and the surrogates during the initial calibration procedure. The absolute retention time for each component for each calibration level is listed on Form VI PEST 1. The average of the retention times is used for the center of the window. The retention time windows for target analytes and surrogates are presented in Table 7-36. The surrogate retention time windows are established from Standard Mixture A. Retention time windows are established for at least three peaks in each multicomponent target analyte. The peaks chosen to characterize the Aroclor should be unique to the particular Aroclor.

Use of the same peak as characteristic of two different PCBs must be avoided. All characteristic Arochlor and toxaphene peaks have windows of ±0.07 minutes.

Table 7-36. **Retention Time Windows for Pesticide/PCB Target Analytes and Surrogates**

Compound	Window (minutes)
TCMX (surrogate)	±0.05
α-BHC	±0.05
β-BHC	±0.05
δ-BHC	±0.05
γ-BHC (Lindane)	±0.05
Heptachlor	±0.05
Aldrin	±0.05
Heptachlor epoxide	±0.07
Endosulfan I	±0.07
Dieldrin	±0.07
4,4'-DDE	±0.07
Endrin	±0.07
Endosulfan II	±0.07
4,4'-DDD	±0.07
Endosulfan sulfate	±0.07
4,4'-DDT	±0.07
Methoxychlor	±0.07
Endrin ketone	±0.07
Endrin aldehyde	±0.07
α-Chlordane	±0.07
γ-Chlordane	±0.07
Arochlors	±0.07
Toxaphene	±0.07
DCB (surrogate)	±0.10

An external standard procedure using calibration factors (CF) is used in Pesticide/PCB analysis. Calibration factors are calculated for each level of calibration using the following equation:

$$CF = \frac{\text{Compound response}}{\text{Mass injected (ng)}}.$$

The compound response can either be peak area or peak height; however, once a choice is made for a particular compound, it must be retained through the entire calibration and sample analysis procedure. For example if peak area is chosen for heptachlor, then the calibration factors for the three calibration levels must be calculated using peak area, and the samples must be quantitated using peak area.

The average CF is calculated and reported on Form VI PEST-2 for single component analytes. The %RSD for the individual calibration factors is also reported and is used as an indication of the linearity of the calibration. The single CF for each of the characteristic peaks for the multicomponent analytes is reported on Form VI PEST-3.

The areas to be checked by the reviewer include:

1. Use of the correct calibration solutions at the correct concentration in the proper order for both columns

2. Determination of proper retention time windows for target analytes and surrogates on both columns

3. Determination that adequate resolution has been achieved between peaks on both columns, 90% is the standard

4. Calculation of calibration factors for each analyte for each column

5. Determination of the linearity of the calibration for the single component analytes and surrogates.

Linearity in the calibration is assessed through the %RSD. The standard for target analytes is less than 20.0%. The SOW allows α-BHC and δ-BHC to have RSDs up to 25.0%. The two surrogates have allowable %RSD up to 30.0%. Up to two target analytes on each column may exceed the 20.0% criteria, but may not be greater than 30.0%.

There is a requirement in the SOW to supply at least one chromatogram from each of the Standard Mixes A and B that displays calibrated compound peaks registering between 50 and 100% full scale deflection. The purpose of this is to ease calculation of the resolution and to allow identification of the apex of the peak, which defines the retention time.

The evaluation of the sample results obtained from systems that do not meet the resolution criteria depends on how much overlap exists between the two co-eluting peaks. The existence of overlap in the calibration means that the peak areas or height are influenced by both compounds. Results for both compounds in samples should be qualified as either estimated results (J) or unusable (R) depending on the severity of the problem.

It should be recognized that the actual sample may contain any of the known problem pairs of co-eluting target analytes in Table 7-37. The contents of the Standard Mixes A and B are designed so that these problem co-elutions are avoided in the calibration. This permits an accurate calibration for the individual components to be obtained. It does not correct for quantitation inaccuracies that may occur in actual samples.

Table 7-37. Co-eluting Target Analytes in Pest/PCB Analysis

γ-BHC	β-BHC
4,4'-DDE	Dieldrin
4,4'-DDD	Endosulfan II
4,4'-DDT	Endosulfan sulfate
4,4'-DDT	Endrin aldehyde
Methoxychlor	Endrin ketone

Calibrations for target analytes and surrogates that do not meet the linearity criteria are not capable of generating good quantitative data using the calibration factor calculation. All individual compound results reported from non-linear calibrations are to be flagged as estimates (J or UJ).

Incorrectly calculated retention time windows can lead to misidentification of target analytes in samples. The reviewer should calculate the correct retention time window and use the recalculated window to evaluate all reported sample results.

4. Calibration Verification

Continuing calibration consists of analysis of an instrument blank, the mid-level concentrations of Individual Standard Mix A and B, and the PEM. These must be performed every 12 hours of operation with the Standard Mix A and B alternating with the PEM (Table VI-38). Acceptable sample results must be bracketed by acceptable calibration verification sequences. The 12 hours are defined as the time lapsed from injection of one instrument blank to injection of the last sample in the sequence. Injection of the next instrument blank restarts the 12-hour clock.

The data to be reviewed for continuing calibration are found on Form VI PEST-6 and -7, Form VII PEST-1 and -2, chromatograms and data system printouts. The items to be verified are that:

1. The calibration verification sequence is performed within the 12-hour requirement (Table 7-38)

2. Resolution between individual peaks in the Standard Mixes and the PEM is at least 90%

3. Retention times for all components are within the retention time windows established during the initial calibration sequence

4. Calculations for percent difference are performed correctly and are within the ±25% criteria

5. Endrin and DDT breakdown criteria are still being met.

Table 7-38. Analytical Sequence for PEST/PCB Analysis

Time	Injection Number	Injection Contents
-	1 - 15	Initial calibration sequence (Table 7-35)
0 hr	16	Instrument blank
	17	PEM
	18	First analytical sample
	19...	Subsequent samples
12 hr	-	Last sample in set
0	1st injection past 12:00 hr	Instrument blank
	2 -3 past 12:00 hr	mid-level Individual Standard Mixes A and B
	4...	Samples
next 12:00 hr	-	Last sample
0	1st injection past 12:00 hr	Instrument blank
	2	PEM
	3...	Samples
next 12:00 hr	-	Last sample
	1st injection past 12:00 hr	Instrument blank
	2 -3	mid-level Individual Standard Mixes A and B
	4...	Samples

Table 7-38. Analytical Sequence for PEST/PCB Analysis, *continued*

Time	Injection Number	Injection Contents
etc.	etc.	etc.
	After last sample	Instrument blank
	after last blank	PEM or Standard Mix A and B

The calibration verification is assessed through calculation of the percent difference in quantitation between the initial calibration and the re-analysis of the target analytes and surrogates in the Standard Mix A and B and the PEM. Percent difference is calculated as:

$$C_{found} = \frac{\text{Peak Response}}{CF}$$

$$\%D = \frac{C_{found} - C_{true}}{C_{true}} \times 100$$

where: Peak response is the area of the peak or the peak height.
CF is the calibration factor from the initial calibration.
C_{found} is the amount of the component calculated from analysis of the standard.
C_{true} is the amount of analyte in the standard.

The evaluation of the sample results obtained from systems that do not meet the resolution criteria depends on how much overlap exists between the two co-eluting peaks. The development of overlap in the calibration verification means that degradation of the system is occurring. Results for both compounds in samples analyzed since the last in-control calibration verification should be qualified as either estimated results (J) or unusable (R) depending on the severity of the problem.

In a similar line of thought, failure to meet retention time windows is a sign of system degradation. Samples analyzed since the last in-control calibration verification are suspect and the reported target analyte identifications may be unusable (R). If no peaks other than the surrogates are present in the chromatogram, then the reported non-detects (U) are reliable. The situation should be noted in the reviewer's narrative and brought to the attention of the supervising TPO.

When calibration verifications fail to meet the percent difference criteria, reports of target analytes from associated samples since the last in-control calibration verification are flagged as estimates (J or UJ).

5. Blanks

Blanks are used to evaluate sample contamination that arises from either the field or the laboratory. The blanks performed in the course of a Pesticide/PCB analysis include field blanks, method blanks, instrument blanks, and sulfur and GPC cleanup blanks. Method blanks are performed for each analytical batch of 20 samples. Instrument blanks are performed at least once every 12 hours of instrument operation. Cleanup blanks are performed each time a cleanup is performed on part of a sample batch. If all the samples in the batch are taken through the same cleanups then the method blank may also function as the cleanup blank(s). The data to be reviewed are found on Form I PEST,

Form IV PEST and the raw data chromatograms and data system printouts. If separate cleanup and method blanks have been performed then there should be a separate Form IV PEST filled out to identify each of the blanks and the associated samples.

Blanks are prepared by spiking analyte-free portions of either water or a soil substitute (sodium sulfate) with surrogates, then taking the blank through the entire analytical process simultaneously with all of the associated samples. If instrument analysis of a batch of samples is split between two or more instruments then the blanks should be analyzed on each instrument used. The idea is that no compounds other than the surrogates are found in the blank.

Results are never corrected based on blank contamination. Instead the review actions depend on which blank is contaminated and the magnitude of the contamination. The blank with the highest contamination level is used as the standard for evaluation if different types of blanks are found to be contaminated. If contamination is found in the blanks but not in the samples, note may be made of the observation on the reviewer's report but the sample data is not flagged. A five-times criterion is used for evaluating the sample results in the case of blank contamination. If the sample results are greater than five times, the amount of contamination found in the blank, the data are not flagged.

If sample concentrations are less than five times the amount of contamination found in the blank, then the data is flagged as undetected (U). The CRQL may also be raised to the level of contamination found in the sample. When massive contamination is indicated in the blanks, all sample data may be flagged as unusable (R). The decision to flag all data as unusable should be discussed in the reviewer's narrative.

In reviewing the blank and sample data, note should be made of any dilutions or variations in sample/blank weights that may alter the apparent concentrations of blank and sample results and make not acceptable results look acceptable. An example of this is when a blank and diluted sample both exhibit, say, 50 ppb 4,4'-DDT, but a ten-fold dilution factor correction of the sample gives reported results of 50 ppb for the blank and 500 ppb for the sample. The 500 ppb in the sample is totally attributable to laboratory contamination and therefore the five-times criteria does not apply.

There are cases when samples appear to have been contaminated, but the blanks are clean. An example is when dilution of a sample exhibits target analytes that are not seen in the undiluted sample. Another example is when a sample exhibits a hit for a target analyte, but the sample duplicate does not. Although this can result from non-homogeneous samples, random contamination does occur in the laboratory and should not be ruled out. In these cases the sample result is flagged as undetected (U) and an explanation placed in the reviewer's narrative.

Instrument blanks are used to evaluate carry-over from samples containing high levels of target analytes to subsequent injections on the instrument. If instrument blanks have not been performed following injection of high level samples, subsequent samples need to be closely evaluated to determine if detected analytes are really in the sample. If this is thought to be the case, the data can be flagged as undetected (U) and an explanation made in the reviewer's narrative.

6. Surrogate Spikes

The surrogate compounds, tetrachloro-*meta*-xylene (TCMX) and decachlorobiphenyl (DCB), are added to all samples and blanks at the levels indicated in Table 7-39. Surrogate compounds are also present in all calibration mixes, PEM and resolution check solutions (Tables 7-32, -33 and -34). Surrogates are calibrated just like target analytes, with the calibration factors calculated from Individual Standard Mix A.

Table 7-39. **Sample Concentration of Surrogate Spikes in Pest/PCB Samples** (Assuming a normal sample size of one liter for water samples and 30 g for soil/sediments)

Surrogate	Low Level SOW Water μg/L	Multi-level SOW	
		Water μg/L	Soil/Sediment μg/kg
TCMX	0.040	0.200	13.3
DBP	0.040	0.200	13.3

The data to be reviewed with regard to surrogate spike recoveries are found on Form II PEST, Form VIII PEST and the raw data chromatograms and data system printouts. Acceptable surrogate recovery limits are listed in Table 7-40. The retention times for surrogates are checked in each sample and must be within the calculated retention time windows on both columns.

Table 7-40. **Recovery Acceptance Limits for Surrogate Spikes**

Surrogate	Low Level SOW Water	Multi-level SOW	
		Water	Soil/Sediment
TCMX	60-150	30-150	30-150
DBP	60-150	30-150	30-150

If low, but present, surrogate recoveries are observed, this is an indication that reported positive results and non-detects for analytes are probably biased low and the results should be flagged as estimated (J or UJ). If surrogate recoveries are very low (<10%), the non-detected analytes are to be further flagged as unusable (R). This is particularly significant for the first surrogate, TCMX, as extremely low recovery is possibly a sign that the sample was taken to dryness during the sample concentration steps.

High recoveries of surrogates should result in flagging of detected target analyte concentrations as estimates (J). Undetected target analytes are probably reliable and the CRQL is not flagged.

Surrogate recoveries on blanks and/or laboratory control samples that are outside specifications are cause for special concern. Although it may be an understandable random occurrence, when coupled with unacceptable sample surrogate recoveries, doubts are created about the reliability of any sample results. A discussion in the reviewer's narrative is appropriate.

7. Matrix Spikes/Matrix Spike Duplicates

Matrix spike and matrix spike duplicate (MS and MSD) are required to be performed and the recoveries calculated on at least one sample out of each sample set of 20 samples of a similar matrix. However, the results on the MS and MSD are not by and of themselves used to qualify data. The compounds that are used in the matrix spike solution are listed in Table 7-41 along with the associated accuracy (%R) and precision (RPD) quality objectives. The MS and MSD compounds are spiked into water and soil/sediment samples to achieve the levels listed in Table 7-42. Surrogates are added to the spiked samples, and they are processed just like any other analytical sample. MS and MSD are not required to be performed in the Low Concentration SOW.

Table 7-41. Pesticide Matrix Spike Compounds and Recovery Acceptance Limits

Compound	Water		Soil	
	%R	RPD	%R	RPD
γ-BHC (Lindane)	56-123	15	46-127	50
Heptachlor	40-131	20	35-130	31
Aldrin	40-120	22	34-132	43
Dieldrin	52-126	18	31-134	38
Endrin	56-121	21	42-139	45
4,4'-DDT	38-127	27	23-134	50

Table 7-42. Pesticide Matrix Spike Compound Concentrations in Sample Assuming a One Liter Sample for Water and 30 g Soil/Sediment

Compound	Water µg/L	Soil/sediment µg/kg
γ-BHC (Lindane)	0.5	16.7
Heptachlor	0.5	16.7
Aldrin	0.5	16.7
Dieldrin	1.0	33.3
Endrin	1.0	33.3
4,4'-DDT	1.0	33.3

Recoveries (%R) for matrix spike compounds are calculated as:

$$\%R = \frac{SSR - SR}{SA} \times 100$$

where: SSR is the spiked sample result.
SR is the unspiked sample result.
SA is the spike amount.

Precision (RPD) is calculated as:

$$RPD = \frac{2|MSR - MSRD|}{MSR + MSRD} \times 100$$

where: MSR is the matrix spike percent recovery (%R).
MSRD is the matrix spike duplicate percent recovery (%R).

If the sample chosen for the MS/MSD needed to be diluted, then the MS and MSD should be performed on the diluted sample (reduced sample size) rather than dilute the MS or MSD extract after spiking.

The data to be reviewed are found on Form III PEST-1 and PEST-2, and the raw chromatograms and data system printouts. The reviewer should recalculate several of the recoveries and RPD numbers listed on Form III to verify that calculations were performed correctly. In a strict sense the MS and MSD recoveries are applicable to only the sample that was spiked. High or low MS compound recoveries can be related to the behavior of compounds of similar chemical structure or similar volatility (Table 7-29) or the recoveries may be indicative of problems with the results obtained for all target analytes in the sample.

On the other hand repeated inability to generate acceptable matrix spike results over a period of time is indicative of system-specific analytical problems in the laboratory. This situation should be investigated as it may suggest that no results being generated by the lab are usable.

8. Laboratory Control Samples

Laboratory control samples (LCS) are particular to the Low Concentration SOW and take the place of a matrix spike requirement. The compounds, concentrations, and recovery acceptance limits are presented in Table 7-43. A duplicate of the LCS is not required, and precision (RPD) is not calculated. A one-liter portion of analyte-free water is spiked with the LCS compounds and the surrogates, then treated exactly like any other sample.

Table 7-43. Pesticide Laboratory Control Spike Compounds and Recovery Acceptance Limits

Compound	Acceptance Limits %R	Spike level µg/L
γ-BHC (Lindane)	56-123	0.10
Heptachlor epoxide	74-150	0.10
Dieldrin	33-130	0.20
4,4'-DDE	50-150	0.20
Endrin	56-121	0.20
Endosulfan sulfate	50-100	0.20
γ-Chlordane	33-130	0.10

Recoveries (%R) for laboratory control sample compounds are calculated as:

$$\%R = \frac{SSR}{SA} \times 100$$

where: SSR is the spiked sample result.
SA is the spike amount.

The data to be reviewed are found on Form I LCP, Form III LCP and the raw data chromatograms and data system printouts. The reviewer should check to insure that recoveries are calculated correctly, that the LCS was performed at the rate of one per batch of 20 samples and that there are no transcription errors.

Whereas the matrix spike process is subject to the vagaries of the matrix of the sample selected to be spiked, the laboratory control sample is viewed as analysis of a perfect sample with no matrix effects. Inability to generate acceptable data for the LCS makes all sample data suspect and subject to qualification. If LCS recoveries are high, then associated results for target analytes are estimates (J) for those analytes reported above the CRDL and acceptable for those compounds reported as less than the CRDL.

When individual LCS compounds recoveries are low, then related target analyte results reported greater than the CRDL are estimates (J) while the non-detects are unusable (R). If more than 50% of the LCS components are reported with less than acceptable recoveries then all target analyte compounds reported above the CRDL are estimates (J) while none of the non-detected analytes are usable (R).

Surrogate recoveries and internal standard performance criteria must be met for acceptable LCS recoveries to be valid.

9. Regional Quality Assurance and Quality Control

These are suggested in the National Functional Guidelines to consist of checking Performance Evaluation sample results, field duplicates, blind spikes and/or blind blanks. Region III[6] reviews the results of Performance Evaluation samples and requires that all analytes present in the PE sample be correctly identified and quantitated. Region III also evaluates the results of field duplicates in terms of RPD. The RPDs obtained from the field duplicates are cross-checked against those listed as Data Quality Objectives in the Quality Assurance Project Plan.

10. Pesticides Cleanup Checks

The cleanups commonly used with pesticide/PCB analysis are sulfur cleanup, Florisil cartridge filtration and gel permeation chromatography (GPC). Florisil cleanup is required for all extracts. GPC is performed on all soil/sediment extracts and those water extracts that appear to contain high molecular weight interferences. Sulfur cleanup is performed on those extracts that contain sulfur. It consists of mixing the sample with either mercury or copper to form the metal sulfide that is insoluble. The Florisil and GPC cleanups, unless performed correctly, can result in substantial losses of the target analytes from the sample extracts. For this reason details concerning the Florisil and GPC cleanups are reported in the deliverables on Form IX PEST-1 and PEST-2, and the GPC/Florisil raw data, chromatograms and data system printouts.

The Florisil filtration is used to separate polar materials from the target analytes. Each lot of Florisil cartridges is checked by filtering a check solution through a representative cartridge, then analyzing the check solution. The check solution contains 0.5 mL of the mid-level individual Standard Mix A (Table 7-34) along with 0.05 µg 2,4,5-Trichlorophenol. The phenol is a polar compound and is supposed to be removed from the extract through the filtration process. Acceptable results are for the analytes in the Standard Mix A to be recovered in the range 80-120%, while no more than 5% of the trichlorophenol can be present. Further no additional peaks other than those in the calibration mix should be present in the chromatogram. Percent recovery is calculated as:

$$\%R = \frac{Q_d}{Q_a} \times 100$$

where: Q_d is the quantity determined by analysis.
Q_a is the quantity added.

The calibration of the GPC has been discussed above in the SVO section (Item 16). The calibration is verified at least every seven days through calculation of the recovery of check standards consisting of the matrix spike solution (Table 7-42) and a PCB combination of 1016 and 1260 at 2 µg/mL each. The matrix spike compounds must be recovered in 80-110% and the patterns of the PCBs are to be unaltered. The sample

---

[6] Region III Modifications to National Functional Guidelines for Organic Data Review Multi-Media, Multi-Concentration (OLM)1.1-OLMO1.9), September 1994

processing program of the GPC when used for pesticides/PCBs is changed from the SVO program to dump the bis(2-ethylhexyl)phthalate and collect the methoxychlor and perylene. The criteria is that all of the corn oil and >85% of the phthalate are dumped to waste, while >95% of the methoxychlor and perylene are collected.

Sample data reported under conditions of unacceptable Florisil and/or GPC cleanup check criteria is to be qualified and the situation reported to the Regional TPO. Cleanup checks that list zero recovery of analytes or surrogates mean that target analytes that are reported as undetected in samples should be flagged as unusable (R). High recoveries of the check compounds suggest problems with volume adjustment. Related sample data may be flagged as estimated (J). Undetected target analytes are probably reliable.

11. Target Compound Identification

Target analyte identification in pesticide/PCB analysis is based upon retention time matching for the single component analytes. As has been discussed earlier in Chapter 2, there are many causes for false positive or false negative identifications based on retention time matching. As quantitation levels are forced to ever lower values, the probability of false positives increases dramatically. The single most important contributing factor is the presence of noise and background garbage in the sample extracts. The coincidental presence of two unrelated components in a sample showing up in the right retention time windows on both columns approaches certainty as the background in the sample increases. An example is shown in the chromatograms (Figures 7-3 and 7-4). Toxaphene and the aroclors, the multicomponent analytes have an added level of confidence available through pattern matching in addition to the retention times.

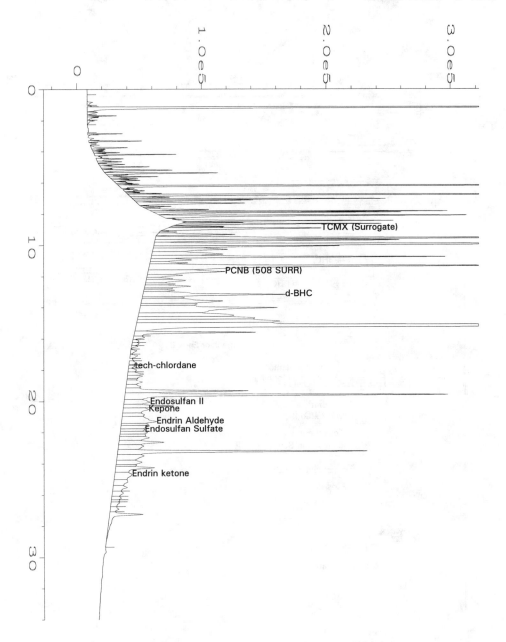

Figure 7-3. **Sample chromatogram for pesticide/PCB analysis illustrating a noisy background (Front column)**

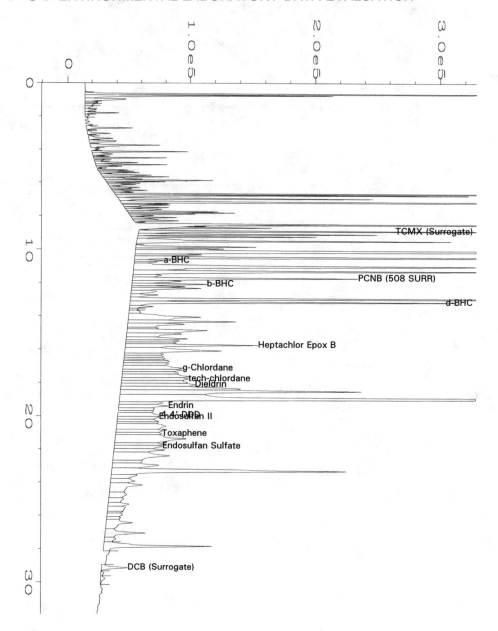

Figure 7-4. Sample chromatogram for pesticide/PCB analysis illustrating a noisy background (Rear column)

The data to be reviewed are found on Form I PEST, Form X PEST, and the raw sample chromatograms and data system printouts. The criteria for acceptable identification is that the component and both surrogates must elute within the correct retention time windows on both columns. Any pesticide analyte present in greater than 10 ng/uL concentration must be confirmed by GC-MS. The GC-MS confirmation is indicated by a "c" being placed in the Q column on Form I PEST for the analyte.

The GC-MS confirmation is accomplished by either examination of the SVO extract for the pesticide or re-analysis of the Pest/PCB extract on the GC-MS. A standard of the target pesticide must be analyzed on the GC-MS system as either part of the initial calibration of the GC-MS or as injection of a single standard on the instrument. If the latter option is chosen, the concentration of the single standard should be 10 ng/uL for single component pesticides, 50 ng/uL for PCBs and 125 ng/uL for toxaphene. An appropriate blank must be analyzed by GC-MS within the same time frame to verify that the suspected component is not due to laboratory contamination. If the suspected pesticide cannot be verified by GC-MS, the pesticide should be flagged as undetected (U), and the CRQL for that component is raised to the concentration of the GC-MS standard used in the confirmation process. A user defined flag (X, Y, or Z) is placed with the result as a qualifier, and a discussion of the flag included in the reviewer's case narrative. Included in the data package should be the mass spectrum of the suspected target and the standard reference mass spectrum. For multicomponent target analytes, at least three of the characteristic peaks should be examined by MS and the data included in the deliverables.

The appearance criteria of the chromatograms is detailed within the SOW. Baselines of chromatograms must return to below 50% scale prior to the elution of α-BHC. After the elution time of α-BHC and up until the elution time of the surrogate decachloro-biphenyl the chromatographic baselines must be below 25%. Sample chromatograms containing target analytes must be scaled so that the largest component peak is less than 50% scale height. For diluted samples the highest target analyte peak must be between 10-100% scale. If electronic data systems have been used to reprocess the chromatograms to achieve these criteria, both the original chromatogram and the reprocessed chromatogram must be present in the data package.

The reviewer needs to be aware that large amounts of either target analytes or non-target analyte materials in the sample can shift target analytes out of their retention time windows while leaving the surrogates unaffected. Multicomponent analytes are subject to weathering, where exposure within the environment has led to depletion of the earlier eluting components of the analyte. The later eluting components are, in general, unaffected but the characteristic pattern is distorted. The chromatograms need to be examined closely for these phenomena, as no evidence of them will be found in data system quantitation reports. Blank chromatograms also need to be closely scrutinized and compared to sample chromatograms for possible contamination by artifacts.

When qualifying identifications from pesticide analysis the choices are either to flag the reported compounds present as non-detected (U) in the case of a false positive or flag the result as unusable (R) in the case of a false negative. There should be substantive discussion in the reviewer's narrative and gross problems with identification brought to the attention of the Regional TPO.

12. Compound Quantitation and Reported Contract Required Quantitation Limits (CRQL)

An external standard calibration using calibration factors is employed to generate quantitative results from the pesticide/PCB analysis. The data to be reviewed are found on Form I PEST, Form X PEST-1 and PEST-2, the sample preparation logsheets, the sample chromatograms, the data system printouts and the case narrative prepared by the laboratory.

If the pesticide has been confirmed by GC-MS, the amount reported for the pesticide should be that generated from the GC-ECD analysis, not a value obtained from the GC-MS analysis.

The calculation of the amount of the pesticide present in the water sample is:

$$\text{Concentration } \mu g/L = \frac{(A_x)(V_t)(Df)(GPC)}{(CF)(V_o)(V_i)}$$

where: A_x is the area (or peak height) of the target analyte.
CF is the calibration factor for the mid-point standard in the initial calibration.
V_o is the volume of the sample extracted in mL.
V_i is the volume injected into the GC in μL.
V_t is the volume of the sample extract in μL. If GPC was not performed then V_t is 10,000 μL, if GPC was performed the V_t is 5,000 μL.
GPC is 1 if GPC was not performed, GPC is 2 if GPC was performed.
Df is the dilution factor and is calculated as:

$$Df = \frac{\mu L \text{ extract used for dilution} + \mu L \text{ dilution solvent}}{\mu L \text{ extract used for dilution}}.$$

For soil/sediment samples the results are calculated as:

$$\text{Concentration } \mu g/L = \frac{(A_x)(V_t)(Df)(GPC)}{(CF)(W_s)(V_i)(D)}$$

where: A_x is the area (or peak height) of the target analyte.
CF is the calibration factor for the mid-point standard in the initial calibration.
W_s is the weight of the sample extracted in grams.
V_i is the volume injected into the GC in μL.
V_t is 5,000 μL.
Df is the dilution factor calculated as above.
GPC is 2.
D is the dry weight factor.

$$D = \frac{100 - \% \text{ moisture}}{100}.$$

All soil and sediment samples are corrected to a dry weight basis. Dry weight factor (D) is calculated from percent moisture (% moisture). Percent moisture is determined by placing a known weight of the sample in a weighed container (Tare), drying the sample overnight in a 105°C oven and reweighing.

$$\% \text{ moisture} = \frac{g \text{ wet sample} - g \text{ dry sample}}{g \text{ wet sample}} \times 100$$

where: g wet sample is the weight of the wet sample in grams before drying minus the weight of the container.
g dry sample is the weight of the dry sample in grams after drying minus the weight of the container.

When different quantities are calculated for the same component on the two different columns, the value reported on Form I PEST is the lower of the two values. Both values are reported on Form X PEST along with a percent difference (%D), which is calculated as:

$$\%D = \frac{\text{Conc}_H - \text{Conc}_L}{\text{Conc}_L} \times 100$$

where: Conc_H is the higher of the two values.
Conc_L is the lower of the two values.

For the multicomponent analytes, the quantity of each of the characteristic peaks is calculated, then the average of the values obtained for the individual peaks is reported. Percent difference of the average values obtained for the two columns is calculated as above and reported on Form X PEST.

The CRQL is adjusted for dilutions and other factors. The calculation of the adjusted CRQL for water samples is:

$$\text{Adjusted CRQL} = \frac{(V_x)(V_t)(V_y)(Df)}{(V_o)(V_c)(V_i)} \times \text{CRQL}$$

where: V_o is the volume of the sample extracted in mL.
V_i is the volume injected into the GC in µL.
V_t is the volume of the sample extract in µL. If GPC was not performed then
V_t is 10,000 µL; if GPC was performed the V_t is 5,000 µL.
Df is the dilution factor as above.
V_x is the sample contract volume 1000 mL.
V_y is the contract injection volume, either 1 or 2 µL.
V_c is the contract sample extract volume, 5,000 µL if sample was processed by GPC; 10,000 if not.

For soil/sediment samples the adjusted CRQL is calculated by:

$$\text{Adjusted CRQL} = \frac{(W_x)(V_t)(V_y)(Df)}{(W_s)(V_c)(V_i)(D)} \times \text{CRQL}$$

where: W_s is the weight of the sample extracted in grams.
V_i is the volume injected into the GC in µL.
V_t is 5,000 µL.
Df is the dilution factor as above.
W_x is the sample contract weight 30 g.
V_y is the contract injection volume, either 1 or 2 µL.
V_c is 5,000 µL.
D is the dry weight factor

$$D = \frac{100 - \% \text{ moisture}}{100}.$$

The reviewer should check to insure that the appropriate equations have been used to calculate results, and that the results are mathematically correct. CRQLs should also be checked to insure they have been adjusted properly. When a choice of two values is to be made for a reported analyte, the correct choice is generally the lower of the two values. When inappropriate calculations or reported values are discovered, the correct values should be placed in the data and notation made of the change in the reviewer's narrative.

The presence of large off-scale peaks can interfere with adjusted CRQL. At the reviewers discretion the CRQL can be flagged as unusable (R). Smaller interferences may justify flagging the reported CRQL as an estimate (UJ).

13. Overall Assessment of Data

The Overall Assessment of Data is a written narrative prepared by the reviewer. It is used as a place to express qualifications and concerns about the sample results not expressly covered in the other areas of review. Besides the data package, the reviewer may wish to refer to the Quality Assurance Project Plan and the Sampling and Analysis Plan. Reviewers may wish to consider to what purpose the data will be applied as a guide to their summary of the data usability. Thus data known to be proceeding directly into the legal arena will be viewed in a different light than data being used to prepare an initial evaluation of a site and is to be followed by further sampling and analysis efforts.

E. Metals and Other Inorganic Analytes

The target analytes for metals analysis under the inorganic SOWs are listed in Table 7-44. The Forms included in the deliverables are listed in Table 7-45.

Table 7-44.   Target Analytes and CRQL of the Inorganic SOW

Analyte	Method	Low Level µg/L	Multi-level µg/L
Aluminum	200.7	100	200
Antimony	200.7, 204.2	5	60
Arsenic	200.7, 206.2	2	10
Barium	200.7	20	200
Beryllium	200.7, 210.2	1	5
Cadmium	200.7, 213.2	1	5
Calcium	200.7, 215.1	500	5000
Chromium	200.7, 218.2	10	10
Cobalt	200.7	10	50
Copper	200.7	10	25
Iron	200.7	100	100
Lead	200.7, 239.2	2	3
Magnesium	200.7, 242.1	500	5000
Manganese	200.7	10	15
Mercury	245.1, 245.2, 245.5	0.2	0.2
Nickel	200.7	20	40
Potassium	200.7, 258.1	750	5000
Selenium	200.7, 270.2	3	5
Silver	200.7, 272.2	10	10

Table 7-44.   Target Analytes and CRQL of the Inorganic SOW. *Continued*

Analyte	Method	Low Level µg/L	Multi-level µg/L
Sodium	200.7, 273.1	500	5000
Thallium	200.7, 279.2	10	10
Vanadium	200.7	10	50
Zinc	200.7	20	20
Cyanide	335.2	10	10
Fluoride	340.2	200	-
NO_2/NO_3-N	300.0, 353.2	100	-

Table 7-45. CLP Forms Included as Deliverables with Each Sample for Metals

Form	Title
I-IN	Inorganic Analysis Data Sheet
II(Part 1)-IN	Initial and Continuing Calibration Verification
II(Part 2)-IN	CRDL Standard for AA and ICP
III-IN	Blanks
IV-IN	ICP Interference Check Sample
V(Part 1)-IN	Spike Sample Recovery
V(Part 2)-IN	Post Digest Spike Sample Recovery
VI-IN	Duplicates
7-IN	Laboratory Control Sample
VIII-IN	Standard Addition Results
IX-IN	ICP Serial Dilutions
X-IN	Instrument Detection Limits (Quarterly)
XI(Part 1)-IN	ICP Interelement Correction Factors (Annually)
XI(Part 2)-IN	ICP Interelement Correction Factors (Annually)
XII-IN	ICP Linear Ranges (Quarterly)
XIII-IN	Preparation Log
XIV-IN	Analysis Run Log

There are 11 areas listed in the *National Functional Guidelines* as essential to check during the data evaluation process. These are listed in Table 7-46 and are discussed in detail in the following paragraphs.

Table 7-46.   Points of CLP SOW Inorganic Data Evaluation

1. Holding Times
2. Calibration
   - Initial
   - Initial and continuing calibration verification
3. Blanks
4. ICP Interference Check Sample
5. Laboratory Control Sample
6. Duplicate Sample

7. Spike Sample Analysis
8. Graphite Furnace Atomic Absorption QC
9. ICP Serial Dilution
10. Field Duplicates
11. Overall Assessment

There are a variety of methods and analytical techniques covered under the Inorganic SOWs. They are presented in Table 7-47.

Table 7-47.   Methods of Analysis Included in the Inorganic SOWs

Abbreviation	Analytical Technique
ICP-AES	Inductively Coupled Plasma - Atomic Emission Spectroscopy
ICP-MS	Inductively Coupled Plasma - Mass Spectrometry
Hydride ICP-AES	Hydride Generation Inductively Coupled Plasma - Atomic Emission Spectroscopy
GFAA	Graphite Furnace Atomic Absorption
FLAA	Flame Atomic Absorption
CVAA	Cold Vapor Atomic Absorption
Cyanide	335.2 Distillation followed by titrimetric or spectroscopic method
NO_2/NO_3-N	Nitrite plus nitrate expressed as nitrogen; 300.0 ion chromatography; 353.2 automated colorimetric
Fluoride	340.2 ion selective electrode

1. Holding Times

Technical holding times are counted from the date of sampling to the date of analysis. Method holding times are contract requirements and are counted from the verified time of sample receipt (VTSR). The holding times are listed in Table 7-48.

Table 7-48.   Holding Times for Inorganic Analysis

Low-level Analyte	Technical Holding Time	Method Holding Time
Metals	180 days	180 days
Mercury	28 days	26 days
Cyanide	14 days	12 days
NO_2/NO_3-N	28 days[7]	12 days
Fluoride	28 days[8]	26 days

Proper preservation of the sample is also an item subject to review. The proper preservations are listed in Table 7-49. Soil/sediment samples are only cooled to $4 \pm 2°C$. Preservation is to be performed by the field sampler immediately on sample collection. Samples for dissolved metals are to be filtered prior to acidification. pH adjustment is checked with wide range pH paper.

---

[7] Not specifically mentioned in the *National Functional Guidelines*, value is from 40 CFR 136, Table II.
[8] Not specifically mentioned in the *National Functional Guidelines*, value is from 40 CFR 136, Table II.

Table 7-49. Preservation Requirements for Inorganic Analysis Water Samples

Analyte	Preservation
Metals	Nitric acid to pH < 2
Mercury	Nitric acid to pH < 2
Cyanide	0.6 g ascorbic acid if residual chlorine is present; sodium hydroxide to pH > 12; cool to 4 ± 2°C
NO_2/NO_3-N	Sulfuric acid to pH < 2
Fluoride	Cool to 4 ± 2°C

The data to be reviewed are found on Form I-IN, Form XIII-IN, the sample traffic reports and/or chain-of-custody records, the sample preparation benchsheets or log-books, and the laboratory's case narrative. If technical holding time and/or preservation requirements have not been met all data is flagged as estimated (J or UJ). Analyses performed that grossly exceed of the holding times should have the undetected analytes flagged as unreliable (R) as a loss of analytes is the expected result from a lengthy delay of sample processing.

2. Calibration

The calibration criteria will vary depending on which procedure was used in the analysis. The target analytes that can be performed for each of the procedures are listed in Table 7-50. The calibration criteria are listed in Table 7-51. None of these instruments will remain within calibration for extended periods of time, thus daily calibration is necessary with frequent calibration checks.

Table 7-50. Analytical Techniques Used Under the CLP Inorganic SOWs for Metals

Analytical Technique	Analytes
ICP-AES	Al, Sb, As, Ba, Be, B, Cd, Ca, Cr, Co, Cu, Fe, Pb, Mg, Mn, Mo, Ni, K, Se, Si, Ag, Na, Tl, V, Zn
ICP-MS[9]	Al, Sb, As, Ba, Be, Cd, Cr, Co, Cu, Fe, Pb. Mn, Ni, Se, Ag, Tl, V, Zn
Hydride ICP-AES[10]	Sb, As, Se
GFAA	Sb, As, Be, Cd, Cr, Pb, Se, Ag, Tl
FLAA	Ca, Mg, K, Na
CVAA	Hg

Table 7-51. Calibration Requirements for Inorganic Analysis

Analytical Technique	Calibration Procedure
ICP-AES	Blank + 1 point
ICP-MS	Blank + 1 point
Hydride ICP-AES	Blank + 1 point
GFAA	Blank + 3 points
FLAA	Blank + 3 points
CVAA manual	Blank + 4 points

---

[9] Low Concentration SOW only.
[10] Low Concentration SOW only.

Table 7-51. Calibration Requirements for Inorganic Analysis, *continued*

Analytical Technique	Calibration Procedure
CVAA automated	Blank + 8 points
Cyanide	Blank + 3 points
NO$_2$/NO$_3$-N	Blank + 3 points
Fluoride	CRDL + 3 points

The data reviewed for calibration are found on Form II-IN (Part A and B), Form XIII-IN, preparation logs, calibration standard logs, instrument logs and instrument data printouts. There are a large number of solutions analyzed within the course of a metals test protocol. They are normally referred to by their initials, and a summary of what the initials mean is presented in Table 7-52.

Table 7-52. Summary of Solutions and Abbreviations Used in Metals Analysis

Abbreviation	Description
CRDL	Contract Required Detection Limit
IDL	Instrument Detection Limit
CRI	ICP calibration check solution at 2 times concentration of CRDL
ICV	Initial Calibration Verification
ICB	Initial Calibration Blank
CCV	Continuing Calibration Verification
CCB	Continuing Calibration Blank
CRA	GFAA calibration check solution at the CRDL
PB	Preparation Blank
ICSA	Interference Check Standard A containing interferents
ICSB	Interference Check Standard B containing analytes to be checked for interferences
ICSAB	Interference Check Standard A mixed with Interference Check Standard B
LRS	Linear Range Analysis Standard

2.1 ICP-AES and ICP-MS

Calibration for the ICP is single point with a blank. A number of solutions are required as some of the analytes can interact chemically with each other at the concentrations normally used for calibration and to avoid spectral interference with each other. Suggested contents of these solutions and representative concentrations are presented in Table 7-53.

Table 7-53. Suggested Calibration Solutions Used for ICP in the SOW

Solution	Contents	Suggested concentration (ppm)
I	Mn, Be, Cd, Pb, Zn	10 each
II	Ba, Cu, Fe, V, Co	10 each
III	Mo, Si, As, Se	10 each
IV	Ca, Na, K, Al, Cr, Ni	50 (Cr, Ni 10)
V	Sb, B, Mg, Ag, Tl	10 (Ag 1, Mg 50)

The linearity of the calibration is checked through analysis of a standard that contains all analytes except Al, Ba, Ca, Fe, Mg, Na and K. This standard is called the CRI. The concentration of the analytes in the solution is 2 times the CRDL or the instrument detection limit, whichever is the greater. CRI analysis is performed immediately before samples are analyzed and at the end of the sample run, or a minimum of twice in every 8-hour time period. At the moment there are no criteria for CRI acceptance.

Immediately following the calibration, it is checked by analysis of the Initial Calibration Verification (ICV) solutions. EPA provides ICV solutions to laboratories with the CLP. In the absence of EPA provided ICV solutions, the solutions are to be prepared from an independent source, which is defined as a source different than that used to procure the initial calibration solutions. The concentration of the ICV is to be different than that of the calibration solutions and the CRI; however, within the linear range of the instrument. The recovery (%R) of the ICV analysis is to be within the 90-110% of the true value for each analyte. Due to possible rounding errors these limits are expanded by 1% for data evaluation purposes to 89-111%. These are calculated as follows:

$$\%R = \frac{\text{Found}}{\text{True}} \; x \; 100 \, .$$

If the ICV percent recovery is not met, the instrument is considered to not be in calibration for that analyte. The proper procedure is to start the calibration procedure all over again.

The calibration is rechecked during the analytical run through analysis of the Continuing Calibration Verification (CCV) solution. The CCV contains all analytes and is prepared from a source independent from the ICV at a concentration near the mid-point of the calibration range. The concentration is to be different than that used for the ICV. The CCV is run immediately before the beginning of the sample analytical run, after every ten samples and at the end of the analytical run. If analysis of ten samples takes more than 2 hours, then the CCV is performed every 2 hours during the analytical run. The CCV analysis is to be performed exactly like the analysis of regular samples, *i.e.* with the same duration of blank rinse before and between exposures, same number of replicate exposures, and the same exposure time. Recovery (%R) acceptance criteria for the CCV are the same as those used for the ICV.

If the instrument was not calibrated on a daily basis, all results are flagged as unusable (R). If ICV results or the CCV results that bracket the sample analysis are outside the acceptance criteria for recovery, the degree of deviation will dictate the qualification of the data for the affected analyte. Small deviations in the ranges 75-89% and 111-125% indicate that the reported values for target analytes are estimates (J) and should be flagged as such. For undetected analytes, recoveries in the high range (111-125%) suggest that the results are overestimated, and the non-detect is not flagged. However, low recoveries (75-89%) means that results are underestimated, and the non-detected analytes should be flagged as estimates (UJ).

Gross deviations from initial or continuing calibration acceptance criteria means that all sample data for the affected analyte should be flagged as unreliable (R). If the recoveries are higher than 125%, this may indicate that any non-detected results for the analyte might be acceptable.

2.2 GFAA and FLAA

GFAA and FLAA calibration standards are to be made fresh each day and consist of a blank and at least three different concentrations of the analyte. One of the standards must be at the CRDL. Calibration must be performed daily. The obtained calibration must exhibit a correlation coefficient of >0.995.

Immediately following the calibration, it is checked by analysis of the Initial Calibration Verification (ICV) solution. EPA-provides ICV solutions to laboratories with the CLP. In the absence of an EPA provided ICV solution, the solution is to be prepared from an independent source, which is defined as a source different than that used to procure the initial calibration solution. The concentration of the ICV is to be different than that of the calibration solutions and the CRA; however, within the linear range of the instrument. The recovery (%R) of the ICV analysis is to be within the 90-110% of the true value for the analyte. Due to possible rounding errors these limits are expanded by 1% for data evaluation purposes to 89-111%. These are calculated as follows:

$$%R = \frac{Found}{True} \times 100 \, .$$

If the ICV percent recovery is not met, the instrument is considered not to be in calibration for the analyte. The proper procedure is to start the calibration procedure all over again.

The calibration is rechecked during the analytical run through analysis of the Continuing Calibration Verification (CCV) solution. The CCV is prepared from a source independent from the ICV at a concentration near the mid-point of the calibration range. The concentration is to be different than that used for the ICV. The CCV is run immediately before the beginning of the sample analytical run, after every ten samples and at the end of the analytical run. If analysis of ten samples takes more than 2 hours, then the CCV is performed every 2 hours during the analytical run. Recovery (%R) acceptance criteria for the CCV are the same as those used for the ICV.

If the instrument was not calibrated on a daily basis or less than three standards were used, all results are flagged as unusable (R). If ICV results or the CCV results that bracket the sample analysis are outside the acceptance criteria for recovery, the degree of deviation will dictate the qualification of the data for the affected analyte. Small deviations in the ranges 75-89% and 111-125% indicate that the reported values for target analytes are estimates (J) and should be flagged as such. For undetected analytes, recoveries in the high range (111-125%) suggest that the results are overestimated, and the non-detect is not flagged. However, low recoveries (75-89%) means that results are underestimated, and the non-detected analytes should be flagged as estimates (UJ).

Gross deviations from initial or continuing calibration acceptance criteria mean that all sample data for the analyte should be flagged as unreliable (R). If the recoveries are higher than 125% this may indicate that any non-detected results for the analyte might be acceptable.

2.3 CVAA

Mercury calibration standards consist of a blank and from five to eight different concentrations of the analyte, depending on the instrument used. One of the standards must be at the CRDL. Calibration must be performed daily. The obtained calibration must exhibit a correlation coefficient of >0.995.

Immediately following the calibration, it is checked by analysis of the Initial Calibration Verification (ICV) solution. EPA provides ICV solutions to laboratories with the CLP. In the absence of an EPA-provided ICV solution, the solution is to be prepared from an independent source, which is defined as a source different than that used to procure the initial calibration solutions. The concentration of the ICV is to be different than that of the calibration solutions and the CRA; however, within the linear range of the instrument. The recovery (%R) of the ICV analysis are to be within the 80-120% of the true value. Due to possible rounding errors these limits are expanded by 1% for data evaluation purposes to 79-121%. These are calculated as follows:

$$\%R = \frac{Found}{True} \times 100 .$$

If the ICV percent recovery are not met, the instrument is considered not to be in calibration for that analyte. The proper procedure is to start the calibration procedure all over again.

The calibration is rechecked during the analytical run through analysis of the Continuing Calibration Verification (CCV) solution. The CCV is prepared from a source independent from the ICV at a concentration near the mid-point of the calibration range. The concentration is to be different than that used for the ICV. The CCV is run immediately before the beginning of the sample analytical run, after every ten samples and at the end of the analytical run. If analysis of ten samples takes more than 2 hours, then the CCV is performed every 2 hours during the analytical run. Recovery (%R) acceptance criteria for the CCV are the same as those used for the ICV.

If the instrument was not calibrated on a daily basis or less than the required number of standards were used, all results are flagged as unusable (R). If ICV results or the CCV results that bracket the sample analysis are outside the acceptance criteria for recovery, the degree of deviation will dictate the qualification of the data for the affected analyte. Small deviations in the ranges 65-79% and 121-135% indicate that the reported values for target analytes are estimates (J) and should be flagged as such. For undetected analytes, recoveries in the high range (121-135%) suggest that the results are overestimated, and the non-detect is not flagged. However, low recoveries (65-79%) mean that results are underestimated, and the non-detected analytes should be flagged as estimates (UJ).

Gross deviations from initial or continuing calibration acceptance criteria means that all sample data for the affected analyte should be flagged as unreliable (R). If the recoveries are higher than 135% this may indicate that any non-detected results for the analyte might be acceptable.

2.4 Cyanide

Calibration standards consist of a blank and at least three different concentrations of the analyte. One of the standards must be at the CRDL. Calibration must be performed daily. At least one of the calibration standards, generally the mid-level standard, must be distilled and the value obtained compared to the calibration curve. The distilled standard must exhibit a recovery of 85-115% of the undistilled standard.

Immediately following the calibration, it is checked by analysis of the Initial Calibration Verification (ICV) solution. The solution is to be prepared from an independent source, which is defined as a source different than that used to procure the initial calibration solutions. The concentration of the ICV is to be different than that of the calibration solutions; however, within the linear range of the instrument. The recovery (%R) of the ICV analysis are to be within the 85-115% of the true value for each analyte. Due to possible rounding errors these limits are expanded by 1% for data evaluation purposes to 84-116%. The recovery is calculated as follows:

$$\%R = \frac{Found}{True} \times 100 \, .$$

If the ICV percent recovery is not met, the instrument is considered not to be in calibration for that analyte. The proper procedure is to start the calibration procedure all over again.

The calibration is rechecked during the analytical run through analysis of the Continuing Calibration Verification (CCV) solution. The CCV contains all analytes and is prepared from a source independent from the ICV at a concentration near the mid-point of the calibration range. The concentration is to be different than that used for the ICV. The CCV is run immediately before the beginning of the sample analytical run, after every ten samples and at the end of the analytical run. If analysis of ten samples takes more than 2 hours, then the CCV is performed every 2 hours during the analytical run. Recovery (%R) acceptance criteria for the CCV are the same as those used for the ICV.

If the instrument was not calibrated on a daily basis, all results are flagged as unusable (R). If ICV results or the CCV results that bracket the sample analysis are outside the acceptance criteria for recovery, the degree of deviation will dictate the qualification of the data for the affected analyte. Small deviations in the ranges 70-84% and 116-130% indicate that the reported values for target analytes are estimates (J) and should be flagged as such. For undetected analytes, recoveries in the high range (116-130%) suggest that the results are overestimated, and the non-detect is not flagged. However, low recoveries (70-84%) mean that results are underestimated, and the non-detected analytes should be flagged as estimates (UJ).

Gross deviations from initial or continuing calibration acceptance criteria mean that all sample data for the affected analyte should be flagged as unreliable (R). If the recoveries are higher than 130%, this may indicate that any non-detected results for the analyte might be acceptable.

There are no formal guidelines for evaluation of fluoride or nitrite/nitrate-N calibration data. However, the guidelines used for evaluation of cyanide data can be applied with little change to the other analyses.

3. Blanks

Blanks are used to monitor the levels of laboratory or field contamination of the samples. As discussed in Chapter 2, to be statistically significant, blanks need to be monitored on a continuing basis to obtain an evaluation of the success of the laboratory's program for contaminant control. Within metals analysis the blanks that are regularly performed are those associated with field activities, called field or equipment blanks, and those associated with laboratory activities. The two laboratory activities that are monitored with blanks are the sample digestion procedures (preparation blank), and the instrument sample introduction system (initial and continuing calibration blanks, ICB and CCB). The preparation blank is an aliquot of deionized distilled water carried through all the sample preparation steps.

Data related to blank analysis is found on Forms I-IN, III-IN, XIII-IN, XIV-IN and the preparation logs, calibration standard logs, instrument logs and the raw data associated with the calibration and analytical run. ICB are to be performed each time the instrument is calibrated after the verification (ICV) of the calibration. CCB are run after the initial calibration and during the analytical run immediately after every CCV. If the absolute value of a calibration blank is less than the instrument detection limit (IDL) then a IDL-U is entered on Form III-IN, values greater than the IDL are entered as numbers on the form. If the CRDL is exceeded, analysis is to be terminated, the problem found and corrected, the instrument recalibrated and the preceding samples since the last successful blank re-analyzed.

For preparation blanks, values less than the CRDL are acceptable. When preparation blanks exhibit analyte(s) present in greater than the absolute value of the CRDL (Both positive and negative CRDL are encountered in metals analysis.), all samples exhibiting analyte less than ten times the blank amount are to be redigested and re-analyzed. Sample results greater than ten times the amount of analyte found in the preparation blank are acceptable. Preparation blanks are reported in μg/L for batches of aqueous samples and in mg/Kg for solids, assuming the average solid sample size of 1.0 g (0.5 g for microwave preparation).

Sample results are never corrected for blank contamination. Violations are to be reported to the TPO.

Sample results less than five times the amount of analyte found in a blank are generally flagged in review as undetected (U). When evaluating results from solid samples, the calibration blanks are very misleading if the reviewer cursorily just compares the numbers on Form III with the sample results on Form I. The raw data may also be misleading as most instrument printouts will already be corrected for sample size and dilutions. For example a CCB may read a 0.10 ppm level for cadmium on the raw data, and an associated solid sample may be reported at 45 ppm, read directly from the instrument printout. If 1.0 g of solid was digested and taken to a final volume of 200 mL, the blank value needs to be multiplied by 200 to obtain a comparative value, 20.0 ppm in this case. The reported cadmium value of 45 ppm is then seen not to pass the ten-times criteria and should be flagged as undetected (U). Dry weight correction factors need to also be taken into account. If the percent moisture in this example is 50%, then a minimum acceptable sample result would have to be greater than 200 ppm to preclude presumption of sample contamination.

Reviewers should perform calculations and conversions on blank results to insure they are comparing representative values.

4. ICP Interference Check Sample

ICP spectral interferences and generation of interelement correction factors are discussed in Chapter 2. The correction factors must be generated annually. The ICP interference check samples (ICSA and ICSAB) are analyzed at the completion of daily calibration and at the end of operation (minimum of two analyses per 8 hours of run time). These are available from EPA or commercial vendors and consist of the analytes and the concentrations listed in Table 7-54.

Table 7-54. Analytes and Concentrations (mg/L) of the ICP Interference Check Samples

Multi Level SOW

Analyte	ICSA	ICSAB
Al	500	500
Ca	500	500
Fe	200	200
Mg	500	500
Ag	-	1.0
Ba	-	0.5
Be	-	0.5
Cd	-	1.0
Co	-	0.5
Cr	-	0.5
Cu	-	0.5
Mn	-	0.5
Ni	-	1.0
Pb	-	1.0
V	-	0.5
Zn	-	1.0
Al	100.0	100.0
Ca	100.0	100.0

Low Level SOW

Analyte	ICSA	ICSAB
Fe	100.0	100.0
Mg	100.0	100.0
Na	100.0	100.0
P	100.0	100.0
K	100.0	100.0
S	100.0	100.0
C	200.0	200.0
Cl	720.0	720.0
Mo	10.0	10.0
Ti	10.0	10.0
As	-	0.100
Cd	-	0.050
Cr	-	0.100
Co	-	0.200
Cu	-	0.100
Mn	-	0.100

Table 7-54. **Analytes and Concentrations (mg/L) of the ICP Interference Check Samples.** *Continued*

Low Level SOW		
Analyte	**ICSA**	**ICSAB**
Ni	-	0.200
Se	-	0.100
Ag	-	0.100
V	-	0.200
Zn	-	0.100

The data to be reviewed are found on Forms IV-IN and XIV-IN and the instrument printouts and raw data. Passing criteria are for all analytes in the analysis of solution ICSAB to exhibit recoveries within ±20% of the true values listed in Table 7-54. Recoveries are calculated as:

$$\%R = \frac{\text{Found in Solution ICSAB}}{\text{True Value in ICSAB}} \text{ x } 100 \text{ .}$$

If true values are not reported by the source of the solutions, then the laboratory generates true values through repetitive analysis (minimum five repetitions) of the ICS solutions and then inclusion of the mean and standard deviation as an attachment in the raw data.

The ICS data should be carefully checked for positive and negative target analyte results greater than the absolute value of the IDL for elements not included in the ICSA or ICSAB solutions. Positive results are an indication of either laboratory contamination of the ICS test solutions or an improperly generated interelement correction factor for that element. The latter situation can lead to false positive results on samples. If this situation exists, samples reported with high levels of the interference components in the ICSA and hits for the potential false positives should have the false positive results flagged as estimated (J). Negative results in the ICSAB lead to the potential for false negatives in the samples when the interfering elements are present. Reported undetected elements in samples that may be subject to these negative interferences should have the results flagged as estimated (UJ).

Aqueous samples that exhibit levels of the four ICSA interferents Al, Ca, Fe and Mg at least as high as those present in the ICSAB (500, 500, 200 and 500 mg/L, respectively) can be examined for potential false positive and false negative results based on interference correction factor deficiencies. The following guidelines apply:

- If the ICSAB recovery for an element is greater than 120%, positive sample results for the element should be flagged as estimated (J). Results for the element that are reported as undetected are acceptable.

- If the ICSAB recovery for an element is in the range 50-79%, then false negative results can exist. Sample results for the element are flagged as estimates (J or UJ).

- If the ICSAB recovery for an element is less than 50%, then sample results for that element are flagged as unusable (R).

Application of these guidelines to soil/ samples needs to account for reduced sample size and dilution effects upon the levels of the four elements in the ICSA. These calculate out to be 100,000 mg/Kg for Al, Ca and Mg, and 40,000 mg/Kg for Fe.

The contents of the ICSA check used in the Low Level SOW makes interpretation of the effect of interference correction factors for any particular element much more complicated; however, it also makes the results obtained on the ICSAB much more applicable to all samples. With a fair level of confidence, the three bulleted guidelines above can be applied to any sample without any prequalification requirements for the sample contents to match the concentrations of the ICSA.

5. Laboratory Control Sample

The Laboratory Control Samples (LCS) are available from EPA to contract laboratories and consist of both solid and aqueous phases. If the EPA provided samples are not available, the ICV solution can be used, in the Multi-Level SOW for the aqueous LCS. A quality control check standard or NIST Standard Reference Material is suggested as a substitute for the Low Level SOW and the solid phase LCS under the Multi Level SOW. For mercury analysis, an aqueous LCS is not required, while for cyanide the distilled ICV is used as the LCS.

The aqueous LCS have recovery acceptance criteria of 80-120%, with the exceptions of silver and antimony, which have no set limits. Percent recovery is calculated as:

$$\%R = \frac{\text{Amount of analyte found}}{\text{True value of analyte in LCS}} \times 100 \ .$$

The solid LCS recovery acceptance limits are set by the provider of the LCS for each LCS standard. The data supporting the LCS performance and results are found on Form 7-IN, Form XIII-IN, Form XIV-IN, and the preparation logs, instrument printouts, and other raw data. The proper course of action in the case of LCS failure is to first re-analyze the LCS solution, then, if the LCS still fails, redigest and re-analyze the entire batch of samples.

The LCS results are evaluated on an analyte-by-analyte basis. If only a single analyte fails, then qualification of sample data based on LCS failure is limited to that same analyte. General guidelines for evaluation are:

- When LCS recoveries are greater than the acceptance limit, flag associated positive results as estimated (J). Non-detected analytes are acceptable.

- When LCS recoveries are slightly low (50-79% for aqueous samples), flag all results as estimates (J or UJ).

- When LCS recoveries are very low (less than 50% for aqueous samples), flag all results as unusable (R).

LCS recoveries are an indication of the performance ability of the laboratory, when there are limited complicating matrix effects in the sample. Although random failure will occur, repeated inability to meet LCS acceptance criteria bring into question the laboratory's ability to reliably analyze any sample. LCS failures need to be discussed in the reviewer's narrative with this point in mind.

6. Duplicate Sample

Duplicate sample analysis is required at a rate of one duplicate per batch or sample delivery group. If different types of samples are present in the group then one duplicate is to be prepared for the aqueous samples and another duplicate for the solid samples. Duplicates must be performed in exactly the same fashion for all aspects of the sample preparation and analysis. Samples analyzed by two different methods, such as GFAA and ICP, must have duplicates for both techniques.

Duplicates are evaluated by calculation of Relative Percent Difference (RPD). The formula for RPD is:

$$RPD = \frac{2|A-B|}{A + B} \times 100 \,.$$

where A and B are the analytical results for the sample and associated duplicate.

For aqueous duplicates, if the sample results are greater than five times the CRDL, the acceptance criteria for RPD is 20 or less. If the sample results are less than five times the CRDL, then the duplicate acceptance is evaluated on the sample results rather than RPD. The criteria are ±CRDL.

For solid samples the method criteria for RPD are the same as for aqueous samples. With regard to technical usability of the data, various regions may allow evaluation of duplicate results on solids to be relaxed to RPD of 35 or less and ±2 times the CRDL.

When out-of-control duplicate results are encountered by the reviewer, all data on associated samples for the affected analytes should be flagged as estimated (J). The affect on the data should also be discussed in the reviewer's narrative.

7. Spike Sample Analysis

Spike analysis is used to determine the ability to recover a known added amount of the target analyte from the sample. In CLP inorganic analysis there are two types of spikes performed. The first is an addition of target analytes to an aliquot of a sample before the beginning of sample preparation. This is variously called a matrix spike, a pre-digestion spike, a pre-distillation spike or simply a spiked sample. Recovery limits for matrix spikes are calculated as:

$$\%R = \frac{SSR - SR}{SA} \times 100$$

where: SSR is the spiked sample result.
  SR is the sample result; use zero if result is less than IDL.
  SA is the spike added.

Recovery limits for spiked samples are 75-125%. If the amount of analyte native to the sample is greater than four times the amount of spiked analyte, then the recovery limits for spiked analytes do not apply.

The second type of spike is an addition of a known amount of target analyte to the prepared sample immediately before it is brought up to final volume for analysis. This is known in the CLP as a post-digestion spike, post-distillation spike, or an analytical spike. Analytical spikes are required to be performed whenever the matrix spike has failed to be within recovery limits. Analytical spikes for either silver or mercury are not required. The analytical spike level is at two times the native sample amount of the analyte or at two times the CRDL, whichever is greater. The results of the analytical spike are never used to flag sample results; however, the recoveries must be discussed in the reviewer's narrative.

The amount of the target analyte used to spike the sample aliquots is set within the CLP SOW. These various levels are presented in Table 7-55.

Table 7-55. **Inorganic Target Analyte Spike Levels.** (An asterisk designates an analyte not required to be spiked while a dash indicates no set level. Antimony and selenium are specified as being in the +5 oxidation state.)

| Analyte | Low-Level Water µg/L | Multi-Level | | | |
		ICP Water µg/L	ICP Soil mg/Kg	AA Water µg/L	AA Soil mg/Kg
Al	500	2000	*	-	-
Sb	50	500	100	100	20
As	10	2000	400	40	8
Ba	200	2000	400	-	-
Be	10	50	10	-	-
Cd	10	50	10	5	1
Ca	*	*	*	-	-
Cr	50	200	40	-	-
Co	100	500	100	-	-
Cu	50	250	50	-	-
Fe	250	1000	*	-	-
Pb	25	500	100	20	4
Mg	*	*	*	-	-
Mn	50	500	100	-	-
Ni	100	500	100	-	-
K	*	*	*	-	-
Se	50	2000	400	10	2
Ag	50	50	10	-	-
Na	*	*	*	-	-
Tl	50	2000	400	50	10
V	100	500	100	-	-
Zn	100	500	100	-	-
Hg	0.5	NA	NA	1	1
CN	100	100	100	NA	NA
F	400	NA	NA	NA	NA
NO_2-NO_3	200	NA	NA	NA	NA

Data for review of spiked sample results are found on Form I-IN, Form V-IN (Part A & B) and are supported by the instrument printouts and other raw data. When elements have been tested by two different methods (such as ICP and GFAA), spiked sample results will be reported for each technique. Results from analysis of spiked solid samples are reported in terms of dry weight, and the reviewer should check to make sure the conversions were performed correctly. The field blank should never be used as the batch matrix spike.

If the spike recoveries are outside the acceptance range of 75-125%, all positive sample results are flagged as estimated (J). Non-detected sample results are flagged as estimated (UJ) if the spike recoveries are 30-74%. Non-detected sample results are flagged as unusable (R) if the spike recoveries are less than 30%. If spike recoveries are greater than 125%, this indicates that there is a high bias in the results and thus non-detected analytes are acceptable without flagging.

When more than one spike result is reported for an analyte within a set of analyses of the same matrix, concentration and method, and one of the spike results is not in the acceptance range, the data are evaluated on recovery of the unacceptable spike.

8. Graphite Furnace Atomic Absorption QC

Graphite furnace atomic absorption (GFAA) data are evaluated within the context of the Furnace Atomic Absorption Analysis Scheme (MSA tree, Figure 7-5). This analysis scheme developed as a solution to the problem of interferences found during the analysis of complex environmental samples. When samples are encountered that present spectral interferences to the analysis, a calibration is created in the sample itself by Multiple Standard Additions (MSA) at 50%, 100%, and 150% of the approximate sample analyte concentration to overcome the interference. MSA is discussed in Chapter 2. The preparation blank and laboratory control samples are not subjected to the MSA procedure. If preparation blanks fail the analytical spike acceptance criteria, the entire batch fails and must be redigested. The reviewer should not attempt to evaluate GFAA data until a complete understanding of the MSA tree has been achieved. The MSA tree presented in Figure 7-5 has been altered to make clarify some of the decision points presented in the figure in the CLP-SOW.

The decision tree is based upon the analysis of all samples (except matrix spiked samples) with concurrent analytical spikes (post-digestion spikes). "All samples" includes the preparation blank and the laboratory control samples. The data that reports the findings from GFAA analysis are found on Forms I-IN, V-IN, VIII-IN and the instrument printouts and other logbooks/benchsheets.

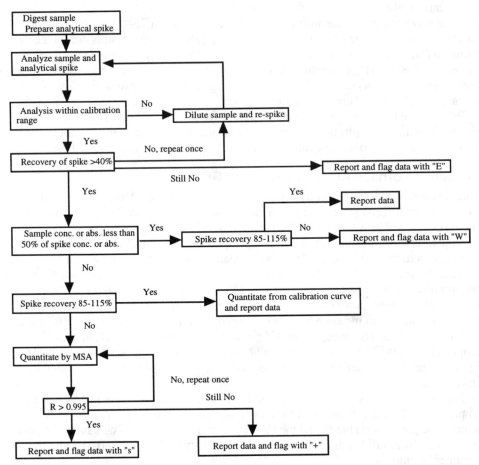

Figure 7-5. GFAA decision tree.

The analytical spikes are prepared at a level equal to two times the CRDL, with the exception of lead which is 20 µg/L. The analytical spike is prepared by adding a volume of spiking solution to the digested sample. The volume of the analytical spike solution added is not to exceed 10% of the volume of the original sample. The volume of the sample is then adjusted by adding water so that the sample and analytical spiked sample volumes are equal.

Each sample and analytical spike is injected and analyzed by the GFAA twice, then the average of the determinations are reported. If the concentration of the sample is greater than the CRDL, the replicate injections must agree within 20% RSD or else the replicate injections must be repeated once. Samples being analyzed by MSA are injected and analyzed only once.

Only 20 injections are allowed between blank and continuing calibration verifications. This means a maximum of ten separate solutions can be analyzed between CCV. As the analytical spike must be analyzed immediately following the related sample, a total of five complete analyses is possible between CCV.

Sample results obtained from replicate injections that do not meet the less than 20% RSD criteria are flagged as estimated (J). If the replicate injections were not repeated, the finding should be listed in the reviewer's narrative.

If the analytical spike recovery is less than 40%, the associated results are flagged as estimated (J or UJ). If the recovery is less than 10%, the undetected analytes are flagged as unusable (R).

If the sample absorbance is less than 50% of that of the associated analytical spiked sample, and the recovery of the analytical spike is not within the 85-115% criteria, then the results for the analyte are flagged as estimates (J or UJ).

If Multiple Standard Addition results are needed for a sample and MSA was not performed, flag the results as estimates (J or UJ). If MSA was performed and inappropriate concentrations were used or correlation coefficient criteria were not met, flag the results as estimates (J). The finding should be discussed in the reviewer's narrative.

9. ICP Serial Dilution

A serial dilution of 1:5 must be performed on at least one sample from every batch of analyses by ICP to determine if physical or chemical interferences exist in the analyte determinations. Field blanks cannot be used to fulfill the serial dilution requirement. If the analyte in the sample is at least 50 times the value of the IDL, then the percent difference between the value obtained from the 1:5 dilution and the undiluted value must be within 10%. Percent difference (%D) is calculated as:

$$\%D = \frac{|I - S|}{I} \times 100$$

where: I is the initial sample result.
 S is the serial dilution result multiplied by five.

A 1:5 dilution is defined as increasing the total volume of the sample by a factor of 5. For example, a 10.0 mL sample can be diluted to 50 mL (a 1:5 dilution) or a 10.0 mL sample can have 40.0 mL water added to it (a 1+4 dilution). A 1:5 dilution and a 1+4 dilution give exactly the same result. However, a 1:5 dilution and a 1+5 dilution give different results (50 mL and 60 mL final volume, respectively).

If the ICP serial dilution criteria of %D<10% are not met, then flag all associated reported data from the batch as estimated (J).

10. Field Duplicates

The data to be reviewed are found on Form I-IN and the associated instrument printouts and laboratory records. The field duplicates are identified on the Sample Traffic Reports or the field sample sheets. The reviewer should calculate relative percent difference (RPD) for the results reported for the duplicate samples. If criteria have been specified for field duplicates in the Chemical Data Sampling and Analysis Plan, then these should be applied. Otherwise, a comparison of the results should be discussed in the reviewer's narrative.

11. Overall Assessment

The Overall Assessment of Data is a written narrative prepared by the reviewer. It is a place to express qualifications and concerns about the sample results not expressly covered in the other areas of review. Besides the data package, the reviewer may wish to refer to the Quality Assurance Project Plan and the Sampling and Analysis Plan. Reviewers may wish to consider to what purpose the data will be applied as a guide to their summary of the data usability. Thus data known to be proceeding directly into the legal arena will be viewed in a different light than data being used to prepare an initial evaluation of a site and is to be followed by further sampling and analysis efforts.

The reviewer may wish to include a discussion of the comparability of results if the same samples have been analyzed by ICP and by GFAA. Sometimes ICP interferences can be detected through this comparison that might otherwise go unnoticed.

References

1. *Environmental Compliance Branch Standard Operating Procedures and Quality Assurance Manual.* U.S. EPA Region IV Environmental Services Division. February, 1991.

2. *US EPA Contract Laboratory Program Statement of Work for Inorganic Analysis,* EPA SOW ILM03.0, 1993.

3. *US EPA Contract Laboratory Program Statement of Work for Organic Analysis,* EPA SOW OLMO3.1, 1994.

4. *USEPA Contract Laboratory Program National Functional Guidelines for Organic Data Review,* Office of Solid Waste and Emergency Response, EPA-540/R-94/012, February, 1993.

5. *USEPA Contract Laboratory Program National Functional Guidelines for Inorganic Data Review,* Office of Solid Waste and Emergency Response, EPA-540/R-94/013, February, 1993.

6. *Region III Modifications to National Functional Guidelines for Organic Data Review,* September 1994.

7. *Superfund Analytical Methods for Low Concentration Water for Organics Analysis,* Office of Solid Waste and Emergency Response, EPA/540/R/94/075, December 1994.

8. *Superfund Analytical Methods for Low Concentration Water for Inorganics Analysis,* Office of Solid Waste and Emergency Response EPA/540/R/94/092, December, 1994.

CHAPTER 8

Department of Defense Program Overview

The Air Force, Army, and Navy have laboratory analytical programs that strive to provide accurate analytical data for site assessment and clean-up. To ensure laboratories produce good data, each agency has implemented a lab review process and has written program documents that describe how labs should perform analyses. None of the programs has remained static over the past decade, and as regulators and laboratories have become more educated and experienced, requirements have become more refined and explicit. With improved methods, instruments, education, and enforcement, analytical data has gotten better over the years. This is seen from the historical U.S. EPA WS/WP performance evaluation studies' precision and accuracy results over the last ten years. The Air Force, Army, and Navy, along with the U.S. EPA and EPA regions, state agencies, universities, and thousands of lab employees have been successful in their goal of improving lab data.

Good, successful, and improved are relative terms and depend on a standard. The Air Force, Navy, and Army have defined these standards differently, and these standards are described in the following Chapters. The goal is to give readers an understanding of the current Air Force, Army, and Navy programs, not merely a recitation of QC acceptance criteria. To develop an understanding some background and explanation is necessary.

A. Compliance

Compliance is a contractual issue -- did the lab follow the method or program guidance that was referenced in the contract? Should they be paid? It is therefore a key business issue and is separate from getting the right answer. However, the issue of compliance is more complex.

Compliance connotes a well-defined standard. The Air Force, Army, and Navy each described their standards in program documents, and data compliant with the standards of one program are not necessarily compliant with those in another program, even when the same source method (such as SW-846 Method 8270) is referenced in both program documents. The reasons for the differences in the programs are plentiful but seem to reduce to slightly different missions and program emphases, different interpretations of reference literature, and the large number of variables in analytical methods. The three programs have far more criteria that are the same than are different, and the differences are mostly small in the greater scheme of environmental clean-up activities. However, the differences are significant enough to cause laboratory chemists to execute different steps at the bench level, use different acceptance criteria for quality control measures, and have different compliance assessment criteria.

Compliance requires a well-written standard, and providing a well-written and communicated standard for environmental analytical chemistry is difficult. As with any subject matter, without regard to which party is more correct, authors assume certain definitions for the words they use, but these sometimes are not the same definitions a reader uses. To complicate matters, terms have rapidly proliferated, evolved, and also become extinct, as the industry has grown. A good example of the evolution of terms is found in the use of method detection limit (MDL). In the mid-1980s, MDL could have meant the 40 CFR Part 136, Appendix B definition, a practical quantitation limit (PQL) concept, or the reporting limit that appeared on a lab report. Today, MDL is used almost exclusively in the 40 CFR Part 136, Appendix B sense, or is explicitly defined. A precise description of requirements is imperative, and the only consistent source of program requirements is in the written agency documents. Compliance is first judged against the written requirements. The following Chapters have a bias toward the written requirements, although they do so in light of past requirements.

It is not uncommon to come across a clearly stated requirement that in some applications seems unreasonable or unrealistic. Sometimes even program documents contain errors. Agency program employees have been conscientious and helpful in clarifying requirements; however, agencies do not speak with one voice in such situations, and written confirmation of program level clarifications is difficult. Laboratory compliance additionally involves a third party, the prime contractor, usually an engineering firm. The prime contractor may choose to have an interpretation different from the agency employee. The following sections attempt to address questionable requirements and state common implementation strategies.

B. Determining Program Requirements

To determine program requirements, one must follow conventions for precedence. Precedence applies to a single document and between documents. Sometimes the precedence of documents and requirements is explicitly stated, but often it is omitted. When omitted, the rule of precedence is that the more subject-specific section of document takes precedence over a more general section. For example, in SW-846 the calibration requirements stated in the Method 8270 take precedence over the general calibration requirements found in section Method 8000. Further, the omission of a requirement in the more specific section is not necessarily proof that it is not required. For example, even though bracketing continuing calibration standards are not required in the Method 8270 text, some interpretations of the method contend that since the requirement is in Method 8000, it also applies to Method 8270.

Precedence is applied in the same way between documents: an Air Force, U.S. Army Corps of Engineers, or Navy program document supersedes the requirements of the referenced method. A project specific Quality Assurance Project Plan (QAPP) supersedes the requirements of the program document since it is the specific application of program requirements. Unfortunately, some program documents state that a lab must meet all referenced method requirements and then go on to specify program specific versions of the method that are different from the referenced method requirements. Some programs try the easy fix of stating that the lab must use the most strict approach, but often the requirements are just different, neither one being more strict. Usually, the general scheme of precedence can be, and must be, applied to determine a single way of performing the analysis. An often overlooked area of precedence is in the contract a lab has with a prime DOD contractor. These contracts often state that lab analyses are to be performed in compliance with a certain DOD program document, when they should refer to the project specific implementation of those requirements, usually found in the project-specific QAPP, and sometimes in the Sampling and Analysis plans.

To discriminate between what is mandatory and what is guidance, most documents now are fairly careful in their use of must, shall, may, and should. Must and shall are reserved for mandatory requirements. Unfortunately, there are some problems even with this tool of communication since some documents are guidance in their entirety, and some do not always phrase requirements in a declarative sentence. A well-known example of the former is SW-846, a guidance document, which frequently uses must and shall. A remedy commonly used by program documents referencing SW-846 is to state that the document is mandatory for their program, and since their program document is enforceable through contracts, it does become mandatory.

C. Program Implementation

Even a careful reading of program requirements will not tell a laboratory how a program is actually and currently implemented. Compliance with written program documents has markedly increased in recent years, but few labs can truthfully state that they are compliant with all the requirements of a program (although complete compliance with project-specific QAPPs should be the norm). The lack of complete compliance is in part the result of the forces discussed earlier, such as clarity of requirements, but also because written requirements are often negotiated for application at a specific site. To state that a laboratory has done AFCEE 9/93 *Handbook* work means only that the project required the 9/93 *Handbook* and not that it was followed. Other programs, though fairly rigorously defined, are simply not implemented entirely. Certainly it is the responsibility of the laboratory to understand and implement all requirements, but in competitive bid situations, there often is no market for a fully compliant version. A fully compliant version of a particular program is usually more expensive than the lab's routine approach to analyzing and reporting sample results. Sometimes it is simply because the specified procedure is different from the mainstream product of that lab, and sometimes it is because the program requirements do require more than is typically performed. The additional costs are reflected in the bid prices, and lab selection is often made primarily on price. Although it is the primes (engineering firms that directly contract with the DOD agency) that usually select a lab, the respective DOD contracts office reviews bid selection and may require additional justification for a higher price subcontractor. DOD programs are particularly sensitive to this negative selection process during the times their programs are changing. Although new program documents are released in their entirety, they are usually implemented over time and projects by the analytical community as it digests and understands the full implication of the requirements. The lab that fully implements and prices the program ahead of the curve is at a bidding disadvantage. Education of primes, labs, and, in particular, the contracts' personnel of the agency requiring the new standards would lessen this negative selection process and hasten the implementation of new requirements. Unfortunately funds and time are rarely available for a proactive approach, even when swift implementation would provide program level cost savings.

References

1. *Sampling and Chemical Analysis Quality Assurance Requirements for the Navy Installation Restoration Program.* Naval Energy and Environmental Support Activity (NEESA), Port Hueneme, CA, NEESA 20.2-047B, June, 1988.

2. *Validation of Analytical Chemistry Laboratories.* U.S. Army Corps of Engineers, HTRW MCX, CEMRD-ET-HC, Omaha, NE, EM 200-1-1, 1 July, 1994.

3. *Chemical Data Quality Management for Hazardous Waste Remediation Activities.* U.S. Army Corps of Engineers, HTRW MCX, Omaha, NE, USACE ER 1110-1-263, October, 1990.

CHAPTER 9

Air Force Center for Environmental Excellence (AFCEE)

A. Description of the AFCEE Organization

The Air Force Center for Environmental Excellence (AFCEE) was created in 1991 to provide the Air Force with environmental design, construction, evaluation and remediation management services. It reports to the Air Force Civil Engineer and its field operating agency located at Brooks Air Force Base in San Antonio, TX. AFCEE has a commissioned Air Force Officer as the Commander and a civilian Executive Director. It has six operational directorates:

1) Environmental Restoration
2) Pollution Prevention
3) Environmental Conservation and Planning
4) Construction Management
5) Design
6) Regional Compliance.

and four support directorates:

1) Environmental Contracting
2) Mission Support
3) Public Affairs
4) Judge Advocate.

The laboratory program comes from the Chemistry group of the Consultant Operations group of the Environmental Restoration (ER) directorate. ER has about 130 people and contains the following groups:

- Base Closure Restoration
- DERA Restoration
- Technology Transfer
- Consultant Operations
- Program Support.

The Consultant Operations group has about 25 people and contains:

- Chemistry
- Hydrology
- Engineering
- Toxicology.

The Chemistry group has about eight government employees and gets support from various AFCEE contractors. The Chemistry group performs stationary and mobile lab audits, reviews QAPjPs and ITIRS, provides field technical support, and determines and coordinates new program guidance. Since guidance, project-specific QAPP review, and lab audits come from the same group of persons, the AFCEE program is substantially centralized and more consistent across the nation than the Corps of Engineers and Navy programs. Information about the entire AFCEE organization can be obtained from their WWW page http://www.afcee.brooks.af.mil.

B. AFCEE Program Overview

1. Technical Requirements Documents

There have been several requirements documents from AFCEE and its predecessor organizations. The Technical Services Division of an AFCEE predecessor organization, the U.S. Air Force Occupational and Environmental Health Laboratory (USAFOEHL), published *Handbook to Support the Installation Restoration Program (IRP) Statement of Work for Remedial Investigation/Feasibility Studies (RI/FS)* in May, 1987, (Version 1.2), April, 1988, (version 2.0), and May, 1989, (version 3.0). In about eight pages, version 2.0 contains the basic laboratory requirements that have remained relatively unchanged until the most recent AFCEE lab document published in February, 1996. In May, 1991, the Human Systems Division, a successor to USAFOEHL, published *Handbook to Support the Installation Restoration Program (IRP) Statement of Work, Volume 1, Remedial Investigation/Feasibility Studies.* The May, 1991 *IRP Handbook* contains about 12 pages of laboratory guidance, and this document is still active today in some of the older Air Force contracts, although AFCEE tries to update laboratory specifications to the newest requirements during the QAPjP review process.

The document that is most frequently referenced in active AFCEE contracts is *Handbook for the Installation Restoration Program (IRP) Remedial Investigations and Feasibility Studies (RI/FS)*, published by AFCEE September, 1993. This document has about 20 pages of lab requirements with the remaining 170 pages discussing hydrology, site models, risk assessment, and project deliverables requirements. This document clarified many issues in the May, 1991, *IRP Handbook.* Although most prime contracts reference the September, 1993, *Handbook*, AFCEE tries to update the laboratory specifications to the newest requirements during the QAPjP review process.

The most recent AFCEE lab requirements document is *Quality Assurance Project Plan* (QAPP), version 1.1, February, 1996. This document has about 300 pages of laboratory requirements. AFCEE released a minor update to the document February 29, 1996. Version 1.1 and the two-page update can be picked up at the AFCEE WWW documents site (http://www.afcee.brooks.af.mil/irp_docs.htm). The version 1.1 QAPP is a highly detailed and prescriptive document that states method reporting limits, target analytes, and acceptance criteria for each method. Version 1.1 corrected many of the errors in the version 1.0 QAPP (published in January, 1996), and the draft QAPP released in the Spring, 1995: unfortunately both of these earlier versions were used for some sites.

The version 1.1 QAPP has not had an official release, but AFCEE has been trying to update lab requirements to version 1.1 during the QAPjP review process. Updating from a handbook version to a QAPP version is quite complex since the QAPP requires special reporting forms, unique footnoting, and has some method criteria that are different from previous versions.

AFCEE is currently working on a version 2 QAPP. A major change will be addition of historically-based QC acceptance limits. More methods, such as immunoassay procedures, are being added to the QAPP.

2. Program Organization

AFCEE contracts with prime engineering firms through a competitive bid process. The contracts are usually multiyear and site contracts. The prime contractors forward their choice of laboratory to AFCEE, and AFCEE then audits the lab. The primes are responsible for laboratory data, and an AFCEE audit is not necessarily mandatory for a laboratory to perform work under an AFCEE contract. However, most primes consider the AFCEE audit an additional level of assurance that the lab will produce data acceptable to AFCEE.

QAPjPs are the responsibility of the prime contractor, and the experienced contractor will work closely with the lab to develop the analytical sections. The experienced laboratory will provide precise method QC descriptions that follow current guidance and clarify any ambiguous areas in the AFCEE guidance and published methods. Any deviations from requirements should be explicitly stated in the QAPjP. The completed QAPjP is forwarded to AFCEE for technical review. Review comments generated by AFCEE are sent to the prime for response. This process may be repeated until all issues are resolved. The lab portion of the final QAPjP often does not follow AFCEE guidance exactly. The deviations occur in—and because of—DQOs, method interpretations, level of review, ambiguities in the guidance documents, and costs. There has been great improvement in the timeliness of the publication and review of QAPjPs, but QAPjPs will often not go final for many years, and they are often in review stages while the work is in progress.

3. AFCEE Laboratory Audits

The Chemistry group of Consultant Operations and their contractors have the responsibility to audit laboratories generating data for AFCEE contracts. An audit is requested by an AFCEE prime contractor who either intends to use the lab, or who is using the lab. The ten-step audit sequence is stated in *Guidance for AFCEE Quality Assurance/Quality Control (QA/QC) Audits of Installation Restoration Program Contact Laboratories*, October, 1991, and is as follows:

1) AFCEE distributes the audit guidance document to prime contractors who are then responsible for distributing the document to subcontractor labs.

2) AFCEE sends a letter to prime contractors requesting submission of QA/QC plans.

3) AFCEE reviews the QA/QC plan before, or during, the on-site lab evaluation.

4) AFCEE sends review comments on the QA/QC plan to the prime and requests a response if the review was completed before the audit.

5) AFCEE arranges an on-site evaluation of the lab through the prime contractor.

6) AFCEE audits the laboratory.

7) AFCEE sends to the prime contractor the on-site evaluation report, the QA/QC plan review, and corrective action requirements.

8) The prime contractor responds to the corrective actions.

9) AFCEE reviews the corrective actions response for adequacy.

10) AFCEE notifies the prime of acceptance or rejection of the lab.

In response to the rapid growth in lab audit requests and lean staffing at AFCEE, the audit process was changed in 1993. The information requested before an on-site audit became:

- Method detection limit studies for all analyses performed
- Performance evaluation studies for the past two years
- A copy of the laboratory Quality Assurance Manual
- Acceptance criteria for recovery of controls and standards.

Upon review of this information, and a request from a prime contractor, the laboratory could receive interim qualification. Interim qualification allows the lab to perform analysis of AFCEE samples before the audit process is completed. The rest of the audit process continues in the manner outlined above.

As can be seen, the lab audit is requested and coordinated primarily through the prime contractors and not through the labs. There are programmatic advantages to this approach. The prime contractor is forced into understanding more of the lab data details, and audits are limited to labs that will participate in the program. In the past there have also been some disadvantages. Since all documentation was sent to the prime contractors, and it was their responsibility to distribute it to the labs, laboratories found it difficult or impossible to educate themselves before being chosen as a laboratory by an AFCEE prime contractor. Furthermore, laboratories found it difficult to participate in prime contractors' AFCEE Request for Proposal (RFP) since being an AFCEE-approved lab was frequently a prerequisite. In conjunction with the time delay caused by the backlog in lab audits, these conditions presented a significant barrier to entry for laboratories. The 1993 allowance for interim qualification reduced the barrier to entry, and it has been further reduced today since the AFCEE lab audit backlog has been reduced, and program documents are now readily available from the AFCEE WWW home page.

The initial on-site audit usually consists of two auditors for three days. The AFCEE team performs a detailed audit of lab systems, methods, and QC acceptance criteria. At the end of the audit, the team debriefs the lab. A formal audit report is mailed to the prime contractor. With the lab's help, the prime contractor responds to the audit findings. It has been the AFCEE goal to perform follow-up audits every 18 months, but follow-up audits are probably performed less frequently, unless there are special circumstances. Prime contractors usually perform their own audits of the lab, or participate in the AFCEE audit. An AFCEE document is currently in preparation that describes the responsibility of the prime contractor for the contract laboratory, field audits and corrective action.

C. Technical Requirements

Two requirements documents are in common use for AFCEE work: the September, 1993, *Handbook* and the February, 1996, version 1.1 QAPP. As stated previously, AFCEE tries to apply the QAPP requirements to even those contracts that reference the September, 1993, *Handbook*. There are significant differences between the programs, and the prime contractor and laboratory should carefully consider moving from the September, 1993, *Handbook* to the version 1.1 QAPP, especially when analytical prices are fixed.

In general, the September, 1993, *Handbook* discusses the laboratory requirements in broader terms and summaries, whereas the version 1.1 QAPP is very detailed and attempts to define all method performance variables. The version 1.1 QAPP is similar to a CLP SOW but does not give the level of detail for lab techniques that the CLP SOW gives.

A key difference between the September, 1993, *Handbook* and the version 1.1 QAPP is the concept of "analytes of interest." The September, 1993, *Handbook* introduced and defined the concept of analytes of interest and it became a central theme of September, 1993, *Handbook* work. In the *Handbook* analytes of interest are defined as those analytes that are potentially present at the site under investigation or are of concern to regulators. The prime contractor must identify all site-specific analytes of interest for each project based on site history and the data quality objectives. AFCEE further clarified the concept by stating that the analytes of interest are the only analytes needed in calibration criteria, LCS and MS spike lists, and target analyte lists, and that allowances must be made for new analytes found at the site as the investigation proceeds. Analytes of interest is a powerful concept, cradled by the DQO approach, with a strong effect on method performance and cost. During initial site investigations, the analytes of interest may be all compounds that a method can readily detect and quantify (such as those analytes given in Tables 2-2 and 2-3 of the *Handbook*). Sites that have a history should have a much shorter list. The cost impact does not lie so much with the number of analytes reported, but more with passing batch LCS QC: if all analytes of a multi-analyte method such as Method 8260 or Method 8270 are required to pass in the LCS, the probability that a few will fail is relatively high, and therefore the requirement for re-analysis is high. This also affects project turn-around time (TAT), sample holding times, and raw data compilation. Some organizations have misunderstood these requirements by confusing analytes of interest with the list of analytes given in Tables 2-2 and 2-3 of the September, 1993, *Handbook*.

The version 1.1 QAPP no longer uses the concept of analytes of interest. It requires that all target analytes of a method (given in the method tables 7.2.x.1) be spiked into the LCS, and be used for batch control. Regarding the analytes of interest, the version 1.1 QAPP has moved away from DQO-based analyses to prescriptive analyses.

1. September, 1993, *Handbook* Technical Requirements

A summary of the lab requirements in this document is given in Table 9-1 and is discussed below.

Table 9-1.   AFCEE September, 1993, Handbook Requirements

Category	Elements	Requirement
Definitions	Preparation batch	Processed at the same time; no open batches
	QC limits	Must use lab historical; if lab less precise than method, use method precision and lab mean; lab may submit alternate limits with justification in QAPjP through prime contractor.
	Analytes of interest	Those analytes potentially present or of concern to regulators must be stated in SAP; only analytes of interest are of concern in calibration, LCS and MS lists.
	Method references	SW-846 is preferred where available; if modified or non-SW-846 method is used, justification must be given.
	Precedence	The project QAPjP takes precedence over SW-846, the AFCEE *Handbook*, and the project-specific SOW.
	Handbook applies to	Fixed, mobile, and field labs
Method blank	Frequency	1/preparation batch
	Surrogate control	Yes, per SW-846
	Acceptance	<QAPjP PQL; one time basis exception: if analyte detected in blank but not in associated samples, no corrective action required
LCS	definition	A blank spike; controls preparation batch; water LCS may be used for soil analyses
	Frequency	1/preparation batch
	Surrogate control	Yes, per SW-846
	Spike list	All analytes of interest
	%R control	Yes; all spiked analytes must be within the limits, or all preparation batch samples must be re-analyzed for that analyte. One-time basis exception: if an LCS analyte is above upper limit and that analyte is not detected in the sample, no corrective action is required, and no data qualifiers are necessary.
	Limits	Mean +/- 3SD; may use SW-846 limits until about 20 or 30 points are acquired.
MS	Frequency	One MS/20 samples; a MSD required when regulatory agency requires it; PCB MS must be run with Method 8080 (no explicit mention of toxaphene); no MS required for air or radiochemical analyses.
	Spike list	All analytes of interest
	Surrogate control	Yes, per SW-846
	%R control	No batch control; use LCS windows, if outside, then re-analyze MS for those analytes. If same are still out, qualify related sample results; qualify all 20 samples associated with the MS even if not prepared in the same preparation batch.
	RPD control	No; *Handbook* states that accuracy measures precision.
	Limits	For %R: mean +/- 3SD for LCS
Samples	Surrogate Control	Meet SW-846 corrective action; re-extract within HT.

Table 9-1. **AFCEE September, 1993, Handbook Requirements,** *continued*

Category	Elements	Requirement
Quantification	ICAL	One standard below PQL; all analytes reported (implies multiresponse); state any variances in QAPjP.
	CSTD	All target analytes including multiresponse; state any variances in QAPjP, use materials "prepared independently" of ICAL (second source required if ICAL not traceable).
	Standard source	Inorganics: NIST Organics: CRADA, NIST, CLP-SRM, A2LA "where available" Document in QAPjP other standard sources.
	Calibration criteria	Meet method specified.
	RT windows	Must be established per Method 8000 7.5.
	Confirmation column	Required when PQL; not for multiresponse; lab identifies "most reliable result;" "should be" done within HT (if not, AFCEE reviews, etc; resample if necessary); must be quantitative.
	ICP	ICS must be analyzed at beginning and end of sequence.
	Quantification	Can use RF or curve; use ICAL except for MS; MS uses daily except when samples are in same sequence as ICAL.
Reporting and detection limits	MDL	Must be done for each analyte but does not seem to be matrix or procedure specific.
	PQL	In *Handbook* Tables; must be used. If different, state in SAP and get AFCEE approval; variances submitted by prime. If regulators require lower PQL, lab must establish PQL and state in SAP and get AFCEE approval.
Sample preservation and	Cooler temperature	Record on chain of custody; no acceptance criteria ("issue too complex"): lab to use judgment - prime to discuss with AFCEE
HTs	Sample storage	2-8 deg C
	Preservation	Normally checked in field, if not, lab to check all upon receipt (except VOA).
	Extraction HT	Extraction definition: completion of sample preparation prior to extract cleanup or volume reduction
	Analysis HT	Includes all dilutions, confirmations, and re-analysis
Lab records	Chain of custody	No mention of internal chain of custody forms for samples or extracts
Reporting units	Water	Inorganics: mg/L Organic: µg/L
	Soil	mg/kg for all, dry basis (dioxin may be wet or dry)
	Soil gas	ppb by volume
	Moisture calculation	Unless SW-846 method specifies, use modified ASTM D2216

1.1 Batch

In the September, 1993, *Handbook*, AFCEE defines the term preparation batch as 20 or fewer samples that are similar in matrix and are prepared at the same time with the same lots of reagents. It further stipulates that open batches are not permitted. The reference to open batches is meant to disallow analyzing an LCS every 20 samples instead of every preparation batch. Some have argued that for organic analyses using surrogates, controlling off the LCS in the first group (of less than 20) samples and off the method blank surrogates in subsequent groups is appropriate and adequate batch quality control. The September, 1993, *Handbook* explicitly disallows this practice, and requires an LCS with each preparation batch.

The September, 1993, *Handbook* states that the batches must contain samples of similar matrix, but the definition is very broad. In general, only soil, water, and air matrices are recognized, unless there is a compelling reason for a finer distinction.

The September, 1993, *Handbook* batch definition is a common, albeit somewhat liberal one. It does not put restrictions on personnel or time, since "at the same time" is open to interpretation.

1.2. Method Blank

The method blank consists of an analyte-free matrix into which all reagents used in sample processing are added in the same volumes or proportions. The method blank must be carried through the complete sample preparation and analytical procedure. One method blank is required for each analytical batch.

A common first question about method blanks is whether they must contain a surrogate matrix for soil analyses. The labs frequently argue that for metals, the most frequently requested soil surrogate, Ottawa sand, might add contamination, and, for organics, the Ottawa sand has no effect on results since it is inert. In either case, the labs argue there is no significant technical or QA advantage. Regulators often prefer a solid matrix in the blank because the blank will then also include the weighing process of sample preparation. The September, 1993, *Handbook* does not state that a solid surrogate matrix is necessary for solid matrices, and in an answer to the same question for LCS, stated that water LCS may be used for soil analyses.

Corrective action must be performed when a method blank contains any analyte greater than the project-approved PQL. Most programs require that corrective action be performed when a target analyte is found at or above the PQL, and the latter rule is commonly used by AFCEE during the QAPP review process. AFCEE made some allowances, on a one-time basis for failed LCS recoveries. Although the definition of a one-time basis is somewhat vague, the intent was to allow acceptance of usable data when the QC failure did not seem to be indicative of an on-going process problem and when the failure probably did not affect the usability of the data. On a one-time basis exception, if the method blank has a target analyte above the PQL, sample results still may be reported if the same analyte is not detected in the sample.

1.3. LCS

The LCS of the September, 1993, *Handbook* is more properly a blank spike since it does not require matrix matching. A water LCS may be used for soil analyses. The LCS must be spiked with the analytes of interest. The LCS controls the preparation batch, in that recoveries for all of the analytes of interest must be within the DQO ranges.

The analytes-of-interest concept for LCS is a pivotal cost and productivity issue for the multianalyte organics methods such as Methods 8260 and 8270. If the analytes of interest are a properly identified subset of the method target analytes given in Tables 2-2 and 2-3 of the September, 1993, *Handbook*, obtaining acceptable recoveries in the LCS remains manageable. However, if the spike list is assumed to include all target analytes given in Tables 2-2 and 2-3, the probability for reruns, missed holding times, missed project turn-around times, and resampling increases dramatically.

In practice and over time, primes and laboratories have been able to implement a workable hybrid of the stated and clarified requirements. As much as is possible, the analytes of interest are identified from historical analytical data and site usage, and these are then used to spike the LCS. The method target analyte and calibration list usually include all analytes given in Tables 2-2 and 2-3 (with any necessary add-ons), and samples are analyzed for the full set of method target analytes. If additional contaminants are found at the site during the site investigation, these are added to the spike list. Often the full list of target analytes is spiked into the LCS, and sometimes the recovery of all the analytes is reported, but control remains limited to the identified analytes of interest. Implementing this solution requires a good amount of work from the prime and the laboratory. Since AFCEE and other regulators have the task of with protecting our environment, they too must be convinced that this approach will not decrease the efficacy of an assessment or clean-up or be cost-inefficient in the long run.

The LCS, along with the method blank, controls preparation batch acceptance. If the recovery of an analyte in the LCS is outside the LCS recovery windows, the LCS and all associated samples, must be re-analyzed for that compound. If instrument re-analysis fails, then the samples must be reprepared with a new LCS and must pass the previously failed spiked analytes. A one-time basis exception may be used to report target analytes not detected in the sample if the batch LCS had a recovery above the upper acceptance limit for that analyte.

1.4 Matrix Spike/Matrix Spike Duplicate

The September, 1993, *Handbook* requires, but downplays, the importance of matrix spikes. One matrix spike is required for every 20 samples, unless another regulatory agency requires an additional matrix spike. The matrix spike consists of the analytes of interest.

Matrix spikes do not control the analytical process but can result in sample result qualification. If the matrix spike recovery is outside the LCS windows, then it must be re-analyzed for the failed analytes. If the re-analysis fails again, the sample results for all 20 samples linked to that matrix spike (whether in the same preparation batch or not) must be qualified for that analyte. If it passes, no qualification is made. There is no requirement to calculate the relative percent difference or qualify sample result data based on the results obtained from the matrix spike pair. It is unclear whether re-analysis to confirm failure to obtain acceptable recovery means instrument re-analysis, or re-preparation and instrument re-analysis.It is important to clarify this point in the QAPjP.

1.5 Method Target Analyte Lists

The default target analyte lists for 33 different analytical procedures are given in the September, 1993, *Handbook*. However, the analytes of interest (those potentially present at the site or of concern to regulators) should be the method target. This opens the door to short lists and to cost savings. In practice though, it is more common to have the method target analyte list be the list given in Tables 2-2 and 2-3 of the *Handbook* with additional analytes of concern added.

1.6 QC Limits

The full spike list usually gets the headlines, but it is the recovery limits that determine whether a full spike list is an issue in the acceptance of data. Clearly, wide recovery limits will make a full spike list easy to pass, while tight limits may make it impossible.

The September, 1993, *Handbook* requires that labs use lab limits generated from their historical data. If the lab historical limits are less precise than the published method limits, then the lab mean and the published method precision should be used. Using the lab mean and the published precision leaves the value of the mean open, probably an oversight by AFCEE.

Apart from the problems associated with calculating accurate historical limits, a programmatic level decision is made when lab historical limits, rather than standardized limits, are chosen. If a program defines standard limits, comparability of data across laboratories is emphasized. In contracts, using lab historical limits allows the program to benefit from on-going improvement as technology and practice narrow QC acceptance windows. In the September, 1993, *Handbook*, AFCEE opted for historical limits, but during the project QAPP review, AFCEE uses the available SW-846 method limits as a de facto outer limit.

1.7 Quantitation

The September, 1993, *Handbook* requires that the multipoint calibration contain a standard below the PQL listed in Table 2-2 and 2-3. From a standardization point of view, this requirement is somewhat problematic for laboratories since SW-846 methods require that the standard be at or below the PQL. From a quality point of view, it would probably have been more correct to require that the low standard be below the QAPP specific PQL, which might be below the *Handbook* PQLs. In practice, AFCEE has requested that lower PQLs be proven in some way (e.g., by demonstrating acceptable recovery of a sample spiked at the lower PQL). Although AFCEE confirmed it meant to say "below" and not "at or below," perhaps the issue is just one of decimal places, and therefore moot.

Quantitation is performed off the initial calibration data with either calibration curves or response factors. If using response factors, the average response factor from the initial calibration must be used. No guidance is given for the acceptance of calibration curves. An exception is made for mass spectroscopy quantitation, which must use the response factor from the daily continuing calibration. Therefore for all analyses except mass spectroscopy, the continuing calibration standards (CCS) are more properly continuing calibration verifications (CCV).

CCVs and CCSs must use materials prepared independently of the initial calibration, and must contain all analytes of interest. The *Handbook* explicitly states that this also applies to multiresponse analytes. Of course this leads to some problems with Method 8080.

AFCEE requires that a quantitative second column confirmation be performed for GC analyses using 2-D detectors when the analyte concentration is greater than the PQL. It is not required for multiresponse analytes, presumably since the pattern of the analyte serves as the second level of confirmation. The confirmation must be performed within holding times. The lab is to report both analyses, and identify the best result.

The September, 1993, *Handbook* requires calibrations be performed according to the published method specifications, but it is important to acknowledge that the published methods contain ambiguities, errors, and choices. It would therefore be prudent to specify the implementation of the calibration requirements in the project-specific QAPP that is reviewed by AFCEE.

1.8 MDL/PQL Requirements

The laboratory is required to establish method detection limits by the SW-846 or the 40 CFR Part 136, Appendix B procedure. There is no requirement for instrument-specific MDL studies, or, as AFCEE later clarified, matrix specific MDL studies. Water MDLs, with a conversion factor, may be used for soil methods.

PQLs are listed in Tables 2-2 and 2-3 of the September, 1993, *Handbook*. If a project requires different PQLs, these must be specified in the SAP, and approved before the start of the project.

1.9 September, 1993, *Handbook* Method and Class-Specific Requirements

The September, 1993, *Handbook* primarily addresses programmatic level quality assurance and therefore does not specify many method- or class-specific requirements. Still, there are some that are worth discussing.

As with many programs, Method 8080 presents a challenge since it contains multipeak and single-peak target analytes. The nine multipeak analytes of Method 8080 are toxaphene, technical chlordane, and the seven PCB mixes. The September, 1993, *Handbook* includes either eight or nine of the multipeak analytes: it is unclear whether the reference to chlordane is meant to mean technical, or alpha and gamma chlordane, or all three. Regardless of whether it is eight or nine, the September, 1993, *Handbook* requires that instrument calibrations be checked using all target analytes, including the multipeak analytes. Since target analyte lists usually include all the Table 2-3 analytes, and most multipeak analytes require separate standards, continuing calibrations would be prohibitively long. Often a project can accept more efficient calibration sequences. An example is to calibrate and confirm calibrations with representative multipeak analytes, but report all multipeak analytes if they are not detected in the samples. If, after the first analysis, any multipeak analytes other than the representative analytes used for the standards during the first analysis are suspected, the extracts are rerun under an acceptable initial and continuing calibration standards.

1.10 Clarifications for the September, 1993, *Handbook*

Below is a list of some clarifications for the September, 1993, *Handbook* that have not been published by AFCEE.

Method	Clarification
8010	Remove 2-chloroethyl vinyl ether as a target analyte; the method recommends three surrogates: less, but at least one, may be used.
8260	The PQLs given are actually the SW-846 MDLs; the 8260 PQLs should be 1 ppb for water and 5 ppb for soil.
8140	Stirophos PQL should be 3.4 ppb not 2.4 ppb.
8270	Benzo(k)fluoranthene should be on the target analyte list.

2. Version 1.1 QAPP Technical Requirements

The version 1.1 QAPP contains more details than past program documents. Section 7 uses about 200 pages to describe the QC requirements for 34 methods. The requirements are organized by method, and each method has three tables: the first table states the method target analyte list and PQLs; the second table states the LCS and MS spike list and QC acceptance criteria; the third table states the calibration, QC acceptance corrective action, and flagging criteria.

The version 1.1 QAPP initiated an AFCEE-specific forms and footnoting. These requirements are described in Section 8 of the QAPP. Table 9-2 summarizes the version 1.1 QAPP requirements.

Table 9-2.   AFCEE QAPP Version 1.1, February, 1996, Requirements

Category	Element	Requirement
Definitions	AFCEE analytical batch	Up to 20 environmental samples that are similar in matrix and that are extracted at the same time with the same lot of reagents. MS and MSDs count in the batch count, but LCS and blanks do not. For analyses that do not have a separate extraction or digestion step, an analytical batch refers to samples analyzed sequentially within a calibration period.
	QC limits	Provided in the methods
	Method references	Provides detailed requirements for the 34 definitive methods and more brief requirements for the 17 screening methods.
	Precedence	It is intended that the version 1.1 QAPP be applied uniformly across all projects, but project QAPPs take precedence over the version 1.1 QAPP
	QAPP	Applies to fixed, mobile, and field labs
LCS	Definition	Analyte-free water for aqueous analyses and Ottawa sand for soil analyses
	Frequency	One per analytical batch
	Spike list	All target analytes
	Surrogate control	Yes
	%R control	Yes; re-analyze all samples and LCS for outliers, otherwise flag data.
	Limits	Limits specified in tables in QAPP
MS	Definition	Use only AFCEE samples; used to evaluate method bias due to sample matrix; does not control batch acceptance
	Frequency	An MS/MSD pair per 20 field samples
	Spike list	All target analytes
	Surrogate control	Yes
	%R and RPD control	Calculate values %R and RPD and compare to limits in tables in QAPP. Outliers do not require re-analysis but do require the footnote M for all referenced samples.
	Limits	%R limits are the same as for the LCS; RPD values are given in tables in QAPP.
Blanks	Definition	An analyte-free matrix to which all reagents used in the sample preparation process are added in the same proportions
	Frequency	One per analytical batch
	Surrogate control	Yes
	Control	Perform corrective action if any analyte is > PQL; reprepare and re-analyze all batch samples, otherwise flag data.

Table 9-2.   AFCEE QAPP Version 1.1, February, 1996, Requirements, *continued*

Category	Element	Requirement
Samples	Surrogate control	Yes; after system control is reestablished, reprepare and re-analyze the sample.
Quantification	ICAL	The low standard must be at or below the PQL; use materials prepared independently of the calibration materials.
	CCV	Use all analytes listed in the QC acceptance criteria table; this applies equally to multiresponse analytes.
	Standards sources	Use NIST, EPA, A2LA, or equivalent AFCEE approved source; If an NIST, EPA or A2LA standard material is not available, the standard material proposed for use shall be included in an addendum to the SAP and approved before use.
	Calibration criteria	Use %RSD for ICALs; %D for CCVs; acceptance criteria applies to all target analytes and is stated in the method tables.
	RT windows	Establish per SW-846 Method 8000; use for GC and HPLC; upon RT check failure, re-analyze all samples back to the last good RT check, otherwise flag data.
	Confirmation	For GC and HPLC analyses, quantitation confirmation is required within the holding time; for GC, use second column; for HPLC, use second column or different detector; report results from the first analysis.
	ICP	ICS (interference check sample) is run at beginning and end of each run sequence; upon failure, re-analyze all samples, otherwise flag data.
	Quantification	May use calibration curves or Rfs; when using Rf, use average Rf from ICAL; do not quantitate from CCV Rf
Reporting and detection limits	MDL	Based on 40 CFR Part 136 Appendix B. Perform annually for each method, analyte, matrix, and instrument; use ASTM Type II water for aqueous matrix and Ottawa sand for soil matrix; submit to AFCEE before samples are analyzed; MDL < PQL.
	PQL	Given in tables in the QAPP
	Results reporting	Report results to the MDL; results less than MDL shall be reported as the MDL value and flagged with a U; for results between MDL and PQL, use F flag.
Non-lab QC	Ambient blank	Pour ASTM Type II water into a VOA vial in the sampling area; only needed when analyzing for VOA.
	Equipment blank	After cleaning sampling equipment, use ASTM Type II water to pour over or into, or pump through, sampling equipment; collect and analyze for all target analytes. If there are hits, flag all associated samples.
	Trip blank	Associate a VOA vial filled with ASTM Type II water with the sampling containers before they are sent to the field, during sampling, and when samples are sent back to the lab; use one per cooler. If hot in trip blank, flag sample results.
	Field duplicates	A second sample collected at same location as first; collected simultaneously or in succession; must be blind to lab personnel; measures sampling precision.
	Field replicates	A split; a single sample divided into two parts; must be blind to the lab; used to assess precision.

2.1 Batch

An AFCEE analytical batch is twenty or fewer samples that are similar in matrix, are from the same site, extracted or digested at the same time, and use the same lot of reagents. The batch count of twenty includes matrix spikes but excludes blanks and LCS. The AFCEE analytical batch also extends to methods that do not require separate preparation, such as volatile analyses by purge and trap, and is then defined as up to twenty samples analyzed sequentially within a calibration period. The definition of calibration period is unclear. If a calibration period extends from one CCV to the next, Methods such as 8010, 8020, 8021, and 8011 would have their method blank and LCS rate doubled from previous requirements.

2.2 Method Blank

The method blank consists of an analyte-free matrix into which all reagents used in sample processing are added in the same volumes or proportions. The method blank must be carried through the complete sample preparation and analytical procedure. One method blank is required for each AFCEE analytical batch.

If an analyte is found in the method blank at concentrations greater than the PQL, all samples must be reprepared and re-analyzed. If data are reported with a method blank that has analytes above the PQL, then a flag (B = analyte found in blank and sample) is applied to sample results of that analyte.

SW-846 allows data to be reported unqualified if the concentration found in the blank is less than 5% of the amount found in the sample, or if the blank concentration is less than 5% of the regulatory limit. The version 1.1 QAPP does not follow this SW-846 convention.

2.3 LCS

The LCS matrix is analyte-free water for aqueous analyses and Ottawa sand for soil analyses. The LCS is spiked with known concentrations of the compounds stated in the appropriate QAPP table of the method, which is commonly the full list of method target analytes. One LCS is required for each AFCEE analytical batch. The version 1.1 QAPP made two significant changes to the LCS: it is now matrix specific, and it is spiked with all method analytes, instead of the analytes of interest.

When an LCS analyte recovery is outside the recovery limits, the associated samples must be re-analyzed for the failed analyte. If sample results are reported with LCS data out of criteria, the lab must apply either a J (estimated) or R (rejected) flag to the failed LCS analyte in the sample. Although flagging requirements are stated in the individual method requirements, LCS flagging is consistent across methods. The decision table for J and R is presented in Table 9-3.

Table 9-3. **LCS Flag Decisions Based on Percent Recovery (%R) of Target Analytes.** Lower control limit = LCL; Upper control limit = UCL.

	LCS Result	
Sample Result	%R <LCL	%R >UCL
Analyte not-detected	R	no flag
Analyte detected	J	J

2.4 MS/MSD

A matrix spike and matrix spike duplicate are to be analyzed for every 20 AFCEE samples. The MS/MSD have the spike lists and recovery limits as the LCS. The RPD limits are given in the appropriate table for the method in the QAPP.

The version 1.1 QAPP increased the matrix spike requirements from the September, 1993, *Handbook*. The September, 1993, *Handbook* required only a single matrix spike (although in practice, a duplicate was usually also analyzed) and did not require the calculation of RPD. The version 1.1 QAPP states that the MS/MSD results are used to document the matrix bias of a method and are not used to control the analytical process. There is no corrective action required when matrix spikes do not fall within limits; however the footnote M (matrix effect) is required for the failed analyte for all samples of the same matrix from that site.

The use of matrix spikes to document method bias for a particular matrix seems reasonable and appropriate, but the footnoting requirements seem incomplete. Since MS/MSDs are required every twenty samples, both passing and failing pairs may be produced, often for such common-place reasons as background interference from occasional highly contaminated samples. However, the corrective action requires that all site samples of the same matrix be footnoted with an M. This seems to require that data already reported with passing matrix spikes be retroactively modified with the M flag. Finally, the M footnote gives no indication of whether the sample results are biased high or low, an important facet of assessing the effect of matrix interference.

2.5 Target Analyte List (TAL)

Each method has a defined target analyte list, and this list is given in the method table in the QAPP. The target analyte lists have remained essentially unchanged from the September, 1993, *Handbook*.

2.6 QC Limits

The LCS and surrogate recovery accuracy and the MS/MSD recovery accuracy and RPD precision acceptance windows are given in the appropriate table of each method. Separate windows are listed for soil and water. The LCS and MS/MSD share the same recovery windows for all methods.

For organics, some of the recovery windows are taken from SW846, some seem to be based on historical data, and others, where there apparently was no acceptable reference for a window available, are just default windows based on AFCEE's analytical judgment. The RPD windows are all default windows, usually 20% for waters and 30% for soils, although some methods, such as SW8310, have wider default RPD windows.

For SW6010A and SW6020, the recovery windows are all 80 - 120% for both soil and water. The RPD windows are 15% for water and 25% for soils. For other inorganic methods, the recovery windows seemed to be based on either referenced methods, historical data, or AFCEE analytical judgment. The precision windows are all based on AFCEE analytical judgment.

Most of the acceptance windows are attainable by a production laboratory. However, there are some exceptions, for example hexachlorocyclopentadiene in SW8270B. Other spike compound windows, such as those for the ketones in SW8240B (these compounds are not target analyte compounds in SW8260A) are relatively wide but will surely cause re-analysis due to the water solubility of these compounds, rather than analytical system control. When developing a project specific QAPjP, the prime contractor and laboratory should review the QC limits closely and propose justified alternative windows if the version 1.1 QAPP windows would lead to unacceptable project performance.

As stated earlier, AFCEE will change the QC acceptance windows to historically based windows in the version 2 QAPP.

2.7 Calibration and Quantitation

In general, for organic analyses, five-point initial calibrations are required and for inorganic analyses, three calibrations standards and a blank are required. The lowest standard of the initial calibration must be at or below the PQL (see discussion under MDL and PQL). Quantitation is performed off the initial calibration data, and there no longer is an exception for mass spectroscopy methods. Initial calibrations are evaluated using %RSD for response (or calibration) factors. All target analytes must meet the specified %RSD requirement. Table 9-4 summarizes the %RSD requirement for a few common methods.

Table 9-4. Initial Calibration Acceptance Criteria

Method	Acceptance criteria
SW8010B	%RSD < 20%
SW8021A	%RSD < 20%
SW8080	%RSD < 20%
SW8240B	%RSD ≤ 30%
SW8260A	%RSD ≤ 30%
SW8270B	%RSD ≤ 30%
SW6010A	correlation coefficient ≤ 0.995
SW7191	correlation coefficient ≤ 0.995

All initial calibrations are verified with continuing calibration verifications (CCVs) and all samples must be bracketed by acceptable CCVs. CCVs must use materials prepared independently of the initial calibration materials, and must contain all analytes of interest. The version 1.1 QAPP explicitly states that this also applies to multiresponse analytes which, again, leads to some problems with SW8080. The version 1.1 QAPP also requires that the volatile and semivolatile mass spectroscopy methods have bracketing CCVs. Although this concept has merit, and is consistent with other gas chromatography detector requirements, it is not fully developed in the version 1.1 QAPP. This GC/MS requirement does not discuss whether a bracketing tune is required, or whether an acceptable CCV obtained after a retune is compliant. The Lab's approach should be clarified in the project – specific QAPjP.

The version 1.1 QAPP requires that a quantitative confirmation be performed for non-mass spectroscopy GC and HPLC methods when the analyte concentration is equal to or greater than the PQL. For GC analyses, confirmation is done with a second column, and for HPLC analyses, confirmation may be done with a second column or dissimilar detector. It is now required that the first analysis be the reported result in the forms (although IRPIMS still requires reporting of both results). The confirmation must be performed within holding times. The version 1.1 QAPP does not explicitly discuss second column confirmation for multiresponse analytes but requires that all hits be confirmed in the method QC tables.

The version 1.1 QAPP removes much of the method interpretation required when using the September, 1993 *Handbook* and SW846. Each method has explicit requirements summarized in tables in the method.

2.8 MDL/PQL Requirements

The laboratory is required to establish method detection limits by a modified 40CFR136 Appendix B procedure. The MDLs must be method, instrument, and matrix specific. Matrix is defined as water or soil. The instrument-specific MDL requirement can be challenging for the multi-instrument lab since sample results must be reported to the MDL, and a not detected result is reported by using the MDL value with a U flag suffix. Although not discussed in the version 1.1 QAPP, approaches other than strict instrument specific MDLs may be acceptable: for example, a statistically pooled MDL (using the pooling equations of 40CFR136 Appendix B), or the highest instrument specific MDL may be appropriate. If it is believed that method detection limit studies by 40CFR136 Appendix B are sensitive and appropriate indicators of method performance, and that instrument performance significantly affects MDLs, then using the MDL of the instrument on which the sample was analyzed is probably the most accurate. If, however, it is believed that MDLs are only approximate indicators of method performance, or project DQOs allow for alternate approaches, then one of the alternate approaches should be considered. The site-specific QAPjP should clearly state which approach will be used, since reporting data with instrument-specific MDLs is often more costly for data reviewers, end-users, and laboratories. MDLs must be below the PQLs listed in the tables in the methods.

The method PQLs found in the tables of the method deserve close attention when preparing project-specific QAPjPs. The version 1.1 QAPP partially corrects the SW8260A PQLs in the 9/93 *Handbook*: the 9/93 *Handbook* SW8260 PQLs (which were the SW8260 MDLs) were multiplied by 10 for the version 1.1 QAPP PQLs. AFCEE used this common theoretical conversion from MDL to water PQL, but in doing so disregarded the SW846 method guidance that the PQLs for SW8260 should be 1 ppb for water samples with a 25 mL sample and 5 ppb for a 5 mL sample. However for SW8240B, AFCEE did follow the same SW846 guidance it disregarded for SW8260A. As a result, the PQLs for SW8240B are attainable, whereas the PQLs for SW8260A cause problems in several areas. For example, the PQL for methylene chloride is 0.3 ppb. Taken together the method blank criteria would require a production laboratory to re-analyze most batches or, depending on instrument run sequence, frequently re-analyze the blank. The standards costs for the low standard of the initial calibration curve would increase substantially given the requirement that this standard be at or below the PQL and the PQLs are not at a consistent level. Finally, although many of the SW8260A PQLs are attainable, some, mostly those below 0.5 ppb, would be difficult to attain while meeting all other method requirements. It seems that AFCEE is using SW8260 as a very sensitive organic volatiles method, and the prime contractor and laboratory should evaluate project DQOs before implementing the version 1.1 QAPP SW8260A instead of SW8240B with add-on compounds.

An anomaly also exists between the SW8080A and SW8081 PQLs. Some of the method SW8080A PQLs are substantially below those of SW8081, contradicting the relative sensitivities of the methods. Some examples for water PQLs are listed in Table 9-5.

Table 9-5.   Some PQL Anomalies in the QAPP

Compound	SW8080A	SW8081
aldrin	0.04 ppb	0.34 ppb
endrin	0.06 ppb	0.39 ppb
dieldrin	0.02 ppb	0.44 ppb

The SW8081 toxaphene water PQL of 0.5 ppb is probably in error since this PQL cannot be attained for this multipeak analyte. With the exception of toxaphene and the PCBs, the SW8081 PQLs would require laboratories to decrease instrument sensitivity since the PQLs are higher than those commonly attainable and requested.

The version 1.1 QAPP requires that results are reported to the MDL. The second column confirmation requirements (Confirmation is necessary only above the PQL.) effectively limits methods with second column confirmation to reporting to the PQL. If analytes are found in the sample below the PQL but above the MDL, the result is flagged with an F.

2.9 Version 1.1 QAPP Method and Class-specific Requirements

The version 1.1 QAPP states some requirements in the method Calibration and QC Acceptance Criteria and Corrective Action tables that are not normally emphasized or have been assumed not to apply to certain methods. For example, the version 1.1 QAPP requires the SW8000A 72-hour retention time studies for methods SW8270B and SW8260A, and requires that retention time windows be applied. If the mass spectro-scopy retention time windows are not met, the data are flagged. These criteria are deleted in version 2 QAPP.

Initial calibration standards verification with standards from a second source is required for organic methods. The acceptance criteria are the same as for the CCV, and although this can be met for many analytes, some will often fail. Some examples are given in Table 9-6.

Table 9-6. Initial Calibration Verification Acceptance Criteria

Method	Acceptance criteria
SW8081	±15% difference
SW8260A	±25% difference
SW8270B	±25% difference

The version 1.1 QAPP, just as the 9/93 *Handbook*, does not provide an efficient and effective analytical sequence for SW8081 when both pesticides and PCBs are required. The stated requirements lead to the same problems as discussed under the 9/93 *Handbook*.

D. Data Reporting

1. September, 1993, *Handbook* Data Levels and Deliverables

The 9/93 *Handbook* does not define any data levels or deliverables, however prime contractors often define a level 1 and level 2 data package. The level 1 data package is the standard laboratory report, which contains the results of all sample and QC analyses but not any raw data. The level 2 data package contains raw data to support the sample and

QC results. Prime contractors are obligated to review raw laboratory data such as initial and continuing calibrations, but the frequency of raw data review is contract specific.

The 9/93 *Handbook* states that third party data validation is not required by AFCEE, but that it may be required for some sites. In practice, third party data validation is contract specific, and if required by the contract, it is usually at a rate of about 10% of the samples reported.

2. Version 1.1 QAPP Data Levels and Deliverables

In the version 1.1 QAPP AFCEE defines two levels of data: screening and definitive. It also defines the deliverables forms (basically CLP-like), and a footnoting scheme. Finally, AFCEE requires delivery of data electronically for their IRPIMS database.

2.1 Screening data

Screening data are defined as data generated by rapid methods with less rigorous sample preparation, calibration, or QC requirements than definitive data. Physical test methods, such as dissolved oxygen, pH, and temperature are designated as screening methods. See Table 9-7 for a list of the designated screening methods found in Section 6 of the version 1.1 QAPP. The version 1.1 QAPP requires that screening methods be confirmed and that the rate of confirmation be defined in the FSP.

Table 9-7. AFCEE Version 1.1 QAPP Screening Methods

Method[1]	Parameter
3550	moisture section of the method
9040 & 9045	pH
9050	conductance
9060	total organic carbon
160.1	filterable residue
160.2	non-filterable residue
170.1	temperature
180.1	turbidity
310.1	alkalinity
360.1	dissolved oxygen
organic vapor (FID and PID)	soil gas screening for halogenated, aromatic, and petroleum hydrocarbons
ASTM D422	particle size
ASTM D1498	oxidation-reduction potential
ASTM D3416	methane
4020	PCBs by immunoassay
4030	TPH by immunoassay

---

[1] EPA methods unless otherwise indicated.

Calibration and QC requirements for screening data are defined in Table 6.1 of the version 1.1 QAPP. Data flagging criteria are also defined. All screening data are flagged with an S flag to denote a screening method. Screening data are further qualified with a J (estimated), R (rejected), or B (blank contamination) if the stated QC criteria are not met. A flag (U) is used when the analyte is not detected above the MDL. The required use of the U flag seems to imply that MDL studies are required for screening methods; however, some methods are not amenable to the MDL procedure defined in the version 1.1 QAPP. Also, although PQLs are given for some of the screening methods, the concomitant F flag (analyte detected between MDL and PQL) is not allowed. The final data qualifier for screening methods consists of an S joined by the most severe other data qualifier. From most to least severe, the allowable flags are: SR, SJ, SB, SU, and S.

Three generalized data forms are provided for reporting screening data and confirm that MDL and PQL values are required for screening analyses.

2.2 Definitive Data

Definitive data may be generated by mobile or fixed laboratories, and are defined as those generated by the methods and QC given in Section 7 of the version 1.1 QAPP. Section 7 contains three tables for each of the 34 methods described. The first table defines the TAL and PQLs, the second, the LCS and MS spike list and acceptance criteria, and the third, QC and calibration checks, acceptance criteria, corrective action, and flagging criteria.

Section 8 of version 1.1 QAPP defines the data review, flagging, and reporting requirements. The five-tier review requirements for the lab are something of a conundrum. It is required that the analyst and section supervisor (or senior analyst) review 100% of the data. After the first and second data review have been performed, the section supervisor applies the data qualifiers, and then the final qualifier. The QA section must also perform a 10% review of completed data packages, and the project manager performs a sanity review on completed packages. If the tenor of the version 1.1 QAPP were broader and instructive, the data review requirements would not be problematic since their intent is fairly clear. However, the version 1.1 QAPP is directive, using "shall" liberally in this section, and in this context, one needs to question whether a data review group may substitute for the supervisor or the QA group. One might also question what is meant by a 100% review (All data should be reviewed prior to issuance of a final report.) and how far assumptions about electronic data and its transfer may go. Finally, depending on how the lab is organized, the review might exclude the LIMS processes within the lab. If the data review requirements are taken literally and conservatively, which a lab interested in reducing compliance liability would do, the review would be above the industry average, add a measurable cost to analysis, and not necessarily improve data quality. Clearly, AFCEE would have been better served in this section by emphasizing the end goals rather than the steps along the way since data review processes vary significantly according to the LIMS used, lab size, and lab management inclination. Given the requirements and the tenor of the text, a lab might be best served by presenting their adaptation of the required data review scheme in the site-specific QAPP, and noting any exceptions in an addendum, as required by the version 1.1 QAPP.

An interesting and new addition to the AFCEE lab requirements is data qualifiers. The data qualifiers (or flags) are generally described in Section 8 and are linked to each method criterion given in the third table for each method in Section 7, and as discussed above, in Section 6 for screening methods. In general, if the failed criteria affects a single

entire sample is
gates, or SPCC criteria,

dation but it would be
e determination.
eview by an independent
to existing data to
e data. A good example
idelines, discussed in
rd usability, and has a
to deficiencies in the
le, if calibration
dard deviation retention
ed as R in the associated
, but usability is very likely
a by the completeness

definition given in Section 4. The _____ pliance) goal is 90% for soil
and 95% for water and presumably, since the version 1.1 QAPP would have been
referenced in the prime's contract with AFCEE, a failure to meet these goals may result
in a reduced payment to the prime and lab, resampling, and diminished ability to assess
the site. If implemented as stated for the completeness determination, the new flagging
requirements become a powerful economic stick.

2.3 Hardcopy Reports

AFCEE now requires CLP-like forms for hardcopy data reports. The version 1.1 QAPP
gives examples of the 27 required forms in Section 8.

3. IRPIMS

IRPIMS is a large database of site assessment data that include many years of field and
lab results data for most AFCEE projects. The lab results comprise about two thirds of
the entire database. It is the responsibility of the AFCEE prime contractor to submit data
electronically to AFCEE, and the prime invariably delegates the responsibility for lab
data to the laboratory. In early 1996, AFCEE released software written in ACCESS
called IRPTOOLS. IRPTOOLS allows hand entry of data and can accept lab-generated
files; it also performs most of the QC checks that were previously performed by Metrica
(the AFCEE contractor responsible for the IRPIMS database) after the IRPIMS files
were sent to AFCEE by the contractor. Although IRPTOOLS allows hand entry of all
data, including lab data, hand entry of lab data, because of its volume, is not a viable cost
or quality option in the long run. However, IRPTOOLS can be useful for editing
(although this opposes QA tenets) and executing the impeded QC checks. Unfortunately,
IRPTOOLS does not yet (by mid-1996) have a stand-alone lab version: the software
requires field data files, rarely available to the lab, for it to perform the lab QC checks.
However, the proficient hacker can set up dummy field files, and then make use of the
lab QC checks IRPTOOLS provides.

References

1. *Handbook to Support the Installation Restoration Program (IRP) Statement of Work for Remedial Investigation/Feasibility Studies* (RI/FS) in May, 1987, (Version 1.2), April, 1988, (version 2.0), and May, 1989, (version 3.0)

2. *Handbook to Support the Installation Restoration Program (IRP) Statement of Work*, Volume 1 Remedial Investigation/Feasibility Studies. AFCEE, May, 1991

3. *Handbook for the Installation Restoration Program (IRP) Remedial Investigations and Feasibility Studies (RI/FS)*, published by AFCEE September, 1993

4. Quality Assurance Project Plan (QAPP), version 1.1, February 1996

5. *Guidance for AFCEE Quality Assurance/Quality Control (QA/QC) Audits of Installation Restoration Program Contact Laboratories*, October, 1991

analyte, just that analyte is qualified in associated samples. If the entire sample is affected, as with refrigerator temperatures, holding times, surrogates, or SPCC criteria, then all analytes are qualified.

The flagging scheme presented is considered to be data validation but it would be more correct if one were to call it version 1.1 QAPP compliance determination. Validation in the environmental industry currently connotes a review by an independent third party, not associated with the lab, which applies standards to existing data to determine usability and seeks a broader contextual review of the data. A good example of a validation protocol would be the EPA CLP Functional Guidelines, discussed in Chapter 7. The AFCEE compliance check is not oriented toward usability, and has a strong inclination towards the R flag, defined as unusable due to deficiencies in the ability to analyze the sample and meet QC criteria. For example, if calibration verifications for Method 8270 do not fall within the three standard deviation retention time windows, all analytes that failed in the standard are flagged as R in the associated samples. By definition, compliance would not have been met, but usability is very likely to remain intact. Data flagged as R are considered invalid data by the completeness definition given in Section 4. The completeness (QAPP compliance) goal is 90% for soil and 95% for water and presumably, since the version 1.1 QAPP would have been referenced in the prime's contract with AFCEE, a failure to meet these goals may result in a reduced payment to the prime and lab, resampling, and diminished ability to assess the site. If implemented as stated for the completeness determination, the new flagging requirements become a powerful economic stick.

2.3 Hardcopy Reports

AFCEE now requires CLP-like forms for hardcopy data reports. The version 1.1 QAPP gives examples of the 27 required forms in Section 8.

3. IRPIMS

IRPIMS is a large database of site assessment data that include many years of field and lab results data for most AFCEE projects. The lab results comprise about two thirds of the entire database. It is the responsibility of the AFCEE prime contractor to submit data electronically to AFCEE, and the prime invariably delegates the responsibility for lab data to the laboratory. In early 1996, AFCEE released software written in ACCESS called IRPTOOLS. IRPTOOLS allows hand entry of data and can accept lab-generated files; it also performs most of the QC checks that were previously performed by Metrica (the AFCEE contractor responsible for the IRPIMS database) after the IRPIMS files were sent to AFCEE by the contractor. Although IRPTOOLS allows hand entry of all data, including lab data, hand entry of lab data, because of its volume, is not a viable cost or quality option in the long run. However, IRPTOOLS can be useful for editing (although this opposes QA tenets) and executing the impeded QC checks. Unfortunately, IRPTOOLS does not yet (by mid-1996) have a stand-alone lab version: the software requires field data files, rarely available to the lab, for it to perform the lab QC checks. However, the proficient hacker can set up dummy field files, and then make use of the lab QC checks IRPTOOLS provides.

References

1. *Handbook to Support the Installation Restoration Program (IRP) Statement of Work for Remedial Investigation/Feasibility Studies* (RI/FS) in May, 1987, (Version 1.2), April, 1988, (version 2.0), and May, 1989, (version 3.0)

2. *Handbook to Support the Installation Restoration Program (IRP) Statement of Work*, Volume 1 Remedial Investigation/Feasibility Studies. AFCEE, May, 1991

3. *Handbook for the Installation Restoration Program (IRP) Remedial Investigations and Feasibility Studies (RI/FS)*, published by AFCEE September, 1993

4. Quality Assurance Project Plan (QAPP), version 1.1, February 1996

5. *Guidance for AFCEE Quality Assurance/Quality Control (QA/QC) Audits of Installation Restoration Program Contact Laboratories*, October, 1991

CHAPTER 10

Conclusion

So now your head is filled to bursting with all this information about the intricacies of data evaluation and you're ready to attack the piles of paper. Evaluating data by the shotgun approach is tremendously unrewarding and inefficient. Before you make that frontal assault on the first piece of raw documentation, it may be more beneficial to pause and make a plan of action.

To make a data evaluation planrequires becoming familiar with the data requirements, then making a determination of what is necessary to check to insure that the data requirements are met. The first order of business is then to collect the needed references. These will include, as appropriate:

1. Federal regulations and rules that relate to the sample results and monitoring

2. State regulationsand rules that relate to the sample results and monitoring

3. Local regulations and rules that relate to the sample results and monitoring

4. Project- or contract-specific Quality Assurance documents

5. Approved analytical method that dictates how the results are to be obtained

6. Specific permit that requires the sample results and monitoring

7. Laboratory Quality Assurance Manual.

These references will directly indicate whether or not the results must reflect exact method compliance and if there are any associated target analyte regulatory levels.

The reviewer next determines what are the essential quality controls and the acceptance limits for the quality control results. The essential quality controls are those that are most indicative of method complianceor data reliabilityat the regulatory limit. These are very useful when they take the form of a checklist. An example of a checklist for evaluation of data pertaining to an NPDES permit is presented in Table 10-1.

The next step is to attack the pile of results and supporting data in a systematic fashion. The checklist guides one in what documentation to look for, what items to evaluate and provides a record of the findings. If any missing data are discovered or there are problems with the data, the reviewer should contact the laboratory (Make a record of the call.) and request clarification or missing documents. If at all possible resolve all questions with the laboratory. Make written notes on the resolutions.

Finally, sit back and make an overall evaluation of the data. Ask yourself if they fit all your and the regulatory agency's needs. Ask yourself if they make sense based on what you know of the source of the samples. Ask yourself if you are personally willing to accept full legal responsibility for the data. If the answers to these questions are "Yes," then the data are acceptable.

Table 10-1.   Model Checklist for Evaluation of Method 625 Data for an NPDES Permit Compliance Monitoring Sample.

Method 625	Permit Parameter	Monthly Regulatory Limit µg/L
Permit #:	Hexachlorobenzene	196
Sampling Point:	Hexachloroethane	196
Date Sampled:	Hexachlorobutadiene	142
Date Reported:	Nitrobenzene	2237
Laboratory:	4,6-Dinitro-o-cresol	78
Lab Report #:	2-Nitrophenol	65
Reviewer:	4-Nitrophenol	162

Quality Control	Requirements	Check	Comments
Initial Calibration	3 pt, one near MDL		
	%RSD <35 or Cal. Curve		
IDC	Each T.A.		
Continuing Calibration	Daily, each T.A. <20% D		
Surrogates	3 minimum	Use Table below	
Internal Stds.	3 minimum	Use Table below	
Method blank	each batch, <MDL each T.A.		
Holding time	7 days to extr.		
Tuning	Daily to DFTPP		
Matrix Spike	Each TA at regulatory level		
Control Charts	Prec. & Acc each T.A.		
PE Sample Date:	Each T.A. acceptable		

Standard	IS	Surr	Standard	IS	Surr
Base/Neutral Extractables					
Aniline-d5			Anthracene-d10		
Benzo(a)anthracene-d12			4,4'-Dibromobiphenyl		
Decafluorobiphenyl			4,4'-Dibromooctafluorobiphenyl		
2,2'-Difluorobiphenyl			4-Fluoroaniline		
Phenanthrene-d10			Pyridine-d5		
1-Fluoronaphthalene			Nitrobenzene-d5		
2-Fluoronaphthalene			2,3,4,5,6-Pentafluorobiphenyl		
Naphthalene-d8					
Acid Extractables					
2-Fluorophenol			Pentafluorophenol		
Phenol-d5			2-Perfluoromethyl phenol		

List of Acronyms/Abbreviations

AA	Atomic absorption
AES	Atomic emission spectrometry
AFCEE	Air Force Center for Environmental Excellence
APHA	American Public Health Association
AREAL	Atmospheric Research and Exposure Assessment Laboratory
ASE	Accelerated solvent extraction
ASTM	American Society for Testing Materials
ASV	Anodic stripping voltammetry
BAT	Best available technology
BDL	Below detection limit
BFB	4-bromofluorobenzene
BNA	Base/neutral acid
BOD	Biological oxygen demand
CAA	Clean Air Act
CCC	Continuing calibration check
CCS	Contract compliance screening
CCV	Continuing calibration verification
CDA	Continuing demonstration of ability (samples)
CERCLA	Comprehensive Environmental Response, Cleanup, and Liability Act (Superfund)
CF	Calibration factors
CFR	Code of Federal Regulations
CLP	Contract Laboratory Program
CRI	ICP calibration check solution at two times concentration of CRDL
CRQL	Contract required quantitation level
CVAA	Cold vapor atomic absorption
CWA	Clean Water Act
%D	Percent Recovery
D	Difference
DAS	Data acceptability screening
DBC	Dibutylchlorindate
DCB	Decachlorobiphenyl
DCPA	Dacthal, 2,3,5,6-tetrachloro-1,4-benzenedicarboxylic acid dimethyl ester
DFTPP	Decafluorotriphenylphosphine
DMR	Discharge monitoring report
DOD	Department of Defense
DOE	(U.S.) Department of Energy
DPD	N,N-Diethylphenylene diamine
DQO	Data quality objectives
ECD	Electron capture detector
ELCD	Electrolytic conductivity detector

EMMC	Environmental Methods Monitoring Council
EOX	Extractable organic halogens
EP	Extraction procedure
EPA	U.S. Environmental Protection Agency
ER	Environmental restoration
FID	Flame ionization detector
FLAA	Flame atomic absorption
FRE	Federal rules of evidence
FTIR	Fourier transform Infrared
FWPCA	Federal Water Pollution Control Act
GC	Gas chromatograph
GFAA	Graphite furnace atomic absorption
GPC	Gel permeation clean-up
GS/MS	Gas chromatography/mass spectrometry
HDPE	High density polyethylene
HEM	N-Hexane extractable material
HPLC	High pressure (or performance) liquid chromatography
HPLC-MS	High pressure liquid chromatography-mass spectrometry
HRGC/LRMS	High resolution gas chromatography/low resolution mass spectrometry
HRMS	High resolution mass spectrometry
ICAL	Initial calibration
ICB	Initial calibration blank
ICP	Inductively coupled plasma
ICP-AES	Inductively coupled plasma atomic emission spectrometry
ICS	Initial calibration solution
ICV	Initial calibration verification
ID	Identification
IDA	Initial demonstration of ability (samples)
IDC	Initial demonstration of competence (samples)
IDL	Instrument detection limit
IPC	Instrument performance check
IPR	Initial precision and recovery (samples)
ISE	Ion-selective electrode
J	Estimated (when used as a data flag)
LCS	Laboratory control samples
LCSD	Laboratory control sample duplicate
LFB	Laboratory fortified blanks
LFM	Laboratory fortified sample matrix
LIMS	Laboratory information management system
LRB	Laboratory reagent blank
MCL	Maximum contaminant levels
MDL	Method detection limit
MF	Membrane filtration
ML	Minimum level
MNP	Most-probable number
MS	Matrix spike
MSA	Multiple standard addition
MSD	Matrix spike duplicate
NBS	National Bureau of Standards (now NIST)

ND	Not-detected
NIST	National Institute for Standards and Technology (formerly NBS)
NJ	Estimated quantity of TIC (when used as a data flag)
NPD	Nitrogen-phosphorus detector
NPDES	National Pollutant Discharge Elimination System
NRDC	Natural Resources Defense Council
NTIS	National Technical Information Service
NTU	Nephelometric Turbidity Units
OCPFS	Organic chemicals, plastics, and synthetic fibers
OERR	Office of Emergency and Remedial Response
OPR	Ongoing precision and recovery (samples)
OSW	Office of Solid Waste
PAH	Polynuclear aromatic hydrocarbons
PARRC	Precision, accuracy, reliability, representativeness, and comparability
PCB	Polychlorinated biphenyl
PDS	Post-digestion spikes
PE	Performance evaluation
PEM	Performance evaluation mixture
PGF	Peak gaussian factors
PID	Photoionization detector
POTW	Publicly-owned treatment works
POX	Purgeable organic halides
PQL	Practical quantitation level
QA	Quality assurance
QAPjP *or*	
QAPP	Quality assurance project plan
QC	Quality control
QL	Quantitation limit
QCS	Quality control sample
Quant	Quantitation
%R	Percent Recovery
R	Unusable
RCRA	Resource Conservation and Recovery Act
RDX	Royal Demolition Explosive
Rf	Response factors
RL	Reporting level (or limit)
RPD	Relative percent difference
RRF	Relative response factors
RRT	Relative retention time
RSD	Relative standard deviation
SAP	Sampling and analysis plan
SASS	Source assessment sampling system
SDWA	Safe Drinking Water Act
SGT-HEM	Silica gel treated n-hexane extractable material
SOP	Standard operating procedures
SOW	Statement of work
SPCC	System performance check compounds
SPE	Solid phase extraction
SVO	Semivolatile organic

SVOC	Semivolatile organic compound
SWMU	Solid waste management unit
TAL	Target analyte list
TAT	Turn-around time
TBPFA	Perfluorotributylamine
TCL	Target compound list
TCLP	Toxicity characteristic leaching procedure
TCMX	2,4,5,6-Tetrachloro-*meta*-xylene
TICs	Tentatively identified compounds
TNT	Trinitrotoluene
TOC	Total organic carbon
TOX	Total organic halogens
TPO	Technical project officer
TRPH	Total recoverable petroleum hydrocarbons
TS	Total solids
TSS	Total suspended solids
U	Undetected (when used as a data flag)
USAFOEHL	U.S. Air Force Occupational and Environmental Health Laboratory
USGAO	United States General Accounting Office
USGS	United States Geological Survey
UV	Ultraviolet
VOA	Volatile organic analysis
VOC	Volatile organic compound
VOST	Volatile organic sampling train
VTSR	Verified time of sample receipt
WQBEL	Water-quality based effluent limitation
W S	Water supply (PE Sample)
W W W	World-wide Web
XRF	X-ray diffusion
WP	Water Pollution (PE Sample)

Index

Note Section

Note Section

Note Section

Note Section